A Herefordshire Tale

—

Claston, Hops, and the Davies Family

A Herefordshire Tale

—

Claston, Hops, and the Davies Family

by

Peter Davies

Published by Peter Davies

PETER DAVIES
12, The Maltings
Dormington
Hereford HR1 4FA

First published in 2007
Copyright © Peter Davies 2007

Set in Times New Roman by Logaston Press
and printed in Great Britain by
Cpod, Trowbridge, Wilts.

I dedicate this book to our dear son Philip
whose enthusiasm for the farm
and care of the family and staff were unbounded

Contents

Acknowledgements

I am indebted to the following people for their assistance, guidance and encouragement in making this book possible:

Andrew Foley
Peter Glendenning
Sue Hubbard and staff at the Record Office
Andy Johnson of Logaston Press
William Lewis
Ron and Jennifer Shoesmith

My special thanks to Celia Brewin for typing my garbled tapes, and to my wife Pam for disentangling the composition.

Introduction

For some time when I have been talking to people about the past, they have remarked that I should record these memories, otherwise they would be lost forever.

In this book I have endeavoured to achieve this end, together with some local records and family history.

Peter Davies, October 2007

In Father's Day

It's only now I'm older
That I recall with joy
The way in which they used to farm
When Father was a boy.

Old Ben did all the thatching
The sharp pegs were hand made,
The best straw kept for thatching,
With twine secured and laid.

Ten ricks were in the stackyard,
All thatched and trim, and right,
Well roofed to stand the winter-snow
And howling winds at night.

And men knew how to scythe then
And other skills by hand,
And there was so much pride and joy
In working on the land.

In summer in the meadows
They made sweet meadow-hay,
All loaded in loose forkfuls
In the old fashioned way.

And the potato harvest
Came in the hessian sacks,
Carried up the old barn steps
On farmlads' aching backs.

Mangold cutting froze the hands
Made hard men out of boys,
But hand-milked cows in cowsheds warm
Were not without their joys.

A man would dig a ditch out
With carefully sharpened spade,
And hedges were not just sliced off
But skilfully cut and laid.

Progress sometimes seems to me
To take a backward turn,
Because from those old timers
We have so much to learn.

And life was at a quieter pace
When Father farmed his land,
And every man had pride of place
By skills of his own hand.

And village life lay round the church
And harvest suppers then,
Were such a happy gathering
Of thankful hearted men.

I'm lucky I remember them
Old Ben, and Mick and such
Without them … back there in my youth
I would have missed … so much.

Foreword

I had a rare treat some time ago: along with my fellow clergy of the Hereford Rural, Ledbury and Bromyard deaneries, I attended a service of Holy Communion in the exquisite little 12th-century Church of St Peter, Dormington, and then popped practically next door for a conducted tour of Claston, one of England's most outstanding hop farms. As we bounced along in a tractor-towed trailer watching the harvester at work on the hedgerow hops, and then as we stood on the gantries over the computer-controlled conveyors and between the kilns, I began to form some startling new impressions of just what is involved in the modern agricultural industry when it comes to harvest.

I don't know if you have noticed, but hops have all but disappeared in Herefordshire. Even as recently as when I moved to this county, there were hop-yards everywhere. When I was in the army and living in Moreton-on-Lugg, Liz and I used to ride our horses through lines of tall hops that bordered the A49. We used to watch the host of men tying strings early in the year and then tried to count the procession of trailer-loads of hops at harvest time. But that's all finished. No hops are grown there any more. The odd virus, changing economic times and a shift to chemical beers (encouraged by big brewers because they are easier and cheaper to handle) devastated this traditional crop and threatened a whole way of life that had existed in this county for generations. And then the fight-back started – at Claston.

Working right at the cutting edge of botanical research and in co-operation with laboratory scientists, Peter Davies, whose family have farmed Claston since the second half of the 19th century, began trial plantings of newly developed strains of the new hedgerow hops (only 8 feet high instead of the old 20, and highly resistant to the wilt virus), and at the same time began developing the machinery that would harvest the new crop and process it. His ground-breaking work has put him at the forefront of world hedgerow hop growing, and has enabled him to produce high quality hops at a fraction of the old cost. And business is booming.

At Claston we, a group of largely middle-aged clergy, saw what the harvest is really all about – God's wonderful gift of a fertile, fruitful world, harnessed by the technological ingenuity of the human race; a highly developed industry producing better and better crops for the needs of society, more and more efficiently, and at ever lower cost. And the good news is that real ale sales are growing, and even the supermarket shelves are now filling with beer that contains natural ingredients and has real taste rather than the wishy-washy chemical products.

I suppose my Harvest Festivals up until now have really been rather naïve celebrations of farming seen through rose-tinted spectacles – a very traditional view of a bygone age. Now I see more clearly the reality of a highly sophisticated industry of dedicated men and women, bringing together the latest advances in modern science and the age old miracle of life in the natural world. Through their inspiration and dedication we are fed and clothed.

Living here in the heart of rural Herefordshire we are blessed in being close to the soil and the whole process of agriculture, unlike big city dwellers whose children still grow up thinking that milk comes from bottles and peas are made in factories. But what we see happening in the fields around us is only possible because of the advances pioneered and developed in places like Holme Lacy College and in the Rowett Research Institute in my own home city of Aberdeen. There is as much science in agriculture now as there is in space flight. And Claston teaches us a remarkable lesson; science can bring us back to natural products by making them economically viable in competition with the synthetic products (like chemical beer) which have become so widespread during the 1970s, '80s and '90s. This could be one of the great boons of the 21st century – science bringing us back closer to nature.

Revd. Jimmy Morrison

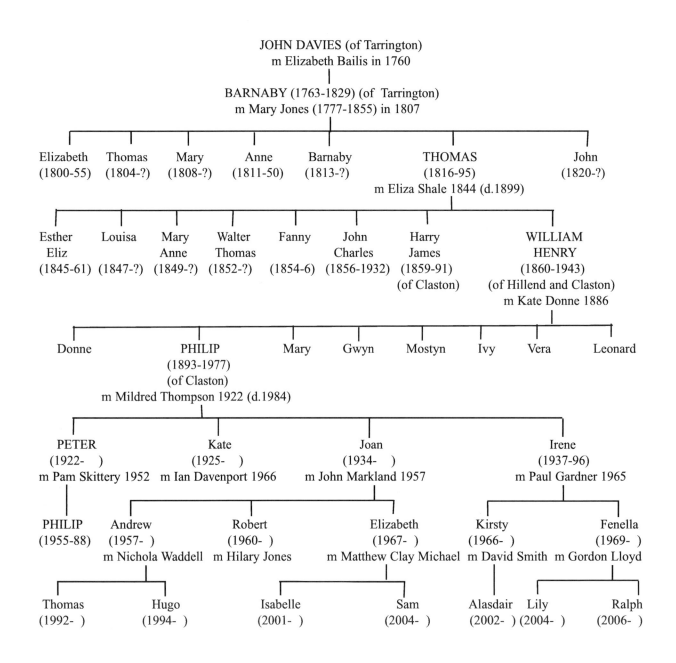

JOHN DAVIES (of Tarrington)
m Elizabeth Bailis in 1760

BARNABY (1763-1829) (of Tarrington)
m Mary Jones (1777-1855) in 1807

| Elizabeth (1800-55) | Thomas (1804-?) | Mary (1808-?) | Anne (1811-50) | Barnaby (1813-?) | THOMAS (1816-95) m Eliza Shale 1844 (d.1899) | John (1820-?) |

| Esther Eliz (1845-61) | Louisa (1847-?) | Mary Anne (1849-?) | Walter Thomas (1852-?) | Fanny (1854-6) | John Charles (1856-1932) | Harry James (1859-91) (of Claston) | WILLIAM HENRY (1860-1943) (of Hillend and Claston) m Kate Donne 1886 |

| Donne | PHILIP (1893-1977) (of Claston) m Mildred Thompson 1922 (d.1984) | Mary | Gwyn | Mostyn | Ivy | Vera | Leonard |

| PETER (1922-) m Pam Skittery 1952 | Kate (1925-) m Ian Davenport 1966 | Joan (1934-) m John Markland 1957 | Irene (1937-96) m Paul Gardner 1965 |

| PHILIP (1955-88) | Andrew (1957-) m Nichola Waddell | Robert (1960-) m Hilary Jones | Elizabeth (1967-) m Matthew Clay Michael | Kirsty (1966-) m David Smith | Fenella (1969-) m Gordon Lloyd |

| Thomas (1992-) | Hugo (1994-) | Isabelle (2001-) | Sam (2004-) | Alasdair (2002-) | Lily (2004-) | Ralph (2006-) |

The Davies Family Tree

CHAPTER ONE

The Background to Claston Farm

Claston Farm is in central Herefordshire, some 5 miles east of Hereford and 9 miles north-west of Ledbury. It is situated in the valley of the river Frome, a short distance from the north bank. The soil is a red loam and the valley is renowned for its fertility. The farm is in the eastern part of Dormington parish and is bounded by Stoke Edith on the east, Mordiford on the south, Lugwardine on the north-west, and Weston Beggard on the north. From time to time Claston farm has included parts of Stoke Edith, Weston Beggard and other neighbouring parishes.

Early occupation is often somewhat difficult to find along river valleys, which may well have been densely wooded, but the polished Neolithic hand axe that was ploughed up at Prior's Court in the 1960s gives some indication that hunter-gatherers were present in the area. However, it is not until the Iron Age that there are firm signs of settlement in the area. On the summit to the south of Claston is the 8-acre promontory fort on Backbury Hill romantically called Ethelbert's Camp. It has a strong triple rampart on the north side and precipitous slopes around the southern part. The eastern side has suffered from an ancient landslip, but north and south-west entrances are apparent. There is no known reason for any relationship with St. Ethelbert.

Eastern Herefordshire had a network of roads during the 300 or more years of the Roman occupation. West of Hereford and stretching through Wales was the military area, but to the east of the main border line an agricultural landscape developed with farms and villas scattered throughout the landscape. The Welsh border road from Chester to Caerleon passed close to the Roman town at Kenchester, a short distance west of Hereford, but a branch probably cut across the north and east of the city heading towards a crossing of the Lugg at Mordiford and thence to Gloucester. The northern boundary of Hereford is marked by another Roman road, heading from Wales eastwards towards Worcester. Even closer to Claston is the section of Roman road that passes north / south through Bartestree – an alternative road leading south to Gloucester. Some five miles further east yet another north / south road passes through Stretton Grandison, again leading to Gloucester.

Although some Roman pottery has been found close to Ethelbert's Camp, the main settlement in Dormington appears to have been towards the centre of the village. About 1911 there was a report of a Roman pavement and a key found close to the vicarage. Trial borings in 1951 confirmed the presence of a pavement 'about 2 ft deep' but no details were given. In addition a 'cigar-shaped enclosure' has been identified south-west of Tower Hill, and nn aerial photograph shows the site of two rectangular enclosures in Bean Acre hop-yard to the east of Moor Mill Cottages. These could be of Roman origin, or possibly later in the Dark Ages. Could Claston have had a Roman origin? There is no evidence, but there has been relatively little ground disturbance in the immediate house area, so there is still hope for excavation to prove this possibility.

Long before the Norman Conquest, Dormington and Prior's Frome belonged to St. Guthlac's Priory in Hereford. With a foundation probablyu earlier than that of Hereford cathedral, the monastic settlement (which was originally in the area of Castle Green, long before the Norman castle was built) owned

1

large areas of land in Herefordshire, although it lost much of its power after the Conquest. Dormington was certainly a pre-Conquest settlement, the name meaning 'Estate associated with Deormod or Deormund'.

Dormington is recorded under the lands of St. Guthlac in the 1086 Domesday Survey. The entry, under Greytree Hundred, reads:

> The Church [of St. Guthlac] itself held Dormington. Estan the canon held it. 1 hide which pays tax. Walter holds it now; he has 1 plough there and 1 smallholder and 1 slave. The value is and was 10s.

The use of 'held' rather than 'holds' may indicate that the Church had lost its land to the current holder Walter. However, it was still listed in the possessions of St. Guthlac's priory in rentals from the reign of Henry VI to that of Elizabeth I. In 1436 lands held by customary tenure included those in Frome and Dormington of William Collyer who paid 30s. 6d. for 'his own messuage and 1½ virgates together with another messuage and 9 acres'. A messuage and a virgate brought in 21s.; a messuage and a virgate 15s.; 2 messuages and a virgate 28s. 4d. Thomas Parks *pro uno cotagio cum clauso eidem adjacente* paid 3s. 4d. and a 'cottage and garden' was let for 16d. Demesne land included a messuage and 9 acres which rendered 8s. 10d. and 16 acres with no house that produced 4s. There were two holdings of free land – Nicholas Walwyn paid 5s. for a messuage and a virgate and David Kardoken, Chaplain of Mordiford, 3s. for a messuage and half a virgate. The vicar of Dormington paid a 'fancy' rent of a pound of cum min. The picture is of a stable agricultural area with relatively low rents.

At the dissolution, during the reign of Henry VIII, the main holding (presumably Prior's Court) was purchased by John ap Rice, who also bought the main house and grounds of St. Guthlac in Hereford (in Commercial Road where the 'bus station, cinema and county hospital now stand). Other parts of the parish belonged to the Stapleton and the Audley families. Most of the parish eventually fell into the hands of the Foley family of Stoke Edith who kept the land until 1919 when most of the estate was sold.

It is tempting to assume that one of the messuages mentioned in the 15th-century rental is that at Claston, but the present farmhouse was not built until about 1670 and was formerly called Clarkstone, this being a place name. It was built on an L-shaped plan with the wings extending towards the north-east and south-east. A modern wing makes the house half H-shaped. In the late 1920s there was a 17th-century timber-framed barn south of the farmhouse (since demolished) and an early 18th-century two-storey granary. However, remains of earlier buildings have been found near to the present house which

The church of St. Peter at Dormington has a nave of 13th-century date, the chancel being early 14th century. It was over-restored in 1877 by Blashill when the timber bell-turret, and south porch were rebuilt, the north vestry added, and the chancel largely rebuilt. The trussed rafter roofs are of 17th century or earlier date

The church contains monuments to the Brydges and Walwyn families and has traces of wall paintings in the nave. The door-knocker, with a feline head with large eyes, is a very fine Norman piece allied to the Herefordshire School of Romanesque Sculpture.

are not shown on the 1677 Stoke Edith estate map, thus providing some evidence that there was an earlier building close to the existing farmhouse.

DORMINGTON COURT

The *Royal Commission on Ancient & Historical Monuments in Herefordshire, Volume 2* (1932), describes Dormington Court, as consisting 'of a central block with side wings, the south-west wing is of  early seventeenth-century date. The north-east wing is of a late seventeenth-century date and the central block was built early in the eighteenth century'. However, Pevsner in his *Buildings of England – Herefordshire,* describes it as being of odd proportions dating generally to the early 19th century. I have been told that the oldest part of Dormington Court was the original rectory, so does that mean that the house was originally in two parts, one the original rectory and the other the farmhouse, and that they were eventually joined by the central block?

Dormington Court in the late 1920s

An article by Henry Phythian-Adams in *Country Life* concerns William Andrew Vevers, who lived at Dormington Court from about 1804. William was born in 1782 to John and Margaret Vevers of Yarkhill Court. The family had come from Yorkshire early in the eighteenth century. William was reared virtually in the saddle and he eventually came to Dormington Court, where he ran a very well-known racehorse stud farm. He produced many successful racehorses by crossing first-class Clydesdale mares with thoroughbred racehorses, producing heavier-weight steeplechasers. He rode in many races whilst living in Dormington, and he actually trained and rode the winner, *Charity*, of the 1841 *Great Liverpool Steeplechase*, now the *Grand National*. He won many other races all over Europe, coming a very close second in the 1846 *Paris Steeplechase*, when he was 65. In 1838, a local parson presented him with a silver tankard 'for the best stallion used in the County of Hereford'. William Vevers married Elizabeth, daughter of Thomas Maddy of Town House, Madley and they raised eight sons and four daughters. William died in 1858. Five of the sons were set up on Herefordshire farms, at Bartestree Court, Yarkhill Court, Dormington, Ivington and Larport Court. Of the younger sons, Henry became a prominent surgeon in Hereford and the medical officer to the city prison and infirmary. The eldest daughter, who was one of the toasts of the county, was known as 'the little white rose of Dormington' and her father prevented a duel being fought over her. She married twice and lived to be 90. There is a memorial to her in Dormington church in the form of a brass plate below the stained glass window in the chancel.

THE FOLEY FAMILY OF STOKE EDITH

In 1670, Thomas Foley of Great Witley, the head of the greatest iron-founding family in the West Midlands, purchased the Stoke Edith Estate from the Trustees of the late Sir Henry Lingen for his second son, Paul. The existing house at that time, which was close to Stoke Edith church, was of traditional black and white construction facing west down the Frome valley. Claston Farm was part of this estate.

Paul Foley was elected M.P. for Hereford in 1679 and became Speaker of the House of Commons in 1695. During this time, he promoted an Act to restore the City Corporation's independence, which had been eroded by Charles II in 1682, and an Act to improve the navigation of the River Wye, which was of great benefit to Herefordshire. This helped to reduce costs not only for his iron-founding business in the county, but also to bring building materials to Stoke Edith before starting, in 1695, to build the great Stoke Edith Park house. Bricks were made locally for the house in Devereux Park, Woolhope, by Simon Peter. By Lady Day, 25th March, in 1696 he had produced 701,900 bricks at 6s. per thousand. By June 1698 he had produced a further 845,000 bricks which were burnt entirely by wood from the estate, reducing the cost in comparison with bricks from Worcester at 10s. per thousand at the kiln. John Phillips, a bricklayer from London, and his team started work in June 1697 and completed the house by early March 1698. Elm, oak and ash were all obtained from trees from the estate, the elm being used mostly for scaffolding for the bricklayers and masons. Some imported deal arrived from Bristol, transported on the river to Mordiford. Two walnut trees were also felled to provide veneers. A slater from

Looking across the Frome valley. Stoke Edith house central and the church to the left

London, Thomas Night, was engaged to lay the roof, for which he used 88,000 slates from Cornwall and 21 tons of lead. Sadly, Paul Foley died in November 1699 at the age of 54, leaving the Stoke Edith estate to his son, Thomas. The building and interior decoration of the house was completed in 1727.

Prior's Court belonged to John Brydges until his death in 1669 and was later, in 1685, purchased by the Foleys, who then became Lord of the Manors of Prior's Frome, Dormington and Claston.

In 1788, Edward Foley, then owner of the Stoke Edith estate, engaged Humphrey Repton to landscape the park and gardens around the house. Part of the plan was to move the Gloucester to Hereford public road, which at that time went from Tarrington, through the park and the hamlet of Stoke Edith, on to Perton and along the southern extremity of Dormington to Prior's Frome and then on to Mordiford bridge. This road, which passed only 30 yards from the south side of the great mansion, was to be moved 500 yards to the north of the house going from Tarrington through to Dormington.

Arrangements had been made with the turnpike commissioners to keep the new road in repair and also to provide a turnpike house at the present Stoke Edith crossroads, and a blacksmith's shop was built there at the same time. There was a

The parterre at Stoke Edith about 1900

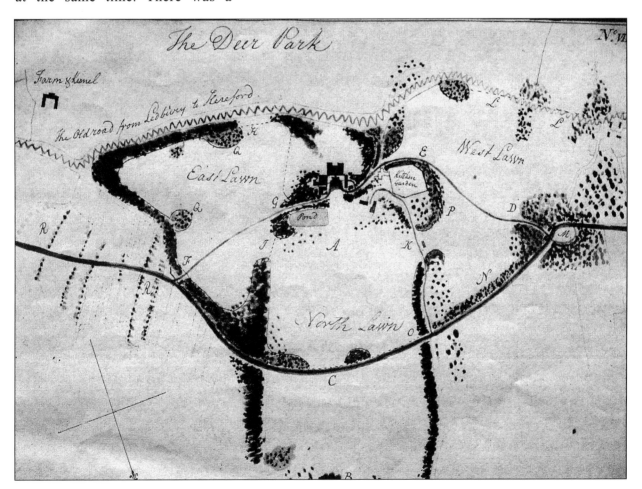

Repton's drawing of the proposed new road

THE NEW ROAD
Estimate

The road from Bartestree to Tarrington

1,400 perches of fencing or thereabouts at 2s. 6d. per perch	£175 0 0
4 arches to convey the water supposed to cost	£100 0 0
5,894 yards of forming 35 feet wide, stoning 13 feet wide	
10 inches thick at 4s. per yard	£1,196 0 0
Total Expence	£1,471 0 0

NB This new cut saves 1 mile wanting 200 yards

circular window which provided views of the road both from the east and the west at the front of the turnpike house.

The construction of the road started in October 1792 and was completed in September 1793, having been built by a team of road builders who were previously constructing carriage roads through the Foley woods.

CLASTON FARM

Claston Farm in 1795

The first record that I can find as to who farmed Claston mentions Thomas Newton. In 1642 he was the Chief Rents Officer for Ross and in 1656 he acquired some of the Claston land and more in 1658. His family farmed at Claston for several generations. The family eventually took over some of Prior's Court and farmed that as well as Claston. The last record that I can find of the Newtons is that a Thomas Newton died in 1816.

It is interesting, looking at the records from the Foley Estate, that when the Newtons were at Claston, between 1771 and 1787 the rent varied between £157 10s. and £244 10s. In 1777, they took over 13 acres of Stoke's Meadow and another £7 10s. was added to the rent. It was fixed then from 1788 to 1799 at £220. In 1782, when the Newtons took over Prior's Court, the rent was £577 10s. This must have been for the two farms, because the rent increased to £660 until 1791. By 1800, it had dropped to £344. The Newton family, by then, had moved to what was known as Prospect Cottage. Whether that was an extra house up at the Prospect or whether Prospect Farm was known as Prospect Cottage at that time is not certain. At that time, Claston must have been a much bigger farm because at the time of the sale in 1919 it amounted to 258 acres.

It is possible, of course, that the Newtons, or even some of the Foley family, farmed Claston themselves until 1815, when William Atwood took over the farm. His sister Catherine, who died on 2 June 1855, was the Governess to the Foley children. In 1856, when his father was farming at Showle Court, John Taylor moved to Claston. Another Taylor, Philip, was farming Prior's Court. John Taylor farmed Claston until 1863. Subsequently my great-grandfather, Thomas Davies, took over the management of the farm for the Foley family.

Claston looking south

My great-grandfather's father, Barnaby Davies, was born in 1763 at Coldmoot, which was then part of Woolhope but is now in Putley, and he married a Mary Jones of Tarrington in 1807. Their son, Thomas, was born in 1816. The first record I have of my great-grandfather's farming career is that he was farming Patrick's Farm in Tarrington, for a rent of £15. He then took over Middle Park in 1837.

At Claston there used to be an ancient barn, built in the seventeenth century, but it fell into disrepair and we finally pulled it down during the Second World War. The building nearest to the house was built in the early eighteenth century, and that included the cider mill and also a cider house. The round kilns at the north end of the building were probably built about that time. I have been told it was about 1740/1750 and this shows that hops had been grown at Claston from that time. In those days, it was on a much smaller scale, with just one 8-acre hop-yard. There was a brewery in Fownhope and it is more than likely that some of the Claston hops would have gone there, and probably the rest to the breweries in Hereford, of which there were three.

At Moor Mills, which is now a private dwelling, there used to be a water corn-mill, which supplied all local inhabitants. The underground channel to take the water from the river to the mill is still apparently in very good condition, but has recently been sealed up. The road that came through Claston farmyard went to the mill and crossed the river over a bridge by the mill. Several of the local footpaths, including one from Prior's Court and the one across the front meadow at Dormington, were all direct routes for local inhabitants to go to the mill.

There also used to be a windmill in Dormington and I could never find out where it was until fairly recently when looking at a map of 1842, which shows a field above Tower Hill called Windmill Field. Presumably that was where it was. The very old thatched, black and white cottages on Tower Hill were once the farm cottages for Claston Farm, and the lane from the old main road up to the cottages was originally a bridle path. My father told me he could remember horses pulling the steam engine and the threshing box up that road. It was a good road then, but now it is just a derelict track.

7

A coach accident at Frome bridge in 1852

DORMINGTON CHURCH – LIST OF PATRONS AND RECTORS

Patrons	A.D.	Rectors	A.D.
Abbot & Convent of Gloucester		Richard de Dowelaund	1308
The same		Walter de Dowelond	1331
The same		Walter de Hodenake	1335
The same		Roger de Syde	1349
The same		Thomas Comeles	1375
The same		Thomas Wyche	——
The same		Richard More	1442
The same		Thomas Hunt	1449
The same		Richard Castell	1458
The same		Joseph Tyler	1506
The same		Richard Badham	1535

After the dissolution of religious houses:

Patrons	A.D.	Rectors	A.D.
John Prise, gent		John Lynton	1546
Crown (by lapse)		John Badham	1560
Gregory Prise (with Bartestree Chapel)		John Badham	1566
The same		Brian Blackway	1576
Thomas Prise, esq.		Anthony Jones	1661
The same		Robert Griffiths	——
The same		Francis Smith	1668
The same		Thomas Holl	——
The same		Robert Cox	1684
Paul Foley, esq.	1685	Thomas Avenant	
The same		John Nash	1691
Thomas Foley I	1699	Sylvanus Woodhill	1703
The same		Henry Smith	1713
Thomas Foley II	1737		
Thomas Foley III	1749	Thomas Wickins	1760
The same		John Landon	1776
Thomas Foley IV	1777	Thomas Jennings	1782
Edward Foley I	1808	E. Howells	1822
The same		L. E. Brown	1845
Edward Foley II	1846	A. Norris Cope	1886
Emily Foley	1900		
Paul Foley	1928	E. Coles	1930
The same		Maurice Berkley	1935
The same		E. G. T. Simey	1947
Henry Foley	1959	William McDonald	1973
The same		Eric Churchus	1985
Andrew Foley	1996	David Bowen	1996

CHAPTER TWO

The First Farming Records of the Davies Family : 1840-1923

Thomas Davies, my great-grandfather, was farming Patrick's Farm at Tarrington and the Middle Park in 1837, but in 1846 he took over Highnam and by 1859 also the Moorend in Weston Beggard as well as Weston Corner, which was another little farm adjacent to the Moorend. He also took over the Stoke Edith lime kilns in July 1859.

The Stoke Edith lime kilns

The 1842 farm map, detailing the different names of the various fields, showed that there was then only one hop-yard planted with hops. In 1864 Thomas Davies took over the management of Claston Farm for the Foley family. In 1865, he grew 9½ cwts per acre in the old hop-yard, taking sixteen days to harvest the crop, and the hop dryer, James Gwilliam, was paid 20 shillings per week – £2 13s. 6d in total. Some of these hops may have been sold to a brewery in Fownhope and some to the three breweries in Hereford. I have a farm diary of 1864/65, showing hops being sold to Flowers brewery, one of the three in Hereford, at £6 per cwtt in September and £5 per hundredweight in October. In fact, we continued to sell hops to Flowers brewery, which eventually became part of Whitbread, until the 2004 crop when the farm was sold.

Thomas managed Claston for the Foleys until 1866, when he took on the tenancy. Whilst manager, he claimed 'remuneration for my time and trouble in managing the farm, journeys to markets and fairs, and expenses thereon and in paying the labourers wages etc':

Note of hand for £150 interest £4 10s. per annum.
Note of hand for £100 interest £4 10s. per annum.

> Extract from accounts 15 June 1865 regarding wages:
> John Hill – minding crows 25 days @ 6d. per day;
> Women – hop tying, 8d.–10d. per day;
> J. Heavens – hoeing 10 acres of peas @ 3s. per acre;
> J. Heavens – hoeing 5 acres of wheat @ 4s. per acre.

When the railway was built in 1861, Thomas Davies had a reduction in the Moorend rent of £15, in lieu of the land for the railway. All this land was owned by the Foley family and was sold by Lady Emily for the railway on condition that she would be able to have the trains stopped at Stoke Edith station whenever she wished to use the train. Later, there were 138 men working on the line from Hereford to Worcester and the railway was making a profit.

In 1865 records show:

Dormington Poor Rate for Claston	£9 13s 1¹/₂d
Stoke Edith Poor Rate	10s 9d
Dormington Income Tax	£2 11s 10¹/₂d
Weston Beggard Income Tax	6s 6¹/₂d
Stoke Edith Income Tax	4s 11¹/₂d

Farm accounts for 27 July 1866 show:

William Cook – mowing 7 acres of clover @ 2s 6d per acre
William Cook – mowing 35 acres of grass @ 3s per acre
William Cook – rowing up 13 acres of hops @ 1s 8d per acre

Accounts for 20 August 1866 show:

William Cook – cutting 10 acres of peas @ 4s per acre
William Cook – cutting 5¹/₂ acres of oats @ 2s per acre
William Cook – cutting 16 acres of wheat @ 7s 6d per acre
James Harwood – 2 days @ 1s 8d per day, other men 1s 6d

Sale Prices in 1866:

Wheat:	5s 8d per bushel
Barley:	3s 6d per bushel
Hops:	£6 per hundredweight
Fat ewes:	62s each
Fat cows:	£604 at 7d per pound

Great-grandfather Thomas Davies

In 1846, Lady Emily Foley and Thomas Newton, late of Claston, then at Prospect Farm, had given two cedar trees to be planted on the north side of the church. Lady Emily's tree was cut down in 1877 during the restoration work to give more light and make the church more visible from the road. In 1881 a broad arrow was cut on the corner-stone of the north-west corner of the church, which was made with Reverend Brown's consent on a government trigonometrical survey.

My grandfather, William Henry, was born at the Moorend in 1860. He was the youngest of Thomas' eight children and in 1886 he married Kate Donne, daughter of Thomas & Mary Donne, whose family were farming at Tretire, a village in West Herefordshire. Her father, however, was a tailor living in London and had become the owner of three gentlemen's outfitters shops in London, Birmingham and Bristol. William Davies and Kate Donne were married by the Rev. E.B. Scott on 21 October 1886 at Wood Green Church, Tottenham, London.

Hillend

Kilns at Hillend

11

The Restoration of Dormington Church,

CLOSED JUNE 12, 1876, REOPENED FEB. 13, 1877.

"SOLI GLORIA DEO."

ABSTRACT OF ACCOUNTS.

Donations and Contributions Received.

	£ s. d.	£ s. d.
For the Nave ...	1201 10 1	
„ the Chancel ...	303 0 0	
		1504 10 1
By Collection on day of opening ...	23 17 11	
Donations for a new bell and other improvements	92 15 6	
For lowering a tomb and railing ...	3 7 6	
For musical purposes ...	5 5 0	
		25 5 11
		£1629 16 0

Expended on the Restoration

	£ s. d.	£ s. d.
of the Nave ...	1201 10 1	
„ Chancel ...	303 0 0	
		1504 10 1
A new bell, &c. ...	46 9 7	
Other improvements	54 5 5	
Lowering tomb, &c. ...	3 7 6	
Musical purposes...	2 6 9	
		106 9 3
		1610 19 4
Balance ...		18 16 8
		£1629 16 0

The balance is devoted to—

	£ s. d.
Iron gates for porch	12 12 0
Musical purposes	2 18 3
Other requisites	3 6 5
	£18 16 8

List of Contributors to the Fund for providing a new Bell, and other Improvements and Requisites in the Church and Churchyard.

	£ s. d.		£ s. d.
The Right Hon. and Ven. The Lord Saye and Sele, Archdeacon ...	5 0 0	The Rev. James Browell, Cowfold	5 5 0
The Rev. W. C. Fowle, Rural Dean ...	1 1 0	William F. Browell, Esq., Tunbridge Wells	2 2 0
The Misses Atwood, Worcester	5 0 0	Mrs. Brown, Penymaes, Hay	1 0 0
Mrs. Bird and Miss Green, Weybridge...	5 0 0	Miss Brown, Oldbury	1 0 0
Thomas Blashill, Esq., Architect	2 2 0	The Vicar and Mrs. Langton Brown	7 0 0
Edward M. Browell, Esq., Feltham	5 5 0	Collected by Master Brown	0 10 0

* The second bell has this inscription, "Soli Gloria Deo, 1862."

List of Contributions to Bell Fund, &c.—Continued.

	£ s. d.		£ s. d.
Brought forward ...	37 10 0	The Rev. R. Muckleston, Dinedor	5 0 0
Mrs. Joseph Cotterill, Portobello, N.B.		Mrs. E. B. Penny, Cullompton	5 0 0
Mrs. and Miss Evans	5 0 0	The Rev. William Poole, Hentland	5 0 0
H. W. Foley, Esq., Prestwood ...	2 0 0	The Rev. W. F. Powell, Hinton Court	1 0 0
The Rev. Wm. A. Frith, Welby Rectory	0 10 6	The Rev. A. H. Price, Digwardine	2 2 0
Miss Hakewill, Exmouth	0 10 0	The Rev. John Purton, Oldbury	5 0 0
By Mr. Hall, Dormington Court—		The Rev. John Winter, Tarrington	0 10 0
Mr. John Pitt, Bosbury ...	1 0 0	The Rev. John Woollam, Yarkhill	0 10 0
Mr. Thomas Pitt	1 0 0	Henry Vevers, Esq., Hereford	5 0 0
Miss Pitt	1 0 0		92 15 6
Mr. Chandler, London	0 10 0		
Mr. James	0 10 0	**Special Donations—**	
Mr. Bezant, Hereford	0 10 0	The Misses Atwood, for lowering tomb, &c.	3 7 6
Small sums	0 10 0	Miss Glover, for musical purposes	5 5 0
Miss Hansell, Norwich	5 0 0		101 8 0
Mrs. Howard	5 0 0		
The Rev. J. Howard	5 0 0	Collected on the day of Re-opening the Church	23 17 11
R. Hereford, Esq., Sufton	2 0 0	**Preachers—**	
The Rev. H. T. Hill, Felton ...	1 0 0	The Lord Bishop of Hereford	£125 5 11
Mrs. Hodgkinson, Lincoln (deceased)...	0 10 0	The Rev. W. C. Fowle.	
Second donation ...	1 0 0		

List of Contributors.

	£ s. d.	£ s. d.
For the Nave—		
The Right Hon. Lady Emily Foley ...	1060 5 0	
Edward S. Hutchinson, Esq. ...	25 0 0	
The Parishioners, by a voluntary rate, May 26th, 1876		
Thomas Bradstock ...	1 14 9	
Francis Link ...	1 1 0	
Luke Preece, Wooton ...	5 10 9	
Henry T. Taylor, Prior's Court	26 6 3	
Thomas Davies, Claston	34 7 9	
Henry S. Hall, Dormington Court	34 1 9	
J. W. James, Bartestree...	1 7 3	
Charles Harwood	0 12 6	
H. W. Foley, Esq.	0 14 0	
	105 15 6	
Less Collecting ...	0 10 5	
		105 5 1
Interest at the Bank ...		11 0 0
		1201 10 1
For the Chancel—		
The Vicar and Mrs. Langton Brown ...	303 0 0	
		1504 10 1
Collection on opening day and other Donations, as per separate List ...		125 5 11
Total Contributions in Cash ...		£1629 16 0

Some Particulars of Expenditure.

For the Nave :—

	£ s. d.	£ s. d.
Messrs. Collins and Cullis, Builders	1118 15 2	
Thomas Blashill, Esq., Architect ...	74 18 0	
Share of Bill for Faculty ...	5 4 5	
Potter's Bill—Brass Pulpit Desk ...	2 12 6	
		1201 10 1

For the Chancel :—

	£ s. d.	£ s. d.
Messrs. Collins and Cullis	281 18 9	
Architects Commission ...	18 13 0	
Share of Faculty Fees ...	2 3 3	
		303 0 0

For the New Bell :—

	£ s. d.	£ s. d.
Messrs. Warner and Sons ...	40 8 10	
Messrs. Collins and Cullis	5 10 0	
Carriage ...	0 10 9	
		46 9 7

For Improvements, Furniture, &c. :—

	£ s. d.	£ s. d.
Messrs. Collins and Cullis	22 13 8	
Architects Commission ...	1 11 9	
Payments as by list following	30 0 0	
		54 5 5

For Special Purposes :—

	£ s. d.	£ s. d.
Lowering Tomb and Rails	3 7 6	
For Musical Purposes ...	2 6 9	
		5 14 3
		£1610 19 4

All Saints' Day, 1877.

A List of Payments for Furniture, Improvements, &c.

	£ s. d.
Six dozen kneeling Hassocks ...	3 19 0
A New Surplice and Communion Napkin	2 4 3
A large Pewter Flagon and Alms Plate	1 15 0
Window Blinds, &c. (Morris) ...	1 17 6
Carpet and extra Desk (Maddox)	3 0 0
Ironmongery, Mats, Brooms, &c.	3 0 8
Fuel for Stoves (Preece)	1 9 0
Work done in the Churchyard ...	3 15 0
Grass Seeds for ditto (Cranston)	1 0 0
A New Pall (Walmesley)	2 16 6
A New Bier (Cullis)	2 5 0
Carriage of Chair, &c. ...	0 7 0
	£30 0 0

Presented to the Church.

A Quarto Prayer Book for the Reading Desk by Mr. and Mrs. E. K. Jakeman.

A Handsome Carved Glastonbury Chair for the Chancel, by the Rev. W. H. Lambert, Stoke Edith.

A liberal supply of Lithographic Drawings of the Church, in its old and restored appearance, by the Architect, Thomas Blashill, Esq.

An Harmonium will be placed in the Chancel, (when thoroughly dry,) by members of the family of the late Mr. and Mrs. Vevers, of Dormington Court.

Much gratuitous assistance was also rendered in hauling gravel and turf for the Churchyard, by Messrs. Thomas Davies, H. S. Hall, and H. T. Taylor.

LANGTON EDWARD BROWN, *Vicar.*
THOMAS DAVIES, *Churchwarden.*

In 1876, Thomas Davies took over the Hillend. He was Churchwarden of Dormington Church and was heavily involved in the restoration of the church in 1876-7. Lady Emily Foley was then Patron of the church and was the main benefactor for this restoration. I understand that when she attended a service at Dormington, she always notified my great-grandfather and he and his fellow Churchwarden had to meet her at the church gate to escort her into church. When the collection was taken, she always put a velvet bag, containing five sovereigns, in the collection.

Harry James Davies, who was a brother of, but only one year older than, my grandfather, took over Claston in the 1880s when my great-grandfather moved to the Pigeon House. Unfortunately, he was killed in 1891 when his horse bolted and ran under a sally (willow) tree. Harry was caught in a fork of the tree and broke his neck. His wife, Isabella, continued to farm Claston until she married again and my grandfather moved there in about 1900. My father was actually born at the Hillend in 1893, as were most of his brothers and sisters, and I remember him telling me that there was a little field opposite the Hillend buildings where they all learnt to ride their ponies.

The golden years of hop growing were during the later part of the 19th century, when 72,000 acres (29,000 hectares) were growing in the English countryside. In this period, William Henry Davies became a very large hop grower, growing over 1,000 pockets on his various farms – Ockle, Moorend, Weston Court, Hillend, Pigeon House and Claston. By the early part of the 20th century, the golden years of hop growing were over. This was as a direct result of the Government raising the tax on beer from 7s. 9d. to 23 shillings a barrel. Beer consumption fell and with it the demand for hops. However, William Davies is better known for his herd of Hereford cattle which he started to promote and with a heifer from which he won the supreme championship at the Royal Show one year. The heifer, called Miss Vera, was subsequently exported to the Argentine. He also was the first man to export a substantial number of cattle, over 60 I believe it was, to the Argentine. The picture

Claston Farm in the 1880s

Grandfather bushelling hops at Hillend. His wife is on the right and Father is slightly behind

13

Miss Vera, who was supreme champion at the Royal Show and was exported to the Argentine

Stoke Edith station with the cattle loaded in trucks on the way to the Argentine

Late 19th century Ryeland sheep were much larger than the modern variety

shows the train, with the cattle in, at Stoke Edith station. My grandfather's eldest son, Donne, was very efficient and was well-known for his skill in breeding Hereford cattle, becoming the youngest man to judge at the Royal Show and at Smithfield. Unfortunately, when my grandfather started him off with the herd, he selected some cattle for my Uncle, but Uncle Donne, without my grandfather's knowledge, swapped some of the cattle, taking better animals for himself, which upset my grandfather greatly.

My grandfather was one of the founder members of the Ryeland sheep herd book and it is interesting to see the photographs, showing that the Ryeland sheep were very large animals at that time. It wasn't until many years later that they did the same as the Hereford cattle breeders, that is to in-breed the sheep to produce small carcasses to provide small joints for the housewife, following the American idea.

My grandfather had a sale of the live and dead farming stock on 5 March 1908, when I imagine he gave up the tenancy of the Hillend. The sale was conducted by A. & D. Edwards, Auctioneers, of Leominster. The 226 lots realised £1,079 7s. 6d., of which Wargents of Canon Frome purchased 25 lots for £55 13s. 6d. The sale of 179 sheep included 40 ewes, some of them in lamb, and 47 baby lambs, sold in lots of five ewes, making prices of £15 10s. to £19 10s. per lot. There were seventeen cattle, thirteen wagon horses and nine ponies. Two of the wagon horse mares made £40 each. There were also 24 lots of furniture.

My father and his brothers were educated as boarders at Lucton School, Aymestrey, to which they travelled by pony and trap to

Left: Grandfather William Henry Davies
Above: My father on the white pony.
All boys wearing Lucton school caps

Hereford station, then on by train to Leominster where they were met by a horse-drawn vehicle to complete the journey. On leaving school, after a short time working in Meats Coal Office in Hereford, my father went to the bankers' college in Birmingham and then started work at the National Provincial Bank, as it was in his day but is now NatWest, in Broad Street. He had planned to work in the bank for several years, with his friend Wilfred Watkins from Woolhope, to gain experience, then to emigrate to Canada. At the outbreak of the First World War, he and his brother, Norman, and Wilfred Watkins joined the Shropshire Yeomanry. They went on to serve on East Coast Defences as part of a cavalry unit. I remember him saying that while there they had a fabulous time – they were all farmers' sons and Lord Cawley was their officer. They used to buy fields of grass for the horses and paid local farm workers to cut the grass for the horses, whilst they retired to the pub. He said that they used to go out very early in the morning on coastal defence and then went back to breakfast, eating huge meals of up to ten eggs with their bacon. Later, the yeomanry were dismounted to become part of the Shropshire Light Infantry and my father was sent out to the Middle East to fight the Turks. Sadly Wilfred Watkins was shot and killed at Father's side in their first engagement with the Turks. This must have been a shattering blow to my father. He was made Paymaster to the regiment but later, unfortunately, he got enteric fever and was very lucky to survive. He said men were dying and they were burying them just outside the bedroom windows; some people were so ill that they couldn't tell the nurses that scorpions were eating their toes. My father lost all his hair one night, he had thick black, curly hair but when he woke up one morning it was all in the bed. He was then sent to Cyprus, which he said was a marvellous place, to convalesce. Later on, he was badly wounded in his hand in an orange grove near Bethlehem in Palestine, during hand to hand fighting. He recovered and went to France at the end of the war where he spent a short time fighting the Germans. He was eventually invalided out of the army in 1919 with a bad heart. It was interesting that no insurance company would take him on for a life insurance policy but he lived to be 83!

When my father came out of the army, he obviously didn't have any money and by then, for several reasons, everything had gone wrong for my grandfather. He had been spending too much time on public work. He was a County Councillor, Chairman of the Board of Governors of the Workhouse, as well as being

Back row: Grandfather, Auntie Mary
Middle row: Uncle Donne, Auntie Gwen, Grandmother (baby Uncle Leonard), Uncle Mostyn
Front row: Father, Auntie Vera, Uncle Norman, Auntie Ivy

LOT 8

A Grazing and Mixed Farm

KNOWN AS

"CLASTON"

together with

A Pair of Cottages

extending to an area of about

179 a.   0 r.   3 p.

Situate in the Parishes of DORMINGTON, STOKE EDITH and WESTON BEGGARD.

Let, together with other lands, to Messrs. W. H., N. and D. Davies on a yearly tenancy expiring 1st January, 1920.

LANDLORD'S OUTGOINGS :—

Commuted Tithe Rent Charge—Rectorial	...	...	£2	15	0
Vicarial	...	...	34	13	2
Impropriate	...	...	2	3	6
Extraordinary	...	...	1	6	3
			£40	17	11

Claston Farm at the time of the sale in 1919

17

one of Queen Victoria's local mounted bodyguards. Some of his farm managers took advantage of this, becoming dishonest, and when his wife died in 1915 he lost heart and his business collapsed.

Uncle Donne was farming at The Pigeon House, Weston Beggard, and it was agreed that my father would take over Claston, but, shortly after he started farming, most of the Stoke Edith estate was put on the market. With great difficulty, Father managed to buy Claston, which had then been reduced to 170 acres. He eventually secured a loan and paid £9,000 for the farm.

My father married my mother, Mildred Thompson, whose father, John, farmed at The Hyde, Woolhope, in November 1922.

THE HOUSE

Stone and tiled, contains :—

Dining Room, Drawing Room, Office, Kitchen, Scullery, Dairy, Wash-house and Coal House, Conservatory (claimed by the Tenant), four Bedrooms, Bath Room and W.C. (Fittings and Water Tanks claimed by the Tenant) and four Attic Rooms.

The Farm Buildings

Variously constructed of stone and brick, slated or tiled, comprise :—

Three Hop Kilns, Hop Room, Granary, Cider Mill, Press and Cellar, Cart Horse Stable for six, Loft, Nag Stable for two, Loose Box, Loft, seven-bay Wain House with Granary over, and two Loose Boxes. Cow House for fourteen, Root House, Calves' Cot, and two Fold Yards with Shedding. Stone, timber and thatched four-bay Barn and two floors, Cow House for seven, iron French Barn. (French Barn claimed by Tenant.)

Pair of Modern Brick and Slated Cottages

each containing Kitchen, Back Kitchen and three Bedrooms ; Pig Cot and Privy.

SCHEDULE

No. on Plan	Tenant	Description	Acres	Total Acres
		PARISH OF DORMINGTON		
1	W. H. ; N. & D. Davies	Grass	21·357	
2		Arable...	11·423	
3		Grass	11·373	
4		Arable and Pair of Cottages ...	5·288	
8		Grass	2·108	
9		Pond	·159	
10		Orchard	3·502	
11		House and Buildings... ...	1·857	
12		Grass	8·279	
13		Do.	19·694	
14		Do.	·798	
15		Do.	·759	
Pt. 22		Orchard	·090	
37		Hop Yard	8·425	
38		Grass	12·707	
40		Orchard	2·779	
41		Arable...	20·560	
73		Do.	10·050	
74		Do.	5·680	
Pt. 75		Grass	2·925	
		PARISH OF STOKE EDITH		
6		Grass	4·924	
7		Do.	·460	
35		Do.	6·599	
		PARISH OF WESTON BEGGARD		
161		Grass	4·654	
162		Do.	1·800	
163		Do.	·509	
164		Do.	1·614	
165		Do.	8·650	
				179·023
		Total A. ...	...	179·023

This Lot is sold subject to a Right-of-Way for all puposes including the haulage of stone and timber between the points marked A and B on plan.

The Vendor will erect and maintain a fence on the easterly side of field No. 75 on plan.

Subject to charge under the Improvement of Land Acts of £23 17s. 2d. p. a., payable half yearly on the 24th day June and the 25th day of December, for the term of 34½ years in respect of the erection of Cottages.

Timber valuation, £139 11s. od.

Sale details of Claston

CHAPTER THREE

Childhood Days : 1923 – 1939

My mother's father, who lived at The Hyde at Woolhope, wasn't very well at the time, so a few weeks after I was born she took me over to see him. We stayed overnight and because there was no cot, I was put to bed in one of the drawers out of a chest

I was born on 27 September 1923 during the hop-picking season; apparently this was an occasion for a great celebration. My father bought a barrel of beer for the hop-pickers and all the farm staff to wet the baby's head. My early memories are of a happy home and it was my paternal grandfather, then living at Claston, who used to show my sister and me how to plant seeds and plants and how to look after them – at an early age he provided me with a lifelong interest in plants and agriculture in general.

One event in my childhood was so significant that even though it happened when I was only four years old, it has remained in my memory. This was the fire at the big house at Stoke Edith – the late 17th-century Stoke Edith Park, the beautiful home of the Foley family, where in Lady Emily Foley's time royalty was entertained. It was on 16 December 1927, when there had been a spell of very cold frosty weather, and my father went over to help rescue furniture and various items. It wasn't until a long time later, probably in the 1960s, when we went to see Mr Foley on business that my father noticed a huge Ming vase. He said to Andrew Foley, 'That's the first time I've seen that since I carried it out of the big fire'. He then told me that he and the head-keeper, Bert Dominey, had rescued all of Mrs Foley's jewellery from her bedroom. I am grateful to Andrew Foley for allowing me access to the following account of the fire, written by his uncle:

THE FIRE AT STOKE EDITH

The fire was discovered by a housemaid who was going downstairs about 7.30 to start her work and found the back stairs in the South East wing full of smoke when she got between the second and first floors. She ran back upstairs to the footman, who was just getting up and he ran down the back stairs in the South West wing, went through the dining room into the schoolroom, which was full of smoke, and he then woke up my father and mother.

My father told the housemaid to get all the other servants downstairs at once and rushed off to switch on the fire alarm bells to the cottages and the roof siren. He then telephoned Hereford City Police Fire Brigade and Ledbury Brigade.

Meanwhile, the footman had run out a hose from the hydrant on the main stairs outside the dining room and started playing it onto the panelling in the schoolroom.

The roof siren failed before reaching full pitch and this was attributed to ice. But the alarm bells brought the estate men in very quickly as they were all just getting up and the loud bell on the stable roof was heard well and

---

Stoke Edith in the 18th century

brought many others in. The result was that the whole of the Stoke Edith firemen were there within 10 minutes and many other helpers within 20 minutes or so.

The Stoke Edith firemen assembled, as per standing orders, in the stable arch and were puzzled to find no one there to tell them where the fire was – it was at that stage invisible from outside the house – until they were beckoned into the house by the servants who, as per standing fire drill orders, had assembled by the back door.

My father told the Stoke Edith firemen to take the fire engine to the pond and lay hose for a jet inside the house and one outside on the East front; two men to come into the house to man interior hydrants and two to lay out hose from exterior hydrants to cover the South front if required. His plan was to try and contain the fire in the South East wing or at any rate the East front.

A Stoke Edith man, Wargent the blacksmith, took over from the footman and was told to keep his jet playing from the main staircase up the well to prevent the fire getting into the skylight. About this time the pressure on the hydrants started to fail which was later attributed to the thick covering of ice on the pond in the park (men were later sent to smash the ice which restored the hydrant pressure but this was much later in the day). But the Stoke Edith fire engine was by now pumping and Wargent was given the hose which had been laid into the house.

My mother had started to organise the servants to take furniture and pictures out and they were soon joined by all the other helpers and started with the dining room.

Just as things were getting organised like this, a very silly and disastrous thing happened. Winser, my mother's personal maid was seen climbing along the wide ledge of the coping outside the third floor windows – going to the north from her bedroom window on the east side. Nobody ever found out how she got there or why – the generally accepted story was that she went back to her room to collect some personal belongings after going downstairs though she stoutly denied that she had ever been able to get downstairs (if so, how did all the other maids get down?). Be that as it may, there was now a panic-stricken woman on the roof who had to be got off somehow.

The Stoke Edith fire escape ladder kept slipping back on the icy north courtyard and could not reach the ledge of the coping. Bond, the chauffeur, tried going out onto the ledge from a third floor west window and climbing round the north front but was stymied by the north pediment which was ice bound.

The fire was now well into the roof on the East side and spreading northwards and downwards through the East side. Hoses were diverted to keep the fire off the NE corner, where Winser was, pending the arrival of the Hereford Brigade who carried life lines.

The north elevation of Stoke Edith in 1715

The Hereford Brigade arrived shortly afterwards having been somewhat delayed by the icy roads. It was under Inspector Hoskin who immediately telephoned for their second fire engine to be sent with more men; he set most of his men to work in the house and two men to deal with Winser. The Ledbury Brigade arrived about the same time.

By about 8.15 there were three fire engines at work still trying to confine the fire to the east side; most of the hoses were being used inside the house (Wargent was reinforced on the stairs by a Hereford hose) but some outside on the NE corner.

I was told that the men on the second floor were completely defeated because the fire was behind the panelling, which was as dry as kindling. As fast as they split panels open to get hoses in, they were driven back by the fire bursting through the opening. It was impossible to get into the roof space because there was only one way in and the roof space was already

An interior view of Stoke Edith House. Nash's parlour, late 18th century

full of smoke. The men on the second floor were slowly driven back towards the west side though Wargent and the Hereford man were still keeping the fire off the skylight and stair well. The arrival of the second Hereford fire engine allowed more hoses to be used but it became clear that nothing would save the roof.

Meanwhile Dent, the tenant farmer of Perton Court, organised the many helpers into salvage gangs working from room to room on the first and ground floors and going from the east side to begin with. These gangs got the whole of the furniture, books, ornaments and even the curtains out of those two floors except out of the schoolroom. They got most of the pictures out of the second floor and a little of the furniture from bedrooms on the west side – they could get heavy things out of the bedrooms because of bringing them down the staircase on the west side.

Sometime a bit after 9 o'clock – nobody could ever remember exactly when – the fire broke through into the skylight and its dome and although Wargent and the Hereford man were able to stay on the stairs for a few more minutes, falling debris forced them to retreat, the skylight crashed down and the stair well became a perfect well ventilated chimney for the fire. A few minutes later, debris from the roof started to come through the ceiling of the painted hall which crashed in about 9.30 bringing down a lot more burning debris. The order was then given to evacuate the house for all firemen and those salvage gangs still working on the west side bedrooms.

To go back to Winser who we left in a panic on the NE corner of the roof, Inspector Hoskin detailed P.Sgt Brommage and PC Glazzard to get her down with a ground party to help. The Hereford ladders reached to just under the wide coping and Glazzard performed the hazardous feat of climbing over Brommage's shoulders at the top of the ladder and getting onto the coping where a Davy-line was fired up to him. Winser was most coy about allowing a vulgar cop to strap the harness onto her in her night attire and she then declined to ease herself over the coping into the welcoming arms of PS Brommage on the grounds that it would be immodest, in her scant attire, to present her rear view to another cop. Glazzard was getting a bit bored after his hazardous climb, with spray from hoses freezing on him and apprehensive at the spread of the fire and he so forgot his normal constabulary sangfroid as to apply his heavy fireman's boot to Winser's bottom. She went down on the davy-line and bumped her head on landing; Glazzard hurried back down the line and Brommage made haste back down the ladder and they both then got on with fire-fighting.

There is not much more to say. After the skylight to the main staircase and the ceiling of the painted hall came in, the whole house became a chimney and fire-fighting was concentrated on trying to keep the outer walls cool to guard against their collapse and on watering down generally. Particular attention was paid to the silver strong room which was in the basement in about the middle of the house and which had not been cleared on purpose because it was fire-resistant; also to some safes on the first floor on the NW side which contained old papers.

Icicles after the fire at Stoke Edith

The chimney blocks were certainly standing at noon (there is a photograph showing this) but the tops of them collapsed sometime during the afternoon.

The S front collapsed either late that afternoon or during the night – I do not know which. This was undoubtedly because that front had no interior walls but did have seven windows making the whole much less substantial than the other fronts.

Watering down went on for another day or so by two fire engines and intermittently thereafter by the Stoke Edith fire engine for another four or five days. The Hereford Brigade were very good about staying on during the first 24 hours – they could call on relief men which the Stoke Edith Brigade could not.

Just after Christmas, a way was cut into the debris to get at the silver strong-room which was found with contents intact but tarnished by water which had seeped through the walls. The contents of the other safes referred to above suffered some heat damage.

When my father took me in the afternoon to see the house, I have an over-riding memory of a huge wall, covered in ice with long icicles hanging from the windowsills, and masses of water pipes from the fire engines lying in the grounds. All that was left standing was the outside walls; the building was never replaced and eventually the walls were demolished leaving just the outhouses and gardens of the original mansion. Sadly there was no chance of this great house being rebuilt.

During my childhood, Father and Mother were very friendly with Mr & Mrs George Bray, who kept a lot of ducks and lived at Dormington Court. There was a pond on the roadside which used to dry up quite quickly in early summer, and their ducks would then find their way across the road and Humble Toft hop-yard, a distance of about 300 yards, to our pond, which very seldom dried up. Father told me that on one occasion they invited Mr & Mrs Bray to an evening meal, caught two of their ducks and then served them roast duck at the meal. Later in the evening Mr Bray commented that it was very strange that two of his ducks were missing. Father then confessed that they had just eaten Mr Bray's ducks, much to his amusement!

During our early years, my sister, Kate, and I had a Scottish governess, Isla Jenkin Paterson, whose father was a grocer in Aberdeen. Until 1933, she taught us subjects such as arithmetic, English, geography, history and religious knowledge, but of course there was no sport. However, she was an excellent tutor and

Tom Jones on left and another man dipping sheep, whilst I watched

we both enjoyed being taught by her. Every day during term-time, unless the weather was too bad, she took us for a walk in the country lanes or on the local footpaths, and we recorded everything that we saw for the first time. She also taught us to stop, look and listen. During our walks she encouraged us to collect things – grasses, wild flowers, leaves and bits of wood. Occasionally, whilst out walking with Miss Paterson, we would see our local road man breaking large pieces of stone (with a special long-handled hammer) into small pieces which he then used for mending pot holes in the lane. Tumps of these larger stones had been put there for this purpose by the council. The road man's job was also to maintain certain stretches of the lane and road, involving cleaning out the ditches, to prevent surface water lying on the road, and also trimming the verges.

Mother used to ask Miss Paterson, when returning to Claston from Scotland at school holiday time, to bring her a supply of oatmeal, so whenever we had porridge for breakfast it was made with genuine Scottish oatmeal. Mother also always used McCloids tea, which she had learnt about through Miss Paterson – this would arrive through the post in a huge wooden box.

Well before Christmas, Mother made the Christmas puddings, weighing out the fruit the day before. The next morning, my sister Kate and I would go into the kitchen before we started lessons and Mother let us stir the mixture before it was cooked as this was thought to be lucky. Christmas Day was special – it was the only time we children were allowed to stay up for supper. We always had a marvellous meal and being able to stay up made this a great event. Another memory of Christmas was the tree, which stood in the corner of the dining room, decorated with real candles, whilst buckets of water stood close by, just in case! At that time we did not have electricity and the candles on the tree were lit just once for about ten minutes, because of the risk of fire, before being extinguished. It was after that exciting event that we had our Christmas presents. Candles were used throughout the house so we both used to go to bed carrying a candle. We were modernized to some extent – we had hot water and an upstairs toilet, however our parents were quite strict and during the daytime we

23

Bert Green with me and my sister Joan.
An old, thatched barn is in the background

were not allowed to go upstairs to use it, but had to go to the outside loo in the garden. What always intrigued me was that there were three seats in this lavatory – it was quite a big place. The two grown-up seats faced the door and a child's seat was on the side. Its original use must have been quite a convivial event!

In 1933, at the age of ten, I started at the Margaret Allen School at St Nicholas Church Hall in Hereford, but only attended for the summer term. At that time there were a lot of boys there including a number of farmers' sons and the two Wright boys, whose father Sid owned a greengrocer's shop in Hereford.

At the beginning of the Autumn term of 1933, I was sent to Hereford High School for Boys in Widemarsh Street, on the corner with Blackfriars Street. It was considered better at that time than the Cathedral School, the other Hereford boys' school. I understand the fees were £2 4s. a term. I enjoyed school, remaining there until 1939, when I took my School Certificate and achieved what was considered to be a reasonable result. One of the disappointments I suppose was that, being a country boy, I didn't get much opportunity for sport, because the sports field was at Wyeside where Hereford Rugby ground is now. The games lessons were 80 minutes long, but by the time you'd walked there from Widemarsh Street and changed, then changed ready to catch the bus back, you never had more than 45 minutes of sport and, in the summer, especially when we were playing cricket, you were lucky if you had one innings with the bat.

Like most people of my generation I have many memories of that period in the 1930s when war was on the horizon, but we youngsters did not even think about it. Often I had lunch at Harris's Café, on the corner next to Macfisheries, between Broad Street and what is now Eign Gate. At that time, lunch cost one shilling and I remember that old Mr Harris, who was short and very fat, was always having his lunch downstairs when we arrived. Later on, while we were having our lunch in the upstairs restaurant, he would come upstairs and have another lunch! He always gave us a very good meal and, when we had a Christmas lunch there, he used to give us cider to drink. Sometimes, if I wanted to buy something and needed to save some of my lunch money, I went to Higgins pork butcher's shop in Widemarsh Street and bought a pork pie for 3d, leaving me 9d to spend.

When we first started school, Kate and I were taken there by a neighbouring farmer, Mr Meredith Owen, of Perton Court. On one occasion after dropping his son David off at the Cathedral School, while he was driving down Widemarsh Street to take me to the High School, we saw a cyclist riding up the middle of the street, reading a newspaper. Mr Owen stopped the car but the cyclist did not see us and, to our amazement, rode straight into us.

At that time, Kate went to the Margaret Allen School, later named the Haberdashers Redcap School and then she went to the Hereford High School for Girls, which was on the corner of Coningsby Street and Widemarsh Street. At the boys' school across the road, the seats in the physics classroom were in tiers and there used to be a scramble amongst the boys to get a seat at the back near the window. From there it was possible to watch the girls playing tennis – a great attraction!

Later on, my sister and I used to go to school each day by bus; the fare was 4½d return. Father used to give us 6d to cover the travel, so we had 1½d pocket money every day. We saved this up to buy Milky Ways – these were cheaper than Mars Bars, which we liked much better!

When we were a little older, we used to catch the bus for Claston in St. Peter's Square, but the service eventually moved to the new bus station, built on the site of the old County gaol in Commercial Road. One of our great delights was to catch the Leicester coach if we were there early enough, as it left at 4.20 p.m., rather than the Ledbury bus at 4.30 p.m. Ours was the only stop before Ledbury, but on Bank Holidays and special occasions, we were not allowed on this busy coach. There would often be up to five coaches at these times, all packed with people leaving Hereford on the long journey to Worcester, Stratford-on-Avon and finally Leicester.

At school, discipline was quite strict and on one occasion, when I was still going to school by bus, having done something wrong, I was kept in at the end of the day and missed the bus home, so I had to walk. On another occasion, when the same thing happened, I was walking through Tupsley and saw the master who had kept me in. He was working in his garden and asked, 'Why are you walking?' I replied, 'Well, it's the only way I can get home'. 'Oh', he said, 'you can't walk home'. So he got his car out and brought me home.

When my sister and I were considered to be old enough to cycle to school, this was another way of earning a bit more pocket money, because Father still gave us the 6d each day.

We also used to earn extra pocket money by harvesting and

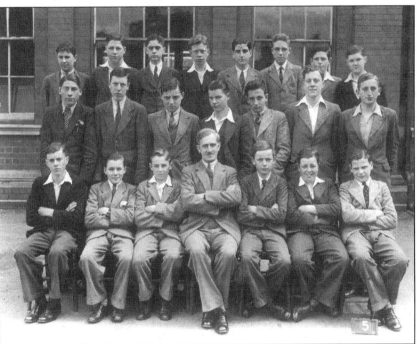

Hereford High School, 1937. Lower VB
Back row: [-], K. Lawley, P.A. Sadler, R.R. Phillips, J.M. Salaverri, N.J. Perry,
E.H. Tompkins, ? Pugh
Middle row: [-], R.G.N. Baker, G.M. Williams, [-], [-], W.J. Langford, J.R. Ford
Front row: D.H. Rock, P.W. Williams, George Preece, A.M. Hartley, Peter Davies,
Frank Pritchard, C.H. Palamountain

selling swedes, with Father's agreement. We built a truck to transport them and used to walk round the surrounding villages selling them at ¼d each. At Claston we had a super stream where fantastic watercress grew and we used to pick bunches, take them with us to school, then at lunch time sell them to the town shops. One of the masters, whose family lived in Anglesey, on discovering that I was a farmer's son inquired if we had any holly on the farm. At that time we had quite a lot and so he asked if I could send some to his mother. Each year, I used to collect bunches of holly, pack them in a box and post them to his mother. He paid me quite well for that service.

Another vivid memory of my schooldays was the annual May Fair, held in the streets of Hereford. On one particular occasion a lot of us boys got together and went to one of the circular Roll A Penny stalls where you rolled a penny down a little slot, trying to make it land within a square that gave a profit. There was only one person operating the stall and no guard around it so whilst one boy attracted attention at one side, another would pop a coin onto one of the winning squares. After the stallholder realised he was paying out a lot more money than usual, he threatened us and sent us away.

Farming was very tough in the 1930s and a lot of farmers went bankrupt. Indeed two farmers in the valley committed suicide. At that time, my father had a milk round as well as the farm. He and one of the men used to take the milk round the local villages in two vans and, when I was old enough, I used to have to help milk the cows before I went to school. Another job I had to do, but which I did not enjoy, was turning the handle of the separator, which was a machine to separate the cream from the milk. Mother then made the cream into butter to be sold on the milk round. I was fascinated by the machine, but it was jolly hard work turning the handle to get it up to the required speed, which used to take quite a while for the five gallons we normally handled at a time. I well remember how my arms used to ache! On Saturdays and Sundays I used to help deliver the milk. There were no bottles then, of course, so you had a metal churn with a lid on it full of milk in the van, plus both a pint and a half-pint measure. You went to the house and sometimes there was a jug or other container outside, with a message to say how much milk to put in, but most times you knocked on the door and the lady came and had a chat and told you what she wanted.

Another place we delivered to was Stoke Edith station, where Father used to let me take the milk to the signalman in his box while he delivered to the station master's house and other railway staff. While in the signal box, I loved hearing the bells which indicated the position of the oncoming trains. When a steam-drawn express passenger train went through the station at speed, the whole place shook. I was always very intrigued to watch the signalman move the long-handled levers to adjust the signals for the next train and also to observe him turn a great wheel which opened the level crossing gates to allow the traffic to cross.

We kept a lot of hens at Claston, so we were able to take eggs and dressed chickens with us on the milk round. The big hen houses were scattered around the farm and in the summer months it was one of my jobs to run around the farm at nightfall to shut them up. The hens normally went into the huts of their own accord, but if you went too early there would often be two or three still outside. Sometimes you could persuade them to go in, but on other occasions they would all come out again and you would have to go back home and start all over again half an hour later.

Hay-making with a hay-loader

After about 1934, Father started killing lambs and then pigs at Claston, so that the milk round became more of a travelling shop. Trade increased and, just before the war began, Father was killing about 24 lambs and 10 pigs a week. He bought most of the animals from local farms in the Lower Frome Valley, but eventually the butchers began to object and said we hadn't got a proper abattoir. There was nothing really wrong with it, for although it was fairly basic, it was very clean and hygienic and nobody was ever ill from eating our meat. For cleaning purposes there was always plenty of hot water, which was heated in a large metal container known as a 'copper', with a wood fire at the base. Originally, this copper was built to provide hot water to do the family washing and the building was called the wash house. The copper was filled with buckets of cold water, pumped from the well and carried by hand.

At that time, Father was renting one of the large parks at Stoke Edith from Mr Foley. This enabled him to keep more cattle, so we had to make a lot of hay to provide for them and always built two large ricks. To help with the workload at hay-making time, Father had an agreement with a Mr Booton, who lived and farmed at Wooton Farm, Checkley, to bring his horses to help us with this task. We needed extra horses at hay-making time as two were needed for mowing, whilst another was used for turning and then swathing the hay ready for loading on to the wagons with the hay loader. The hay loader was attached to the rear of the wagon and it collected and lifted the loose hay on to the wagon. It then took two men to load the wagon and two horses to pull it. Another two horses were then needed to take the load of hay to the barn or hay rick. In return, Father used to help and advise Mr Booton on his hop-growing. I think he grew about eight acres.

Father then increased his labour force by one man, whose name was Tom Hoskins. He lived on Tower Hill in one of the old cottages which are now derelict. Father was apt to make the hay a little too soon, which could cause heating, and one evening the rick got very hot. In fact I think it nearly caught fire and they had to cut into it to cool it down. While they were doing this, Tom spotted the lights down in what is now the Stoke hop-yard, I suppose from a car, and he came rushing about 1/2 mile down the hill to help. Tom's father was alive at that time and was much taller than him and in his haste, because there was no electricity at the house, Tom had put on his father's trousers by mistake and arrived in the hop-yard wearing trousers which were much too long for him *and* he had them on back to front! By the time he arrived, all the work had been done and my father was handing out some cider, which prompted them all to say to Tom, 'You knew we'd done the work and you only came down for the cider!'

THE FERGUSON CLUB JOURNAL

MARKETING OF THE FERGUSON-BROWN

David Markham

1935 was the year in which Harry Ferguson and David Brown reached agreement to manufacture and market the first Ferguson System tractor, the Model A. Two companies were formed, one with responsibility for engineering and marketing, Harry Ferguson Ltd., the other, David Brown Tractors Ltd. (a subsidiary of David Brown and Sons) with responsibility for the manufacturing side.

Because the new tractor was so revolutionary, and so small, it was vital to convince both farmers and dealers that the System worked and could be of benefit to them. Ferguson therefore embarked on an extensive marketing campaign. This took a variety of forms.

Fordson tractor. Ferguson Brown demonstration

In 1935 Father purchased our first tractor, a second-hand Fordson, which was quite a major event on the farm and exciting for us children. There was a report from *The Ferguson Club Journal* on the marketing of the Ferguson-Brown tractor in 1935. I was fortunate enough to be able to see this demonstration which was held in Bean Acre hop-yard at Dormington. The boy on the right in the picture (above) is Dick Walker, who later worked at Dormington Court until he became farm manager at Pomona Farm, Bartestree.

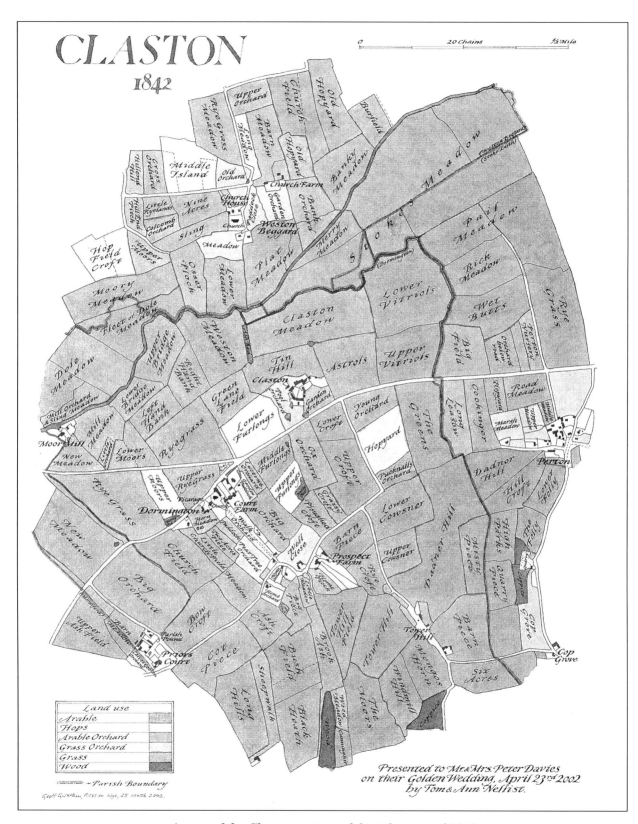

CLASTON
1842

0   20 Chains   ½ Mile

Land use

Arable	
Hops	
Arable Orchard	
Grass Orchard	
Grass	
Wood	

~ Parish Boundary

Geoff G. Gwatkin, Ross on Wye, 25 March 2002.

*Presented to Mr. & Mrs. Peter Davies
on their Golden Wedding, April 23rd 2002
by Tom & Ann Nellist.*

A copy of the Claston section of the tithe map of 1842

28

Hop-pickers arriving at Stoke Edith station.
Note the round topped carriage windows and doors

Wagons collecting hop-pickers baggage from Stoke Edith station

At that time, Father farmed about 200 acres and we just had two hop-yards; the Old Hop-yard and the Vitrols, which have both been in hops until recently. The former had been in hops, probably, since about 1740, as the Tithe Map of 1842 shows 'The Old Hopyard' and also 'the old kilns'. The old kilns were round, the largest had a 13ft 6ins diameter and held about 28 sacks of green hops, while the other two were only 11ft 6ins in diameter and held about 22 sacks each. These kilns all had the original pointed tip to the white cowls, which were a very picturesque feature of the Herefordshire landscape. The cowls were round, with at least a five foot base and were made with cleverly shaped boards going up to a point. At least one-third of each cowl had no boards, to allow the hot wet air to be drawn up and escape, after passing through the hops while they were being dried. The cowls were designed to rotate so that the boarded part was facing the wind, thus increasing the air flow through the hops. In later years, fans were used for this purpose, enabling the hops to be loaded about 2ft 6ins deep, instead of about 12ins as they were when the kilns were originally built. A board about six inches wide and five foot long protruded from the centre of the unboarded part of the cowl, acting as a weather-vane.

One of the great joys of the hop-picking season, as there were only open fires to dry the hops, was to sit in front of the fire at night before the kilns were loaded for the second time that day, to enjoy the warmth, the hum of the fans and the smell of the hops. Several old Welsh miners used to come in at night and help load the kilns after working in the hop-yard during the day. They did not want any payment, but settled just for our local cider. My sister and I used to love to sit in the kilns and talk to these old characters, hearing their stories about Welsh mining and what happened in the pits and about life in the Welsh valleys. At that time the hop-pickers used to come from South Wales by train and the horse and wagon would be sent to Stoke Edith station to collect them and their luggage.

My father used to dry some of the hops in kilns at Lugwardine, but in 1937 decided to build a new kiln at Claston. This was done with local labour and the bricks for the walls were reclaimed from part of the old rick-yard wall. A pure air coke-fired system was installed in this new kiln, which was situated at the house-end of the old cooling room, where in the 1990s we used to hold the Parish Suppers. One of our regular staff, Bill Williams, was in charge of stoking the coke-fired kilns during the night shift. To ensure that he did not go to sleep while resting in the wheelbarrow and let the fire out, he ingeniously fixed it so that if he went to sleep, his head would go forward and he would be tipped out. My father also planted a new 5 acre hop-yard on the south side of the main road, opposite the present farm entrance.

One of the sad things about hop-picking when I was a very small boy was that we used to have to burn sulphur in order to bleach the hops. This gave me a sore throat, so whilst the hops were being brought in, Kate and I were dispatched to stay with our maternal grandmother, who lived in the hamlet at Stoke Edith. However, we were allowed to return for the weekends on a Saturday morning and as we walked the mile along the A438, seeing the chimneys of Claston as we came along the road, was a great sight.

As part of the varied farm business, Mother ran a shop for the hop-pickers and we used to go in there quite often, because she sold sweets. However, there was trouble if we were ever caught with any sweets! Eventually, as we grew older, we were allowed to help serve in the shop. It contained a wide variety of goods including groceries, milk and cigarettes as well as the sweets. Mother also sold meat at the weekend. I remember being in the shop one day when there was a tap on the window and a lady asked for three half-pennies worth of stamps. I couldn't understand what she meant, because stamps could then only be bought in a post office. I went back into the house and asked Mother, who told me the lady was referring to snuff!

Looking back on my schooldays, I suppose one of the over-riding memories was of all the family-owned shops in Hereford city centre, where many of the owners lived above their shop premises. During the term that I was at the Margaret Allen School, we used to walk down to a café on the corner of Broad Street and King Street and I was always intrigued by the shops facing King Street in what is now part of the Cathedral Close. Outside one of those shops, I can't remember which, there were masses of leather goods hanging in front of the window. I suppose the most important place to a farmer's young son was the hop and corn market and the hop warehouse, located in Broad Street. After hop-picking, and right through until Christmas, whenever you walked down there, there was a wonderful smell of hops pervading the air. There were more inns and hotels in Broad Street than there are now. In addition to the Green Dragon, there was the Mitre Hotel, which is now part of NatWest Bank and Gabbs solicitors, and the City Arms, which is now Barclays Bank. On the other side, in-between Wilson's florist shop and the hop market was the Kemble Theatre.

In High Street, running the short distance between High Town and Broad Street, were the Marchant brothers' two shops – one a tobacconist and the other a grocery. A third brother had a chemist shop in High Town. Marchant's grocery shop was a wonderful place where you could always smell coffee beans being roasted and gaze at the hams and cheeses suspended from the ceiling. Roberts Café was in High Street, and a lot of the farmers' wives used to go there for lunch on a Wednesday, market day. My mother occasionally took me there during holiday time. One of the things that I remember vividly about Roberts', which was on two levels, was the way the food appeared from the kitchen, presumably down in the cellar, on a small lift with shelves, operated by pulling ropes.

Further along from Roberts, passing into High Town, was Greenlands, which was really like a mini Harrods in those days. I can remember at Christmas time going down to the toy department, which was fabulous, complete with model railways and the opportunity to go on a journey to see Father Christmas in his grotto and gaze at all the beautiful toys on display in the shop. The Butter Market was quite different from what it is now, as there were no shops in the centre, just tables or trestles where local farmers sold their produce. At Christmas time, this was one of the main places to buy dressed turkeys.

On the north side of High Town were Gurneys and Fearis, both grocers and wine and spirit merchants. One of the great memories at Gurneys was the payment system. The assistant put a ticket and your money into a little cup above her head, screwed it in, pulled a lever and the little cup shot along a wire into a central glass-faced office. There were wires all over the shop with these cups whizzing backwards and forwards and you very quickly received your change. Close to Gurneys was Creswells, the butcher whose son was at the High School with me.

Broad Street, Hereford, with cattle for sale, and the hop-market in the late 19th century

Facing Fearis' across High Town was Wakefield Knight, which was a wool and draper's shop and further to the east, Augustus Edwards, the 'Furrier of the West', with the lovely curved shop window. In Pritchard & Sons, the tailors, the clothes were actually made on the premises.

Leaving High Town for Commercial Street, there was Hardings, the ironmonger, whose shop went right through to Union Street where they had a warehouse across the street. In those days, Hardings supplied the hop growers in the area with all their requisites – chemicals (generally just sulphur and copper), string and also the hessian hop pockets. In the warehouse, there was a Mr Davies from Tarrington, who used to mark all the hop pockets with the year and the name and address of the grower by hand, taking him most of the year to do so. Also in Commercial Street, opposite Hardings, was Goldings, another ironmonger, and the main shop of Wilsons the florists.

Of all the family shops I can remember, I believe Rowberrys, the butcher in Union Street, remained on the same premises longest: sadly closing in 2005.

It was during my schooldays that the Odeon Cinema was built in Commercial Street, whilst the Ritz Cinema was built further down in Commercial Road. It was constructed on part of the site of the old prison, concealing the new bus station at the rear. The former Prison Governor's house at the bus station is now used by travel agents.

High Town, Hereford, looking east towards the Old House about 1920

One of the most important shops in the city in my school-boy opinion was Higgins, the pork butcher's in Widemarsh Street, where he sold his delicious pork pies. Further down, nearer to the High Schools, was the Garrick Theatre and also the huge cooling towers for the electricity works.

Looking back on those memories, I think it is fair to say that my sister and I had a very happy childhood, apart from the Spring of 1931 when my Father, Mother and I were all desperately ill with pneumonia. Two nurses were installed in the house to look after us and I can still remember the pain from the very hot antiflogistin poultices with which they covered my chest. I also remember how astonished the nurses were when on one occasion one of our doctors, Dr Walker, arrived at the house at 6.30 a.m., having been bird-watching in Haugh Wood!

In 1933 and 1935 my two younger sisters were born and helping to look after them added to our enjoyment of life. It was intended that I should stay at school in 1939 for two further years to take my Higher School Certificate, before attending Wye College in Kent to follow a two-year agricultural course. However, this plan was abandoned because, with the outbreak of war, it was considered too dangerous to go to that part of the country. The only sad recollection of my schooldays occurred after I had left school. Having been in the same form as 32 or 33 boys for some six years, we got to know one another really well. Sadly many of them were killed in the ensuing war.

CHAPTER FOUR

Early Days, Working on the Farm : 1939–1951

During the summer holidays in 1939, everyone was getting very concerned about the Germans occupying various parts of Europe. Father, having fought through the First World War, was particularly anxious as he knew only too well all about the horrors of war. However, on 3 September 1939, Mr Chamberlain announced that the U.K. was at war with Germany. Soon after this, Father received a letter informing him that the High School would only be operating on a half-day basis, and he thought that going to school for half a day instead of the normal full day would not be good for my education. It was obvious that there was no chance of my going to Wye College as had been intended, so it was decided that I should leave school to work on the farm, although I was only 15 years old.

MY FIRST JOBS

Hop-picking was quickly upon us following the outbreak of war and I think my first job was hauling the sacks of hops from the hop-yard with a horse-drawn wagon. We were picking about 158 sacks a day, so this meant that there would have been about three or four loads per day. As I was very inexperienced, I had difficulty in controlling the horses; in fact, I know I did not always do so! I remember on one of the very first days of hop-picking whilst working in the Vitrols hop-yard, I had to have two horses to pull the load because it had been very wet and the ground was slippery. Coming along the headland at the end of the first bushelling, to my horror I saw that Mrs Green, who was doing the booking, had made a fire and had laid out her crockery on the headland over which I had to pass. There was no way that I could stop the horses and we went straight over the crockery, creating great havoc! How much damage I did I can't remember, but there must have been a lot of broken china, and when I returned to the hop-yard for the next bushelling I was confronted by a very angry Mrs Green. The booking involved recording the number of bushels of hops picked by each picker and was normally done three times a day. Another of my tasks was to take bundles of wood called faggots to the hop-yard each day for the pickers to make fires on which to boil their kettles.

On returning to the farm, the hopsacks were carried up the stairs to be loaded into the kilns and once the kilns were filled the rest of the sacks were laid out on the lawn ready for the night loads. The first loads of hops would have been dried by about 10 or 11 p.m. and it was the Welsh miners who, after working in the hop-yard all day, used to help to carry up the sacks from the lawn and re-load the kilns for the night drying. They were then rewarded, as I've already mentioned, with some cider which they enjoyed whilst sitting round the open kiln fires, talking of times gone by.

The next job that I can remember doing was helping to feed the cattle. The cattle were all housed in open yards and were fed with either swedes or mangolds. These were pulled by hand; the swedes then being topped and tailed with a special knife. The mangolds had to be handled very carefully because they were rather like beetroot and could be damaged very easily. The tops were screwed off and were then used to cover the large heaps of mangolds to protect them from frost whilst they were left to mature for a week or so. Then they were loaded by hand onto carts and tipped into the clamp in the rick-yard. This was quite hard

John Jones littering cattle in the old farmyard

work because mangolds grew to a large size and were very heavy. Both the mangolds and the swedes were stored in large clamps in the rick-yard, covered first with straw and then with hedge trimmings. This was done by hand and the trimmings were carted in quickly when they were dry and a thick layer put over the mangolds in particular to stop them getting frosted. Each day, some of the mangolds had to be wheeled by barrow into the pulphouse where they were pulped one or two at a time into small pieces and mixed with chaff to be fed to the cattle.

Straw and hay were cut up for chaff. All the equipment for grinding corn, chaff-cutting and pulping was driven by an old Blackstone engine, which had to be heated with a lamp to start it up. We had two grinders, one to roll the corn for the sheep and the other to grind the corn for the cattle. This was then weighed out, enough for a day, using so many shovels full of the pulped mangolds plus a certain amount of chaff mixed together. Then it was carried to the cattle in huge sacks which were nearly as big as me. It was very difficult feeding the cattle, because they would become excited and wanted the food quickly, so you had to be very careful otherwise you were tipped into the manger or knocked over.

A tractor was used for ploughing and for drilling, but all the other work was done with horses and I can remember how tired I used to be in the first year, after starting work at 7 a.m., then walking up and down the fields, harrowing to level the ground and cover the seed after the drill. Of course, when you had finished work in the fields at 5 p.m., you still had to go and feed the cattle which took another hour at least.

Another job was harvesting the sugar beet. The beet was lifted by the horses pulling a special plough, which just released it from the ground and then you had to go and pull it up by hand and lay it in rows, with the tops all to one side. It was then left for a few days for the tops to wilt before they were cut off and the beet piled up. We had a special tool to do this, which was a handle with a knife, maybe 15 inches long, with a spike on the end. You bent down and picked the sugar beet up by sticking the spike into it, then holding it in your left hand you cut off the top and tossed it onto the heap. This had to be done correctly. If you cut too much off you were wasting the sugar beet and if you didn't take enough off then you were penalised when it was examined at the sugar beet factory. The beet was then loaded by hand onto either carts or wagons and hauled into a large clamp. A special fork was used for doing this, which had knobs on the end of the prongs to stop them sticking into and damaging the sugar beet. The clamp was built at the end of the drive at Claston and upon receipt of permits from the sugar beet factory in Kidderminster, it was transported to Stoke Edith station on wagons or a lorry, then hand-loaded into trucks to go to the factory. I shall never forget topping the sugar beet, especially on cold, frosty mornings when handling it with the tops wet and frosty was a horrible job!

Sheepcote, Tractors and Horses

At the beginning of 1940, my father had the opportunity to take over 100 acres of land – the Sheepcote – at Bartestree, which we rented from Mrs Barneby at 5 shillings per acre. Mrs Barneby lived at the Sheepcote and was the owner of this estate. She was a very well-respected lady who played a leading part in the life of both Bartestree Church and the village. She had a very beautiful garden, which was maintained for many years by John Harwood, who was also a Churchwarden at Dormington Church over a long period. Mrs Barneby had two sons who were both in the army and tragically her younger son was the first member of the Herefordshire Regiment to be killed soon after the D-day landings in the Second World War. Her elder son, Colonel H. Barneby, eventually took over the estate from his mother.

Before we became tenants, 70 acres of the 100 acres had been ploughed up and put down to barley, producing only 20 tons of grain altogether. The land was in a very poor state because it had been used continuously for growing grass for producing hay. It was virtually impossible to cultivate or to do anything with it when we began farming it.

Also in 1940, we purchased our first new Fordson tractor, which had iron wheels, no cab, an iron seat and cost £123. I was given the task of driving this and a lot of my time was spent working at the Sheepcote. I would leave home at 7 o'clock in the morning, Mother having prepared my breakfast and lunch. Fortunately Mr Harwood had a room in a disused cottage in the garden where he worked and he invited me to go in at breakfast and lunch-time to eat my food. As he had a fire in there, he used to make tea for me and for any of the other men when they were working there. I remember in that year we were ploughing up, for the first time, a very old pasture at Claston which is now the Greens hop-yard. I had not done any ploughing before and the tractor driver, Fred Jones, who was ploughing in the same grass field would not teach me how to do it. I was using a brand new plough, with painted plough-boards, which made it more difficult anyway, especially as the soil is fairly light and uncorrosive in the Greens, but Bert Green, who did not even drive a tractor, came to my aid. It took us some time to get the paint worn off the plough and the plough-boards shiny so that the soil slipped easily over them, but by the end of the day, much to the tractor driver's disgust, we were making a better job than he was! With this two-furrow Ransome plough, which was also used in the hop-yards, I must have ploughed several thousand acres over the next fifteen years and could easily plough over five acres a day.

Bert Green was not my only tutor, as Barlow Walker, the foreman at Dormington Court, frequently used to pop through the hedge of the hop-yard if I was working nearby after I first left school, to have a chat and give friendly advice as to how to proceed with whatever job I was doing at the time. I remember on one occasion, when I was spreading nitrogen in the Lime hop-yard, he asked how much I had put on per acre, and then asked how much I was supposed to be putting on. This made me realise that I was putting on about four times as much as instructed. As this particular drill had not been used before for spreading sulphate of ammonia, which was a finer type of nitrogen and as I had had no instructions or knowledge of how to set the drill, I was therefore very pleased that Barlow happened to come across to me when I had only done a few rows. At harvest time, we had more hops per acre on the few rows of hops on which I had put the extra nitrogen by mistake than on the rest of the crop.

Before we had the second tractor, I used to have to drive the horse when we were dusting the hops at night in order to control hop damson aphid. This was done with nicotine powder. The tractor driver would drive up one row with the tractor-drawn duster, and I drove up the next-but-one row with a horse-drawn duster which was driven by an engine. All I had to do once I had put powder in the hopper was to start the engine up, put the horse in the end of the row and then run up the next row to meet him at the far end. The horse would go up the row quite easilywithout being held , before being met and led to the next row to be dusted. Occasionally, the engine would back-fire which frightened the horse, making him go very quickly, and I had to run very fast to collect him at the far end! As he would keep up with the tractor, I needed to run up and down the rows equally fast. It was quite hard work but kept me very fit! One of the problems, however, was that the dusting had to be done when it was very calm, and the perfect evening would be when it was about 70° and fairly humid, so that the powder would hang like a fog. Unfortunately, as you ran up and down the rows through this nicotine dust, not only you, but also the horse, kept sneezing.

EWES AND LAMBS

In 1941, for some reason I was given the task of lambing the ewes. At that time, they were kept in the orchard by the farm at night and then taken out to a field during the daytime. I was able to drive them down the main road, now the A438, with just a sheepdog to help me as there was very little traffic in those days. I remember one day, ten ewes lambed in this field and on this occasion I had to carry ten sets of twins back to the farm; one set at a time, with the mother following. Then I had to go back to drive the rest of the ewes to the farm for the night. I was pretty exhausted by the end of the day.

It was then, for the first time ever, that we had an attack of lamb dysentery – something we had never heard of before. It was very infectious and we lost a large number of lambs before the vet discovered what it was.

CROPS AND RICKS

Father pitching corn

The Massey binder

By 1942, with the huge increase in acreage of cereals, we had to replace our old Albion binder, which had been purchased by my grandfather during the First World War. At the beginning of the Second World War, I can remember horses pulling it, but it could also be pulled by a tractor. It was changed for a Massey Harris binder, which cut a much wider swathe and was designed to work at a much higher speed. At that time, I was driving the tractor which pulled it. I was very excited about having this new machine to use for the first time and Bert Green and I went to cut some winter oats in what is now a new orchard by Claston cottages. We assembled the binder quite quickly, although there were no instructions. Unfortunately, we had omitted to do one thing and the binder would miss a little bit of the corn, so that it kept blocking at the end on the outside of the cutter bar. We eventually found out that we had failed to put in a little piece of iron that you just pressed down over the end finger, and when done this eliminated the problem. I had great ambitions to cut these five acres during the evening, but we failed because of this omission.

Our acreage of corn had quickly increased and by the time we had the new binder we had 120 acres. After this had been cut by the binder, all the sheaves had to be collected and placed upright by hand, standing in stacks of six or eight sheaves, called stooks. Then it was left to ripen for at least

Corn ricks at Claston

two weeks before being pitched onto wagons and put into either the barn or into corn ricks. We were about three weeks actually pitching corn which filled the four barns and made at least three corn ricks. It was quite hard work, but once you got the knack of it, you could pitch two sheaves at a time onto the wagon. Pitching was done with a long-handled, two-pronged fork, called a pike, and you stuck the prongs into the sheaves in a special way before putting them on the wagon. Two of you did this together, one on each side of the wagon, with another man stacking them on the wagon, and as long as you lifted the sheaves and put them onto the wagon in the correct way, he could position the load very quickly. However, if you just tossed the sheaves on anyhow it made life very difficult for him and you soon had some sheaves thrown back down at you!

Making corn ricks, or even stacking corn in the barn, was a very skilled job because you had to make sure that not only were the sheaves secure so that they could not slip out of the bay, but also when you started the rick you had to build a stook in the middle to keep the corn ears off the ground, to stop them getting damp. Then you worked round and round that central stook until you covered either the bottom of the rick or the corn bay. Then the process was reversed but starting on the outside, working round and round to the middle to secure the sheaves on the outside of the rick or bay. This second layer was repeated, always with the ears facing the centre, until you had completed the rick or bay. The roof of the rick was made by bringing the outside layer of sheaves in about 12 inches and repeating these layers until there was only a very small space at the top. The roof of the rick was then thatched with wheat straw. When you came to do the threshing, it was amazing how many rats there were actually in the rick. I remember on one occasion, when we were threshing in the rick-yard, we saw a rat go down a hole. So we dug it out and kept digging more and more out, until we had caught over one hundred rats from the one hole!

Bert Green, who lived at Prospect Farm and had worked at Claston since the early 1930s, used to build the ricks, and on one occasion he decided he was going to be very skilled and make a rick with round ends. He rounded one end but found it so difficult that he decided to make the other end square as usual, so the final result looked a little bit like a ship. Consequently, we named that rick H.M.S. Green.

The only corn that was not put into either a rick or corn bay was the winter oats and in August, Tracy Read, the threshing contractor at that time, used to come to our farm first, often with a new threshing machine. Then we loaded the sheaves onto a wagon and instead of putting them into a rick, we put the sheaves onto the threshing machine off the wagon in the field. It was threshed and the straw tied into bundles called boltings, then either stacked into a rick or brought back to the farm because it was very valuable as feed for the cattle.

I remember when we had unloaded the wagons, and looking back it was a very sad thing, that there would be masses of baby harvest mice running around on the bed of the wagon, having been disturbed from their nests in the stooks of corn.

A sketch of an old four-wheel wagon

At that time, we had one old broad-wheeled wagon, two other wagons and a new one made by Percy Cox in Hereford. The broad-wheeled wagon was fairly narrow and it was a very skilled job to load the corn onto it. However, you could still get a very good load on although there were no hay thripples on the front of the wagon, but just two small, wooden extensions. I think I accidentally destroyed this lovely old wagon by going too fast when we had a tractor-hitch put on it. The hay and corn-ricks were all thatched and then, during the winter, Tracy Read's steam-engine used to come to drive the threshing machine and all the corn was threshed. Later, the steam engine was replaced by a Massey tractor. Threshing was jolly hard work, especially if the corn being threshed had to be taken to the granary. For this you had a hand-wound sack-lifter, which was a special sack cart so that you could lift the sacks up to be level with your back. Then you had to carry these 2 cwt sacks across the rick-yard, down one of the cattle-feeding passages and up the granary steps, a distance of about 50 yards, before tipping the corn into heaps in the granary. I don't think this did my back much good. On one occasion George, who was operating the threshing machine, asked me to speed up the steam engine a little, but feeling devilish I put the lever to full throttle. The threshing machine started to rock on its wheel blocks and clouds of dust enveloped it. No-one could remember George moving so quickly as he did then to slow the engine down and what he said to me is unprintable!

DRIVING PROBLEMS

When I was old enough, Mr Lawrence, who had a garage in St. Owen Street, taught me to drive my father's car. Mother asked him how I had got on when he brought me home after my first lesson and his reply was that I was very good at reversing. This was no doubt due to the fact that I had been driving a tractor on the farm for about two years and had also been allowed to drive the car around the farmyard and put it in the garage. There were no driving tests in those days and after a few lessons Mr Lawrence said that I was competent to drive on my own. This, however, was debatable! On the first occasion when I did so, I was sent to Bartestree to fill the car with petrol at Mr Ellerman's garage. The local roadman was pushing his wheelbarrow close to the entrance to the garage and unfortunately, as I approached, I misjudged the distance between his wheelbarrow and the car. Much to the amusement of Mr Ellerman, I gently took the barrow out of the roadman's hands! The latter's language was colourful, but fortunately no damage was done to him, the wheelbarrow or the car.

HOPS AND HOP-PICKERS

As the war progressed, the Government asked farmers in Herefordshire and Worcestershire to plant extra hops because there was a shortage of beer for the troops. Father thought this was a good idea, especially as the Government gave you quota, which was an allowance to sell a given quantity of hops per acre. This is the way in which the hop market was controlled by the Hops Marketing Board. Hence we started planting hops, thereby changing the future farming policy at Claston for half a century. The first new hop-yard that we planted was in the Greens which was planted with a variety called Fuggles. This variety was first produced in 1727 from a plant noticed by a Mr Percy Fuggle, who farmed in Kent. By the end of the Second World War, this one variety constituted 60% of the English hop crop. A normal fertilizer programme included steam bone flour, Patullo Higgs or Hadfield's organic fertilizer, plus sulphate of potash and nitrogen and basic slag. However, it appeared that there had not been a planned fertilizer programme at Claston until Bertie Moore took over farming Dormington Court and was advised to do so by his brother who worked for I.C.I. Father then adopted this method of planning the fertilizing of the hops.

Getting ready for hop-picking was a very time-consuming operation. First of all the cribs, which had been taken apart for storage at the end of hop-picking the previous year, had to be re-assembled. The design of these cribs had not changed for over 100 years. They were about 10 feet in length, with four long ash bars – two at the top and two at the bottom. The ends were narrower, about 4 feet long, so they were not dismantled. Freshly cut bars were put on where necessary and then the cloth had to be stitched onto the top four bars of the crib from which it was suspended. Then you had the very

Cribs had not changed for over 100 years

difficult job of hauling the cribs on wagons to the hop-yard. You could only get about eight cribs on a wagon at a time and had to be very careful not to damage them, especially when turning in through the gateway between the high hedges.

Preparing the barracks for the hop-pickers from South Wales used to be another major operation. As they were housed, first of all, in the cart-stables, the horses had to be moved into one of the cattle sheds and the stables thoroughly washed out. Others were housed in the hayloft above the stables, so that also had to be cleaned. Not only was it all washed out, but the walls were also whitewashed. In later years, the main accommodation for the pickers was in the granary, which was always in a good state of cleanliness, but we had to put up partitions to house each family and I think from memory there were seven of these on each side of the room. Downstairs, one end was Father's garage and that was split into two compartments for two more families. Later on, the whole of the under part of the granary, which had been used as a wagon and implement store, was converted into barracks for further accommodation. Many of the pickers had visitors who wished to stay at the farm at weekends, but this had to be controlled as accommodation was very limited. To overcome this, a permit system was introduced, but in spite of our efforts visitors used to sneak in. Toilets were pretty primitive. There was a stone-built building, underneath which a stream ran before eventually emptying out into a

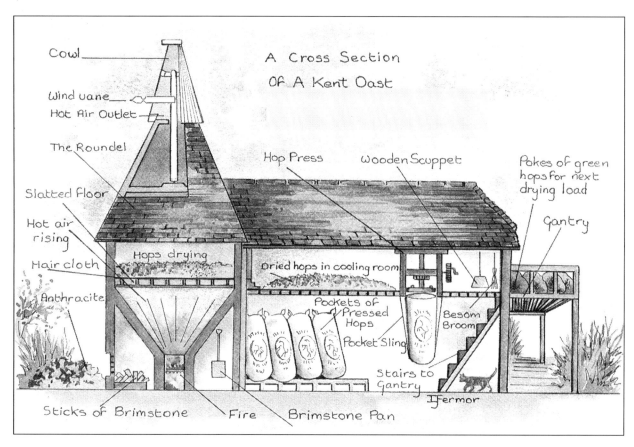

Labels on diagram:
Cowl
Wind vane
Hot Air Outlet
The Roundel
Slatted Floor
Hot air rising
Hair cloth
Anthracite
A Cross Section Of A Kent Oast
Hops drying
Hop Press
Wooden Scuppet
Dried hops in cooling room
Pokes of green hops for next drying load
Gantry
Pockets of Pressed Hops
Besom Broom
Pocket Sling
Stairs to Gantry
Termor
Sticks of Brimstone
Fire
Brimstone Pan

The workings of a hop-kiln

grass field behind the house. This was not a very satisfactory state of affairs, but the authorities in those days said it was all right. Eventually we had to buy corrugated iron toilets and dig holes.

To prepare the kilns in the early days of my farming career, the floor of the kiln was covered with a horse-hair mat called a kiln hair and then goat-hair lifter cloths were spread on top. These would be covered with hops to a depth of 2ft 6ins and the lifter cloths enabled you to drag the dried hops off the kiln. The hops were tipped into large heaps on the floor of the cooling room and left to cool for about twelve hours or longer. They were then pushed with large wood and sacking shovels into very large sacks called hop-pockets, which were suspended through a round hole in the cooling room floor, almost reaching the floor below, being about seven foot high and 2ft 6ins in diameter, when filled with about 1½cwts of compacted hops. In the early days, this was done by someone standing in the pocket to press the hops down with his feet as it was filled, which must have been a horrible job. Later, it was done by a hand-turned mechanical press.

Before the start of hop-picking, the kiln hair mats and the lifter cloths used to be taken down to the river to be washed and the kiln hairs were nailed to the floor of the kiln with special nails. These were short, only about one inch long, but with a head nearly as wide and they were black and very difficult to see when the mats were removed for washing, so some were always missed. Every year a few used to get dropped in the yard and we often had tractors and trailers with punctures caused by the kiln-hair nails. In later years, the kiln hair mats were replaced, and under the goat-hair lifter cloths half-inch mesh wire was used instead to cover the floor, which was more satisfactory.

It was in 1774 that an Act was passed requiring the pockets to be stencilled with the grower's name, year and place of growth; a practice which is still a requirement today. At one time, the pockets were taken

Left: Cooling room showing the steps to the kiln.   Right: Hops in the cooling room

on horse-drawn wagons either to a local brewery or to the station to be transported by train further afield. In the 1930s, I can remember lorries coming to collect the hops which were to be taken to the hop merchants' warehouses in London.

When I left school, the fans which drew the hot air through the hops to dry them were driven by an old Blackstone engine, the same one as we used for chaff-cutting and pulping. It was a very heavy thing to move, but due to lack of space, you could only get one horse in the shed to pull it out and it took two to take it round to the hop-drying kilns. We had an old horse called Prince who was brilliant at this, but one year Father wasn't there and he asked the men to do it. Prince didn't like this and wouldn't pull the engine out, instead he kept backing, so the men started to beat him. I was very worried about this and ran to find Father, who came and was very angry with the men for hitting Prince. He just patted the horse on the head and said, 'Come on,

Claston hop-pockets

41

Prince with Peter in the garden

Round kilns showing the shafting

Prince', and he walked out with the engine immediately! I think the men felt very small. Another problem that we had when we were preparing for hop-picking was that the shafting, which was driven by the engine, was at right-angles to the kilns so the belt had a twist of varying degrees to each kiln. It was quite a tricky job to put the belt on because after putting the first one on, if you were not very careful when you were putting on the next one, if it moved backwards acci-dentally just a tiny little bit, the first belt would come off again. As we had three belts to put on it was quite a challenge.

The gypsy families used to arrive several days before we started hop-picking, with their horses and brightly painted caravans. This was a very noisy and picturesque event; their approach heralded by the clip-clopping of the horses' hooves on the road, the shouts of the men, the barking of the dogs, the cries of the children and the clattering of the pots and pans tied onto the back of the caravans.

The day before we started hop-picking, the carts and wagons were sent to Stoke Edith station to meet the special trains from South Wales on which the Welsh mining fami-lies would arrive. The luggage was loaded onto the wagons with the children and some of the mothers, whilst the majority of the adults walked, many of them stopping at the Foley Arms (now the Tarrington Arms), arriving at the farm much later singing lustily and somewhat unsteady on their feet. Each family was provided with blankets and straw mattresses.

The first day of hop-picking was always a great occasion, bringing together of the Welsh pickers installed in our accom-modation with busloads of pickers from Hereford. In later years there were as many as three 60-seater busloads of people from Wales living in the buildings, as well as six or seven daily buses from Hereford. The first buses arrived in the hop-yard at 6 a.m. but on the first day I had to be there before that because the gypsies and local pickers would arrive at about 5.30 a.m., thinking they could secure places where the best hops were. However, it was all done in a very orderly fashion and there were very few problems. The hops were picked on a piecework basis, so much a bushel, which was a very controversial measure. A bushel was a very large straight-sided basket about three feet high and two feet across at the top, which was used to measure the quantity of hops picked by each picker. For some reason, although the bushel basket held ten gallons, only about eight gallons were counted as a bushel.

Ten minutes before bushelling commenced, the busheller would shout several times in a loud voice, 'Clean them up', which meant everybody should stop picking and pick out any leaves amongst the hops in their crib, ready for bushelling. The busheller had a 'sack holder', who held a hop sack open at the end of the crib for him to tip the hops into. The sack holder counted the number of bushels for each crib in a loud voice as they were put into the sack, and also had to remember to put eight bushels in each sack.

The first busheller I can remember from my schooldays was Peter Green, who always wore a leather apron and a bowler hat and used to cook bloaters at the back of the farmhouse for his breakfast, creating a delicious smell which wafted into our kitchen. The next busheller was Johnny Smith, the son of the ganger who brought the hop-pickers from Wales and he subsequently became the ganger himself. A ganger was a person who signed on and brought pickers from various places, such as South Wales, Tupsley or Hinton.

After I had hauled the hops for several years, we had too many pickers for one busheller and so I started bushelling to help Johnny Smith, but I still had to haul all the sacks home after each bushelling. Measuring the hops, or bushelling, was, I think, my favourite job on the farm. Johnny Smith told me that if I ever had a problem when bushelling a picker's hops, I should not argue with her, but say sorry and admit to having made a mistake, then tip the hops back into the crib, give her the basket and tell her to do it herself. He told me that no matter how hard the picker tried, she would never make the hops measure the same, because once they have been bushelled it flattens them and you get more in the basket. I only had to do this once, and that was with a Mrs Parker, who brought pickers from Tupsley. I think she made it one or two bushels less than I had done, so I never had a problem again!

Hop-picking was quite a ritual really and we always had a strike over payment. Father knew this would happen, so when the pickers were about to start he told them a rate which was lower than that which he thought he would have to pay. Whether we had too many pickers, or not enough, together with the state of the crop would determine how long Father allowed the strike to continue, but it was never very long before he raised the level to what he had planned to pay in the first place and everybody was happy. This payment had already been agreed with Mr George Bray of Dormington Court, the large neighbouring hop farm.

There are lots of stories about hop-picking, one of which I remember vividly. There always used to be ice-cream sellers competing for the pickers' business in the hop-yard and in the second hop-picking after I left school, one of them came to me and asked to be the sole ice-cream seller. I think it was a man called Mr Burcott, who had several ice-cream vans. I replied that provided he gave me an ice-cream every day, I would ban all the other sellers from the hop-yard. So this is what we did and for several years he was the sole supplier of ice-creams and I had an ice-cream every day for nothing! A fishmonger also used to come into the hop-yard every day to sell bloaters and kippers, which used to smell delicious when cooked on the wood fires beside the cribs.

Most of the pickers were very good and picked the hops cleanly with very few leaves. The local people were the best, however, and they always kept picking, even in the wettest weather, as they needed to make enough money to clothe their children for the coming year. The

Busheller Johnny Smith and his mother

43

Bushelling: Cecil Matthews, Harry Darling, Bill Williams

gypsies were marvellous hop-pickers but they tended to pick a lot of leaves as well. Sometimes you had quite a problem making sure that they got the leaves out – the crafty ones took the leaves out of the hops at the top of the crib but left lots of leaves hidden underneath. If you left them unbushelled once or twice, they soon realised that they must pick the leaves out. You also had to make sure that the sack carriers, who carried the sacks to the wagons when filled, kept up with you when you were bushelling, because there was the danger that if a sack was left on the ground when you moved to the next crib, the picker could tip the hops back into the crib for the next bushelling. On one occasion I recall bushelling in the old hop-yard where a lady was in great distress because she had lost her gold watch. We spent a long time looking for it in the hops in her crib until eventually I said 'Well, we'll mark the sack and when those hops are tipped into the kiln and the drier is spreading them, I will tell him to look very carefully and I'm sure he will find your watch'. She offered to give the drier one pound if he found it, which was a lot of money in those days. This was agreed and the sack holder went to the end of the crib and held the sack open. I put my bushel into the crib and as I put my hands into the hops to push them in the basket, I saw the gold watch. She said, 'You knew it was there all the time', but she still offered me the pound, which of course I did not take. I remember on another occasion one of our men working in the hop-yard said he would like to do some bushelling. I reluctantly gave him the basket and he came to one of the South Wales' pickers first. The next thing I knew he had dropped the basket and Mrs Quan was chasing him across the hop-yard with a carving knife, saying she would cut his liver out if she caught him. Presumably he had put too many hops in the bushel!

Some of the gangers who I remember bringing the hop-pickers from Tredegar, South Wales, were Mrs Reardon, grandmother of Ray Reardon, the

A group of workers in the hop-yard.
Back row: Frank Harwood, Alex Phillips, sister Kate, Harry Darling.
Middle row: Bill Williams, Cecil Matthews, John Albrecht.
Front row: Jim Wargent, [-]

famous snooker player, followed by Mrs Smith, mother of Johnny Smith who later became the busheller and gave me good advice when I started bushelling. Amongst the families they brought from South Wales were Mrs Vaughan, who had three successive husbands and nineteen children and lived to be over ninety and Mrs Thomas, who had only one eye, a large family, but only one son, Billy, who worked in the kilns pressing the hops into the pockets.

We had two very nice local, elderly ladies who were not very good pickers. They only had half a crib between them, one picking into the crib and the other into a large box. The busheller had to bushel the hops out of the crib first, usually they only filled one bushel, but any left had to be put into a container. Then the other lady's hops were tipped into the crib from her box. Again these normally only one bushel. Both ladies commented, 'Most disappointing, most disappointing', several times. This performance took longer than bushelling two good cribfuls of hops, so both of us bushellers avoided this crib if possible.

For many years, the hop drier and perhaps one or two others lived in the kilns, sleeping on makeshift beds when they could between loading and unloading the kilns. These workers were always fed by Mother in the house where they used to have their breakfast, lunch and their evening meal, and then she packed a basket for their midnight meal including gin for the drier. This continued until we started working shifts.

Mr Bill Wargent, who was living in the 1940s in the turnpike house at Stoke Edith crossroads, about 3/4 mile away from Claston, had an agricultural engineering business, using the room with the circular window as his office. He would come every Sunday morning to service the old Blackstone engine, which ran continually for six days and nights each week from the start to the end of hop-picking. He used to listen every night before he went to bed to hear if it was running correctly, and said that if it ever stopped during the night he would wake up and come over immediately. Fortunately it never did. Bill Wargent also ran the blacksmith's shop and I remember that when I first left school, I used to take horses to the blacksmith's shop to be shod.

Before the war, the hop-pockets were taken to London by lorry, the lorries being loaded in the evening. Five or six layers of pockets were loaded horizontally and after the third layer, which was very high up, we used to have to put the hop-pockets onto a wagon alongside and then lift them onto the lorry. Unfortunately, the warehouses were all burnt in London during the Blitz, after which we started to store hops on the farms until the brewers wanted them. Some were stored in the cattle sheds or in the barn during hop-picking and then as soon as the picking was finished and the hop-pickers had gone home we moved them back into the kilns and the barracks. We used to store other people's hop-pockets as well at Claston. I remember including Mr Godson's from the Castle, and those from the Hillend and Bartestree Court, eventually all the hop-pockets were collected by the station lorry, taken to Stoke Edith station, then loaded into railway trucks and taken by rail to the breweries. Once I discovered a problem with the very last load. We had got the correct numbers of pockets to go but some were from Bartestree Court and some were from the Hillend and they should all have been from the same farm. I discussed this with the lorry driver, who told me not to worry as only the numbers were checked and they were all the same variety anyway. Thankfully we never heard anything more about it!

I was always very sad when the end of hop-picking came, because during this time the farm was full of life, with lots of people about and the kilns were full of activity. Once hop-picking ceased in early October, the place became dead until the cattle were brought into the yards in mid-November to over-winter.

In 1944, on my 21st birthday in September, for some reason I was sent to the Sheepcote to plough out sugar beet before we started the first bushelling. Although nobody would believe me afterwards, we actually had a snow-storm at Sheepcote whilst I was there. This was early in the morning and when I returned home at about 10.30 a.m. to start bushelling, I told everyone about the snow and they laughed. Maybe it didn't settle, but it really did snow. Of course, being war-time, there was no great birthday parties or anything like that, but Mother cooked a superb meal for us of all the things I liked best, including roast duck. Unfortunately, when we had finished the meal, Father encouraged me to have a cigar to complete the day. I was so ill after it that I never smoked again.

A lorry-load of hops

FAMILY LIFE

In July 1945, Father fell and broke his leg while playing tennis on our court at Claston. He said immediately, 'Fetch a doctor, I've broken my leg'. We were unable to contact any of our usual doctors from Wargrave House, but fortunately Dr Langdale Smith, the Tarrington G.P., was at home and agreed to come straight away. On arrival, he dashed up to the tennis court to assess the situation, then he asked me to fetch his bag from the car. After I had very carefully done this, to my horror he promptly opened the bag and tipped the contents out onto the grass. Soon afterwards Laddie Godsall and I were dispatched to find something on which to carry Father back to the house. We managed to detach a metal door from one of the old round kilns which made an excellent stretcher for this purpose. Dr Smith had established that Father had a compound fracture of his leg and he arranged for an ambulance to take him to hospital, where the following day he underwent surgery to set the leg. Father subsequently spent six weeks in hospital and was unable to walk outside for some time following his return home. This meant that when I was only 22 years old I had to take over the running of the farm, organise the preparations for the hop-picking season, then supervise the work in the hop-yards and the drying of the hops in the kilns. As Father was still unable to get about, I used to take handfuls of dried hops to the house to see if they were dried to his satisfaction.

During the war there was food rationing and we in the countryside were really rather lucky because country people were allowed to rear two pigs, which supplemented the very meagre meat ration. Father used to let our pigs grow very large – much bigger than anybody would want as a bacon pig today – so that we had plenty of bacon throughout the year from these two animals. I'm not sure how heavy they would have been but the butcher came twice during the winter to kill one pig at a time, because that was as much meat as we could cure in one go. The curing or preserving of the meat was done by Mother until later I took over, having been taught this skilled process. The bacon was always very fat because they cut the lean out of it, otherwise it became hard due to the method of curing at that time. However, if the bacon was cooked properly and crisply it was wonderful to eat and of course the hams were fantastic. I remember one year our neighbour, Mr Godson, asked Father if he could kill his pig when we were killing one of ours, so this was done and the butcher, after he had killed the pig, asked Mr Godson if he wanted the offal. He said, 'Oh no, I don't want that', and the butcher was pleased because he was hoping to keep the liver for himself. However, whilst the butcher was busy dressing the pig, we heard Mr Godson coming back saying, 'Liver and bacon, liver and bacon, liver and bacon', and then he told the butcher that he would take the liver. Nothing was wasted from the pig; Mother used the heart and the lungs to make into faggots, and everything else was used in different ways. Even though rationing was very tight, there were always plenty of rabbits about because there was no myxomatosis at that time. I think one of my favourite dishes was rabbit pie, which Mother used to make in late August/early September from half-grown rabbits. She put the prepared rabbit in a pie dish with baby carrots, new potatoes, spring onions and water, covered with pastry. When this was cooked and left to cool, there was not only the meat and vegetables, but a wonderfully tasty jelly too.

During the early years of my tractor-driving, I did all sorts of foolish things and got into many scrapes. I remember on one occasion I was working at Bartestree spreading lime and a wagon-load of bags had been delivered. This was before you had lorry-loads of loose lime. I was spreading the lime with the fertilizer spreader and unloaded the wagon whilst stationed on a bank at the Sheepcote. As I unloaded the top side of the wagon, it tipped over and half of the load of paper sacks fell onto the ground, which I then had to pick up to load the spreader – that taught me a lesson, as being made of shiny paper they were difficult to grasp!

On one occasion when I was driving the tractor taking a large load of hop sacks back to the farm, one of the rear wheels of the wagon came off just after we had left the hop-yard and the axle was dragging on the ground all the way back to the farm. Much to everyone's amazement, my sister Kate, who was sitting on top of the load, did not notice this and much leg pulling ensued.

Another time when I went to cut grass for hay at the Sheepcote, I drove into the field and could not see that somebody had left a set of spikey chain harrows in the long grass by the gate. Unfortunately I drove my tractor over the harrows and very soon had four flat tyres. I then had to walk a considerable distance to Mrs Barneby's house to ask her to explain this embarrassing situation over the phone to Father at Claston and ask for help.

On another occasion in the summer, when it was hot and I had been working long hours, I decided to have my lunch in the field in which I was cutting the grass for hay. After lunch, I lay down to rest and went to sleep. When Father came up at about 3 p.m. to check on my progress, I was still fast asleep and was told in no uncertain manner that I was to work on until I had finished the field.

I will always remember too, while hauling a load of sheaves of corn off the hill, I suddenly felt corn touching my head as I came down the steep bank. I couldn't look round or stop the tractor until I got onto level ground at the bottom of the hill. I then found that the drawbar had buckled and the front of the wagon was virtually touching the wheels of the tractor and the front of the load was very close to my head. That was quite an alarming experience!

Once when we were going to cut corn on the hill, I was sitting on the binder being pulled by the tractor. On the very steep part of the lane just past Stanway, the towing bar came off the binder and I found myself going backwards very fast down the lane. There was nothing I could do – I just had to sit tight. Luckily it didn't go very far before it ran into the ditch, so everything was O.K. and we were soon able to retrieve it.

Another frightening occurrence happened when Frank Harwood was working for us. It was before we had converted the downstairs part of the granary into hop barracks. I was in the tractor house, doing something to my tractor which was stationed in what is now the ladies' toilets, when suddenly there was an enormous explosion. I ran out to see what had happened and Frank appeared amidst clouds of dust, looking very scared. He had been blowing up a wheel which had burst when he had just about finished and, of course, the amazing release of air had blown up all the dust. Quite an alarming experience for him! Talking of Frank Harwood, there was an occasion when Father told me to put his car away and Frank asked me if he could do it instead. Foolishly I let him, while I sat in the passenger seat. He drove the car all right into the garage but then he failed to stop, hitting the wall with the front of the car and we both got into trouble.

TARRINGTON HOPS

In 1946, Father took over the growing of the hops from Mr Godsall at Tarrington. The first year that we had the hops, Father, who knew that they were a variety called Fuggles, duly, marketed them as Fuggles, but apparently Mr Godsall had previously sold them as Goldings – a different variety. There was quite a row as the brewers were expecting Goldings.

Top: Uncle Walter's painting of the old cart stable.
Bottom: The end of the old cart stable. It became a kiln with an elevator to take the sacks up into the kiln

It was in 1946 that we once again started to plant hops to increase our acreage, so that in 1947 we had increased our crop by well over 100 pockets, and by 1950 it had gone from 327 pockets to 655. By 1947 we had to increase the capacity of our kilns and this was done by converting the old cart-stable to another hop-kiln. At this time we had no horses, so we replaced part of the stable block with an 18 foot by 22 foot kiln and we extended the old hop cooling room to this new kiln. This was over the area where the old road from Stoke Edith used to pass through the farm, before crossing the River Frome at Moor Mills and then going on to Bartestree and Hereford. The new kiln held ninety sacks of hops and we had to have a chimney built into it for the coke-fired heating equipment.

POST-WAR HOPS :
ELECTRICITY AT CLASTON

When Father formed the partnership of Philip Davies & Son in 1948, he had quite a battle with the hop trade because they said that this was a different mark – the name on the pocket was called a mark – and it took a long time for him to convince them that the hops were exactly the same, only that he had changed the name to make me a partner. After a couple of years, because of this argument, he decided to put all the hops from

1947 – An Arctic Winter

In January 1947, after very mild spring-like days, a Siberian anti-cyclone brought bitter cold conditions with severe gales and snow, causing drifts of 15 feet. In fact, the old saying "cold enough to starve a crow" applied then. By the 30th January, Dormington was like an arctic wasteland, with temperatures down to -10°C and people were able to walk on the surface of the snow over the tops of the hedgerows. Early February brought more severe blizzards and very hard frosts. Towards the end of February, temperatures were down to -15°C, with storm-force winds causing drifts up to 25 feet deep. A further blizzard struck in early March, with temperatures still down to -15°C. Claston Lane was not visible as the snow had filled the lane and covered the 14 feet high hop-yard hedges on either side.

Snow at Dormington in 1947

The cattle and sheep had all been brought in to the buildings at the farm and for two months we spent all of our time feeding the stock and thawing pipes, which were continuously freezing, to supply them with water. I remember having to walk to Bartestree to collect supplies of food, as the road was impassable to traffic from Bartestree in this direction. Another old saying, "Ice to hold a duck before Christmas, mud and slush after", or the reverse, was certainly true that winter.

When the thaw came in March, we had very heavy rainfall which, combined with the rapidly melting snow, caused a huge flood, the water coming half-way up the field at the back of Claston. There was a 6" layer of ice over the river Frome and this was quickly broken up, when the thaw came, by the rapidly rising water level. I recollect hearing a lot of noise coming from the river just before it started to flood and when I went to find out what was causing this, I discovered huge ice flows crashing into one another and blocking the river bridge. The ice had built up 200 yards upstream from the bridge and in the middle of the river a very frightened rabbit was sitting on the ice. After the severe winter, which caused a very late start to the growing season, we had, to our great surprise, a record crop of hops.

Claston under the name of Philip Davies & Son and that's how we have traded ever since. It shows how easily you can upset a customer by changing the name and I hope that in future the Claston hops will always be sold as Philip Davies & Son.

Towards the end of the 1948 hop-picking, I went to look at the hops one evening while they were being dried on the kilns. When Father went to look at them the next morning, the hop drier, Jim Thomas, was very upset and wanted to know why I was interfering with his hop-drying. Father told me not to go into the kilns again that hop-picking, but said that he wanted me to take over the hop-drying the following year, which I did until 1957 when we had our first hop-picking machine.

Collapse of the Green's hop-yard

In 1950, just a few days before we started hop-picking, the Green's hop-yard collapsed when a cross wire broke due to the very heavy crop. However, we managed to pick 23 cwts per acre of these fuggle hops.

As there was no electricity at Claston, a friend of mine, Laddie Godsall, suggested installing a temporary electric light system in the kilns. To do this, he found a small old generator which was driven by a tractor which also ran continuously to drive the fans in the kilns. One evening, when we had nearly finished installing the wiring for these lights, we realised we had no fuse wire. My sister Kate was then dispatched to Laddie's home in Stretton Grandison to collect this and she drove Father's Wolsley car which looked like new, having had a complete bodywork overhaul. Unfortunately, when returning, she took the left-hand turn to Stoke Edith off the Hereford/Worcester road too fast, not only demolishing the iron railings but also badly damaging the car. She had to walk two miles back to Claston, then Laddie and I went to retrieve the car. In our haste we did not notice that we had left one number plate behind. Father was not amused as he not only had to pay to repair the car but also the railings. The lighting, however, was a great success. When we finished hop-picking, I installed electric light in my bedroom so that I could read in bed, foolishly forgetting that in order to switch the light out I had to go out to the tractor house and stop the tractor.

CHAPTER FIVE

The Effects of the War on the Farm

One of the first changes in farming life after war was declared was the setting up of a War Agricultural Committee in each county by the Government. ThIs consisted mainly of retired farmers, some of them from very small farms, who visited each farm and told the farmer what crops and how many acres of each crop had to be grown, as well as which fields had to be ploughed. This resulted, in a lot of cases, in old pasture fields being ploughed up which were entirely unsuitable for corn crops. I remember all the hill-land had to be ploughed at Claston and in many places on the hill there were only four or five inches of soil, so that in dry years there was a very small crop. It also meant that we had to plough up all the old riverside meadows during the whole of the war and consequently we lost all of the wild flowers that used to be there.

A searchlight was set up at Prior's Court and later moved to Claston, about two years into the war. It was situated in the field behind the house, with the living quarters for the troops in a wooden building about 75 yards away at the top of the field. The headquarters of the searchlight unit was based in Withington at Barnamore House and I remember the RAF girls from there coming across in their gaily coloured running kit to visit the troops. The searchlight never actually picked up a German bomber during the war, but it was attacked once and the troops returned fire with a heavy-duty machine gun which was situated close to the searchlight. They made an ash path from the barracks where they were based down to the searchlight which amused me because, from the air, this must have shown it up much more clearly! The searchlight was used most of all for guiding RAF bombers back from night raids over Europe, as were several searchlights across the West Midlands. To do this the operators would have to point the beams at a certain angle. All the search-lights would be waving up and down, across that line, which enabled bombers to get their bearings if their radios had been damaged.

The Bradbury Lines, which was a fairly new barracks, always had troops based there during the war, and my father became friendly with Major Cann, one of the officers of the Royal Artillery who was based there. He used to come out to Claston with his driver for dinner from time to time. On one occasion, they were having a cold supper, prepared by Mrs Webb, the wife of one of our staff. Somehow or other she got the mayonnaise for the salad and the cream for the coffee mixed up and sent the cream in with the first course, before suddenly realising that she still had the mayonnaise in the kitchen. Nevertheless, she sent it in with the coffee and surprisingly nothing was ever said, but there must have been some very strange expressions on people's faces!

It was during the war that we were asked by a potato merchant to deliver a couple of tons of our potatoes to to the RAF camp at Credenhill. This was done on Mr Ellerman's lorry and when Mick the driver arrived at the camp he was asked if they were King Edward's and he replied 'No. They are Mr Davies!'

Later on in the war, various regiments were stationed in Hereford, including the Royal Ulster Rifles who were there for a year or two. During this time, the RAF camp at Credenhill was set up and there used to be

Peter Davies and his father in Home Guard uniform

terrific fights between the Ulster Rifles and the RAF people on a Saturday night.

Soon after the beginning of the war, the Home Guard was started and my father became the officer in charge of quite a large area, covering Dormington, Stoke Edith, Mordiford, Fownhope, Holme Lacy, Bartestree and Lugwardine. A lot of the training was done at Claston and part of the old barn where the hop-pickers used to live was converted to form a rifle range. At least twice a week, the Home Guard from one of the parishes used to come here for .22 shooting exercises. I wasn't old enough to join the Home Guard then but eventually, although I was still under age, I was allowed to join. When I was old enough I wanted to join the army, but I was refused entry on the grounds that I was more valuable on the farm because there was a desperate need for food production and a great shortage of labour.

The Royal Ulster Rifles played a big part in training my father's company of Home Guard. They allowed us to use one of their training areas in the old lime kilns at Tupsley, for training in the use of Tommy guns and, later let us have ammunition for the Sten guns that we were subsequently issued with. We used to go into these kilns and fire live ammunition at figures which would suddenly appear in front of us. The Ulster Rifles also supplied us with live ammunition to take down to the rifle range at Ross and they came out to help train the troops on various exercises, as well as training us in unarmed combat. On one occasion, later on in the war, there was a big exercise with a Guards Division coming up the Wye valley from Fownhope through Mordiford where Father's Home Guard company was defending the river bridge. Father talked to one of the officers in the Royal Ulster Rifles who advised him how to do this most efficiently. We had been supplied with lengths of old railway line which had been bent into a U-shape especially to be used as road blocks – for this two holes were dug about 3 ft deep in the road and the U-shaped railway lines were dropped into the holes upside down so that they stood 8 ft above the ground, and poles were then placed across them. Father was only supposed to put in one of these barriers, but the Ulster Rifles officer advised him to put in two, to make a complete road block. Eventually, when the Guards Division arrived on the outskirts of Mordiford, the Home Guard held them up for nearly an hour, by which time the officer in charge of the exercise was getting worried and told my father to let them through. I do not know how many people would have been killed if it had been for real, but Father was very pleased to think that his company of the Home Guard had held up the whole of the Guards Division for over an hour.

One of the Home Guard duties was to mount a patrol on Marion's Hill, the hill that goes from the top of the road from Frome to Checkley, right through to Mordiford village. We had an old fisherman's hut to sleep in. There were six of us on duty at a time and you did two hours' patrol and four hours' rest. We never actually saw any enemy activity, but one night we did see a raid on the Rotherwas ammunition factory, although luckily very little damage was caused. However, a house near the factory was damaged and, if I remember rightly, one person was killed.

One thing I remember is that all around the hut at Marion's Hill there were glow worms. There were very many of them and I have never seen them anywhere else in such numbers.

Lots of bombs were dropped in the area. There are three pools, known as the Park Pools, in Woolhope, and the German bombers used to mistake them for the river Wye which was their landmark for the Rotherwas ammunition factory, and lots of bombs were therefore dropped all around the area. The closest bombs to Claston were just over the hill at Checkley, where two or three bombs fell on the south side of the road and one on the north side, just off the road from Checkley up to the top of Tower Hill.

All the Dormington, Checkley and Mordiford members of the Home Guard were crack shots and I don't think they would have missed many Germans if they had had to shoot at them. We used to go on all sorts of night and day exercises. Most training, though, was done on a Sunday morning, mainly at Mordiford. On one occasion, towards the end of the war, I was sent on an officer training course to Stokesay Castle with a friend of mine, Laddie Godsall. We were the only two farmers' sons on this course; all the others came from Birmingham. It was quite astonishing really, because we lived as officers with ATS to wait at table. We had a very good breakfast, then a snack lunch, but always a proper dinner in the evening.

One of the things that we had been trained to do was to clear the enemy out of farm buildings. On the final day of the course, we had to go on an exercise which took us to a farm not all that far from Stokesay Castle. We entered a lovely open farmyard with what looked like hunter boxes, or calf boxes, all around. Our training was for one person to creep up to the door, open it and throw in a thunder flash, whilst the others would provide covering fire. One of the Birmingham chaps crept up to the door, opened it and tossed a thunder flash in as instructed. The thunder flash was quite a big firework which made a fair amount of noise and a huge amount of smoke. However, he did not know that there was a three or four month old calf in this box, which was naturally frightened to death by the flash and the noise of the explosion. A young animal like that will make an enormous bellowing sound if frightened and sure enough it shot out of the calf-box, its tail straight out, making this horrendous noise. The city chap was scared out of his wits and all the rest of them scattered in every direction while Laddie and I were in hysterics as the terrified calf was actually quite harmless! It ruined the exercise of course, because if took us about an hour and a half to recapture the calf, but at the time it really was the funniest thing I think I have ever seen!

One of the weapons that we were trained to use was called a spigot mortar which was an anti-tank weapon. This had an explosive charge like a bomb. It was egg-shaped, about nine inches long and about six or eight inches in diameter and was attached to the end of a long tube with a fin on the end to guide it. This was put onto a sort of machine gun, positioned on a base so that you could swivel it round to point it in the appropriate direction. On the first occasion we had a demonstration of this, a very short, fat officer came out, and he lay on the ground with his hands on the guiding handle of the spigot mortar. It was very funny because he had a very large stomach and as he swivelled the weapon about, his legs came up off the ground. We were tempted to take hold of his legs and steer the spigot bomb by that method!

One day I went to Kidderminster with Mr Llewellyn Evans, the County Council Agricultural Training Officer for Herefordshire. This was long before ADAS was set up. On our way to Kidderminster we passed one of our fields in which Mr Evans spotted some very large docks. I remember that he commented 'Peter, I'm glad to see that you're growing some good docks, I hate to see scrubby little docks growing on a farm!' We went to the Kidderminster sugar beet factory where we saw a demonstration of live spigot mortars being fired and exploding on impact. It really was quite an alarming experience and I was very relieved that we never had to use any.

As another method of defending the villages from the Germans, we buried some 40 or 50 gallon petrol drums, containing a mixture of petrol and oil, in several locations, one of which was the steep bank on the right-hand side just past the quarry on the road up to Checkley from Frome. The areas were prepared and we buried about five of these drums in each location, facing the road. A charge was attached to them and we had the kit to fire one of these at a time, the object being that if you fired it at the moment a German tank went by, you would set the tank on fire.

One of the air raid precautions that we had to take on the farm was to clean out all the ditches around the hop-yards to a depth of three feet for people to take cover in in the event of a raid. For two years, a Colonel Ord from one of the regiments in Hereford, who knew about this vital work, volunteered help to do this in August, which saved us a lot of work.

I'm not sure how we would have known if there was going to be an air raid, so that we could warn the hop pickers to give them time to scramble into these ditches, because there was no radio communication to the hop-yard. I imagine the bombers would have just come and attacked the hop pickers without giving us a chance to warn them, but thankfully it didn't happen.

By 1942, land girls were coming to work on the farms and I remember the first time they came to Claston to do some draining at Longworth, where there were another 40 or 50 acres of land that we were by then renting from Mrs Barneby. These girls had come down from London having never worked on a farm in their lives before and they were just given spades, shown what to do – digging out ditches – and told to get on with it. By the end of the day their hands were covered in black blisters. Another job I remember the land girls doing was thinning out, to about six inches between each plant, the sugar beet that we were growing at the Sheepcote. At lunchtime, Mrs Barneby rang to ask Father if he would go up to the Sheepcote immediately, because, as it was a lovely hot day, these girls were topless whilst singling the sugar beet! Mrs Barneby was very upset about the girls' behaviour. I said I would go, but Father turned my offer down and went himself!

After the evacuation of troops from Dunkirk, soldiers stationed in Hereford used to come out to help us with the corn harvest. One year ATS girls came to help with hop-picking as well, but this was a bit of a

Harvest time. Troops at Claston. The tractor driver is Fred Jones

Youngest sister Irene and visitors around a war-time Red Cross crib

disaster really because they weren't interested in hop-picking, they were just there to have some fun. There were quite a number of problems because the soldiers spent most of their time trying to stuff green hops down the ATS girls' blouses! Father only kept the girls for a few days because their behaviour really played havoc in the hop-yard with the rest of the hop-pickers.

The last troops that were stationed in Hereford were the Suffolk Regiment, who also came out to help with the hop harvest, bringing their Bedford trucks which they used to haul the hops from the hop-yard to the kilns. The regiment was inspected by King George VI before they left for the Far East and landed in Singapore just as it was captured by the Japanese. Sadly I believe they were either killed or captured without a single shot being fired. They were a super bunch of chaps, quite a lot of them were from London but some of them were country people and they all thoroughly enjoyed their hop-picking and worked really hard at it.

We had one horrifying experience during the war when troops and police arrived looking for an army deserter. He was eventually spotted on the farm and then suddenly disappeared again. After a long hunt, we saw the soles of his boots at the end of a drain which he must have crawled up. We then had great difficulty getting him out because he was so tightly wedged in by his effort to escape capture. Had we not found him, he would have died because there was no way that he could have extricated himself from the drain.

There was one tragic accident during the war when two planes collided over the Sheepcote at Bartestree. There was an RAF training camp at Madley, where they had single and twin-engine planes, training navigators, wireless operators and, later, glider pilots. On this occasion, a number of these planes were, I should imagine, having a sort of dog fight over the Sheepcote and unfortunately two of them collided. A single-engine plane crashed at Stalls Farm and both the crew were killed. The pilot of a larger plane managed to land relatively safely in one of the fields at the Sheepcote, but the pilot couldn't stop before the plane crashed through a hedge and hit a tree, killing all eleven young RAF personnel. Mrs Barneby, who lived at the Sheepcote, made it her business to find out the names and addresses of all those killed. She then wrote letters to their parents to tell them how sorry she was and to explain exactly what had happened, reassuring relatives that the victims would not have suffered.

At one stage during the war there was an Indian regiment posted somewhere in the vicinity and they used to come on training exercises, with their mules as pack-horses, from Weston Beggard, through Claston farmyard and up over Tower Hill. It was quite a picturesque sight to see these Indians in their traditional turbans and uniform, and their beautiful mules heavily laden with all sorts of kit.

On one or two occasions, we saw German bombers passing overhead, not really looking for targets but more, I think, trying to escape British fighters. We often saw Hurricanes and Spitfires. Once during harvest time I was very intrigued by a loose barrage balloon. I was driving the tractor up the main road, aiming to turn right into the field by the cottages and was intently watching a Spitfire firing at this balloon to try to bring it down. Unfortunately I drove into the gatepost, severely damaging the radiator of the tractor. I must say that I was in considerable trouble over that and my father was not amused.

The Rotherwas munitions factory was in full production during the war and one of the operations carried out there was filling 400lb bombs. This was done on a piece-work basis. One of the ingredients was a liquid substance which had to be put in to the bombs after it had been heated to a certain temperature. The operators discovered that if they heated the substance just one or two degrees higher than the correct temperature, they could do the job much more quickly and therefore earn more money. Unfortunately, on one occasion they heated it just a little too much and two of the 400lb bombs exploded. Luckily it happened during a break-time and not as many people were killed and injured as otherwise might have been the case. At Claston we heard the explosion which shook the house. Masses of windows in Hereford were shattered. One of Father's Home Guard company's duties was to guard the Rotherwas factory, so he and I quickly changed into uniform and hurried down there to check whether any Home Guard men were needed for rescue operations. We went via Holme Lacy bridge and by the time we reached Holme Lacy village, we came across masses of very yellow-faced munitions workers who were running up the road, trying to escape, thinking there would be more explosions. Although the blast caused much damage, the factory was eventually able to carry on producing munitions.

Approaching D-day, lots of Americans were stationed in the area and some of them were members of armoured units. I was driving my iron-wheeled tractor then and when I was working at home, I used to put planks across the road so that I could bring the tractor back to the buildings without damage to the road, rather than leaving it in the field across the road overnight. On one occasion, I had just put the planks down opposite the gate into the Claston drive and was ready to come across, with the front wheels of the tractor at the edge of the road, when a whole squadron, or maybe more, of American tanks appeared over the brow of the hill and came down the road, travelling very fast. They were not bothered about my planks and just dashed past smashing them all to smithereens. Luckily I wasn't actually on the road but it was quite a frightening experience nevertheless. None of them stopped, they just kept going, possibly not being able to stop because of their great speed.

On one occasion, when I had stopped for breakfast while mowing grass for hay at the Sheepcote, on what eventually proved to be D-day, I heard loud explosions. I wasn't sure what they were as they sounded to be a great distance away, but when my father came up to check my progress I asked him if he had heard them too. He hadn't because it was only in one particular place at Sheepcote that you could hear them. Father listened from there and as soon as he heard them, he knew that 16 inch naval guns were being fired. I wondered how he could be certain of that and he told me he remembered from when he had fought the Turks out in Egypt that there had been one particular naval bombardment involving battleships

Claston after the war. The two depressions in the field to the rear of the main buildings are where the searchlight and machine gun were positioned. See detail below

firing 16 inch shells and he recognised the sound. When we later heard more of the details about what was happening on D-day, we learned that battleships were indeed firing 16 inch guns. That was the first indication we had that anything was happening and it was quite interesting that there was just this one place from which you could hear these guns and if you moved more than just 50 yards away you couldn't hear them any more.

Towards the end of the war we started to have Italian prisoners to work on the farm. First of all they worked under the Agricultural War Committee and they did a lot of hand-draining work. Unbeknown to us, the supervision wasn't as good as it should have been and a few years later we were puzzled to find that there were wet places in the field. When we dug down to follow the drains, we discovered that every now and then two drainpipes had been left out so that the drains couldn't work properly. After the Italians, we had German prisoners who were much better workers, but they only came in ones and twos and we were responsible for them. They were dropped off at the farm and we looked after them for the day and then they were collected at night. One of these prisoners, John Albrecht, eventually asked if he could come and work on the farm permanently. We took him on and he remained on the staff for over forty years. He was a wonderful man; his English wasn't very good but he had an excellent memory and quickly took a great interest in the farm, soon knowing everything that was going on. He lived in the farmhouse for many years and as Father and Mother got older, he used to light the fire for them and take them their early morning tea. He was a much respected member of our staff.

For the duration of the war, windows on any buildings had to be covered with black material so that no light was showing outside to attract bombers. Throughout the war, car headlights had special fittings attached which dimmed the lights to comply with these blackout restrictions. As there were no heated car windscreens, driving on Home Guard duty on frosty and foggy evenings with the windscreen open, as it could be in those days, was the only way to find your way about. This was a very unpleasant business.

During the war, strict petrol rationing was quickly introduced but extra allocations were allowed to reserved occupations, farmers being among these. Petrol was only to be used for business purposes, penalties being imposed for improper use. Bicycles were the only means of transport for country people wishing to go to town and to the cinema; this was only during the winter months as at other times we were working from 7 a.m. to 9 p.m. and there were no holidays at all.

CHAPTER SIX

Marriage, Mechanisation & Expansion : 1951-1972

In 1951, because of the increase in the acreage of hops and therefore the quantity of hops that we were producing, it was necessary to build another kiln. This was the first kiln on the farm to be fitted with an automatic stoker which burnt small coal. We were able to do this as the MEB had by now put a mains electricity line across part of our land to take electricity to Tarrington, thus enabling us to have mains electricity for the farm. Before that, we were drying the hops on hand-stoked coke kilns. Sadly, looking back on it now, we decided to knock down the two small round kilns, which we now realise were of historical interest, and build a square kiln in their place, to increase the drying capacity.

In the same year we took the hill-land out of cereal production and planted it with grass. Looking back, we planted a very interesting mixture of seeds – Giant Lurgen Irish/Italian rye grass, leafy Lurgen Irish perennial rye grass, New Zealand certified mother seed (hawks base strain), evergreen perennial rye grass, Aberystwyth S23 perennial rye grass, Aberystwyth S101 perennial rye grass, Aberystwyth S143 cocksfoot grass, mixed Timothy grass, mixed climate late-flowering single cut red clover, Vale of Clwyd English once-grown medium early red clover, American Alsace and white clovers (15% white), English trefoil clover, mixed climate wild white clover and blended mineral rich herbs ($13^1/_2$ lbs to the acre).

We also replanted the Vitrols that year with a variety of hop called Earlybird. It was the first time that we had grown this particular variety on our farm and it proved, in the long-term, to be a very successful Golding variety at Claston. In fact it was with this variety that we became well-known in the hop world, as it was the variety with which we won our first gold medal for Goldings.

In the 1950s we started using Shoddy, a waste product from the carpet factories, as a fertilizer for the hops because, with the increased acreage, we did not have enough farmyard manure and Shoddy produced very good results. Of course then it was practically 100% wool.

In December 1951, we bought a Weeks hop sprayer. This was a big step forward because it was the first sprayer ever produced that was power-driven, e.g. driven by the power-shaft connected to the tractor. This replaced an old engine-driven sprayer which had been converted to be drawn by a tractor, but was originally designed to be drawn by horses.

In the spring of 1952, we bought our first Ferguson tractor, costing £415, which was £50 less than the Weeks sprayer. That spring we also bought our first Land Rover.

From the late 1940s, the method of pest and disease control in hops was changing from dusts to washes and about 1951/52, the first organo-chlorine sprays became available for the control of hop damsel aphid. This was a revolution, introduced because the nicotine dust was becoming very ineffective, even though the nicotine content had increased from $2^1/_2$% to $7^1/_2$%. I don't think when we started using these new organo-phosphorus sprays, we had either been informed or knew of the risks we were taking. However they were very effective and we only ever had one accident using these new sprays, but even that was the fault of the tractor driver himself, because when he was mixing the chemical he accidentally spilt some in his Wellington boot. Obviously his sock soaked the chemical up but instead of immediately taking

MARRIAGE : STANWAY

1951 was a very important year in my life because I had become engaged to be married to Pamela Skittery, a farmer's daughter from Little Marcle, and as we had a problem finding a house near Claston, we decided to build one if we could get planning permission. Luckily, my father's brother-in-law was the Conservative agent for Hereford and, as a result, he knew the Conservative Member of Parliament at that time, J.P.L. Thomas, one of whose great friends was a Socialist Member of Parliament, Aneurin Bevan. He was the Minister responsible for Planning, so J.P.L. Thomas asked him if it would be possible to get planning permission for our house on the farm. This he was able to do and in 1951 we started building in the field to the south of Claston. The house was named Stanway after the village in Gloucestershire where my mother's father, John Thompson, was a tenant at The Home Farm before he came to farm at The Hyde, Woolhope. Because Stanway was built on a sloping field, the bricks from the walls of the two round kilns taken down at Claston were used to level the ground for the base of the house.

Stanway – Our home for 26 years

Our house was built by W.A. Greening and Son, builders in Hereford, who were a very careful and thorough firm. Pam and I used to get rather frustrated as the building work progressed in fits and starts. Once the base had been completed we went to have a look and found that it was just a concrete pad in a fairly large field. We were both astonished that it looked so small, and it did seem strange to see sheep lying in the sun on the base of our future home! When Mr Greening eventually started to build the walls, he would only build so many bricks high at a time, and then leave it for days to settle before eventually coming back to continue building. It did show, however, that by taking care and time in building up the lower courses, very little maintenance was needed later. Apart from the extensions we made, the only thing we had to do in the two decades plus that we lived there was to have one new tile put on the roof and that was because it had been damaged when the television aerial was being erected! There was never any subsidence nor did we ever have any cracks in the walls nor doors jamming and the only time we had any water-pipes frozen up was in 1963 in a little back hall, which had been added later, but nothing ever froze inside the house. After our marriage, Pam and I spent twenty-six very happy years at Stanway.

Our wedding day was arranged for 23 April 1952. Before the wedding rehearsal it had been agreed that Rev Simey, the vicar of Dormington, who was assisting with the service, should take the actual marriage as Rev Jones of Little Marcle was blind and sometimes found this part of the service difficult. However, Rev Jones was rather late for the rehearsal and, against our wishes, Rev Simey decided to start without him. In the middle of this Rev Jones appeared and was furious to find that the rehearsal had started in his church without him. There were angry exchanges between the two vicars, resulting in the Rev Jones saying 'I will take the marriage vows myself'.

John Weyman Jones, Olga Ruff, Father, Mother, Digby Blanch, myself, Pam,
Mr and Mrs Skittery, Sister Irene, David Skittery

The wedding duly took place, the service being conducted amicably by both vicars, and the reception was held in a marquee on the tennis court at Pam's home. When we left after the reception, we found that some of the young men had played a prank on us, blocking the narrow driveway with a large farm cart. To the amazement of everyone there my cousin, Digby Blanch, who was my best man, pulled this heavy cart out of the way single-handed.

We then proceeded to Ledbury to see Pam's grandmother, who was unable to attend the wedding. On leaving, the taxi driver held the car door open so that she and her elderly house-keeper could toss rice over us, which was rather unexpected and must have been an old custom.

his boots and socks off and washing his feet before going home to get some clean socks, which he should have done with any chemical if this happened, he continued until lunch-time and still did nothing about it. By the evening he became ill and had to be rushed to hospital with organo-phosphorus poisoning. Fortunately he recovered, but it was a very worrying incident and a very foolish thing for him to do, as he did not obey the instructions on the tin. He also failed to report the accident to the farm Safety Officer.

At Claston, we had always grown cider apples, originally to make cider for consumption by the farm workers, this being part of their pay up to the late '30s, and I had, when a teenager, actually made the cider in our old cider mill, using a horse to turn the stone which crushed the apples. I used to feel sorry for the horse, having to trudge round and round the stone for most of the day. We had sold cider fruit to Bulmers ever since they had started buying apples from farmers and one old orchard near the farm buildings, which had been planted many years before as an experimental orchard for the company, was pretty derelict by 1952. In place of that, we planted a new standard orchard which became known as Cottage Orchard, being

*Peter ploughing with the new Fordson Major,
shortly after his wedding*

Cattle in Cottage Orchard

the field by the farm cottages. This was the first orchard that Father and I had planted and was the beginning of commercial cider fruit production on the farm.

1952 was a very good year for hops and in total we produced 722 pockets, which was a record for Claston. We had, in fact, nearly doubled our production of hops in only five years and this total was not exceeded again until 1958, when we produced 871 pockets on an increased acreage. By that time we had ceased growing potatoes, but were still buying young cattle, keeping them for a year and selling them at the big cattle sales in Hereford, where they were bought mainly by the big beef grazing producers in Leicestershire. Our fat lambs were sold in Hereford market and a lot of our cereals were grown for our own cattle and sheep consumption. We also continued to grow sugar beet because not only was this a profitable cash crop at that time, but the tops of the beet provided valuable food for the animals.

In 1948, we had entered a sample of hops in the Brewers Exhibition, which was the national hop competition held in London, and we won third prize for the Fuggle variety. We again won a prize at this exhibition in 1952, which was a major landmark in the history of hop-growing at Claston. That year we had some very fine hops and although we had won no prizes at the local ploughing matches, we were advised to enter the hops in the Brewers Exhibition by Mr Lovatt, a hop factor. A hop factor was the growers' marketing agent. We therefore entered both Goldings and Fuggles and to our amazement, despite our lack of success in the local competitions, we won first prize for the Goldings class for Herefordshire and Worcestershire and also won the gold medal for the best Goldings sample in the U.K. This was the first time the gold medal for Goldings had ever been won in Herefordshire. In addition, we won second prize in the Hereford & Worcester class for Fuggles and the silver medal for the whole country. Goldings, incidentally, were the top grade of aroma hops and were very highly valued by brewers at that time. My grandfather, John Alfred Thompson, had won a gold medal for Fuggles back in

Cattle ready for market

Fat lambs

1906, so we were naturally very proud of our achievement, which surpassed his win. There was a great celebration and a huge number of letters of congratulation were received from the hop world. I remember that going to London to visit the exhibition to look at the hops and receive the prizes was very exciting, especially as I had dried these hops myself. Father had selected the area in the hop-yard from which the prize winning hops were picked, and which we held back from hand-picking until they were at their best, but I actually did the subsequent drying.

Hop-picking machines started to become popular in 1953 when one was put in at Dormington Court. I think it was one of the first to be fitted on a farm in Herefordshire, although there had been one hop-picking machine in the 1930s at Hillend, Weston Beggard. Father was reluctant to buy a hop-picking machine because the early ones, whilst being a great step forward, were causing a lot of damage to the varieties of hops we were growing then and you didn't get as good a yield, or price, for the hops.

In 1954, we purchased a large hop-yard at Marden, on a farm called the Vauld, in partnership with the late John Turner, where traditional Fuggles were being grown, and we continued to do this until 1972 when the hops were removed and an orchard was planted.

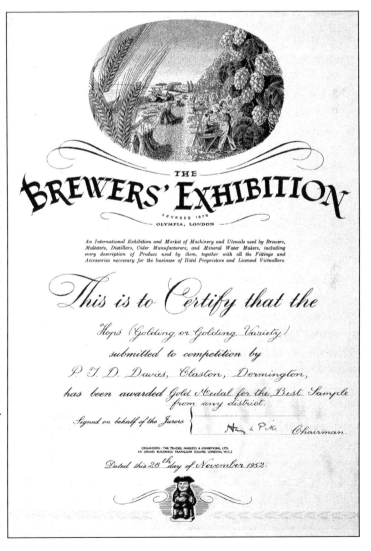

1952 Gold Medal certificate

By 1957, hop-picking by hand was becoming more difficult as many of the pickers were not willing to work more than 6 hours per day. We had 336 names of crib holders on the books. Five bus-loads of hop pickers were coming from Hereford daily and there were two bus-loads from South Wales living on the farm, as well as several gypsy families in their caravans and about twenty local families. There were seventeen staff working in the hop-yard and fourteen in the kilns, and we picked for four weeks and two and a half days. By 1952, the price we had to pay the pickers per bushel of hops had risen from 2½d to 12½d and it remained constant until 1957. Due to the problem of finding so many hop pickers, we decided to install a machine. The hop-picking machines had become much more efficient and it was a difficult decision to know which machine to buy of the two models available. One was the Bruff hop-picker, which was made at Suckley, and the other was the McConnell-Hinds machine, made in Malvern. Father talked to both manufacturers and when he asked George Hinds, the maker of the McConnell-Hinds machine, where we would obtain spare parts if something broke down, he received the reply that it would never happen, so Father, knowing this was very unlikely, bought the Bruff machine! Whilst the McConnell-Hinds machine was better-engineered, the Bruff machine eventually became the most successful hop-picking machine in England.

We had to build a new barn to accommodate our first mechanical hop-picker, which had cost £5,400. I dread to think what one would cost today if you could even find one. The barn was built by Dales of Leominster. They had mistaken their instructions and built it with the centre of the building level with the end of the red kiln building instead of 2 feet off centre as it should have been, to allow space for the elevator to convey the picked hops to the storage area above, before going into the kiln. This error was

Mary Pullen bagging off hops from the picking machine

not discovered until they had completed the steel work when it was a massive task to move it, especially as the steel pillars were already set in concrete.

We had intended in 1957 to pick half the hops (about 400 pockets) by hand and the other half with a machine, but it was a very wet hop-picking which made it so difficult for the hand-pickers that we ended up picking a total of 600 pockets with the machine. To do this we started work at 6 a.m. and worked right through until 11 p.m. I had wanted to work a 2-shift system, but the staff insisted on working right through. A number of people were required in the hop-yard to load the trailers, all of the loading being done by hand then. You had to have somebody cutting the bines about three feet from the ground and then a tractor with driver to pull the trailer, with two people in the front of the trailer pulling and loading the bines by hand. I remember the look on my father's face as the first hops went into the machine was one of absolute horror because it seemed to be so brutal, appearing to shatter all the hop-cones, but this was partly an optical illusion.

Loading the kiln

During that September, we had over nine inches of rain. In fact, the old saying 'rain before 7, fine before 11' did not seem to apply just then. When we had finished picking the hops, the hop-yards looked like a sea of mud. In fact, during hop-picking you couldn't walk to the hop-yards and the mud on the headlands came up over the front axle of the tractors. The men in the hop-yards also refused to work in shifts as was suggested, but continued to load the trailers all the time, so they were supplied regularly with hot coffee laced with rum. Several hop-yards had fallen down at Dormington because, due to the ground being so soft, the anchors holding the wire-work pulled out and the yard collapsed. We inspected our hop-yards several times a day and on one occasion I actually saw anchor rods moving. We immediately stopped picking hops so that all the tractors could be used to strain the wires while new anchors, with larger blocks, were put in to hold

Dried machine-picked hops in lifter cloths on cooling room floor

the wire-work up, thus saving the hop-yard, as the hops would have been almost impossible to pick if the wire-work had collapsed onto the ground in these very wet conditions.

During hop-picking in 1957, we received a telephone call from the well-known television personality, Leslie Thomas, who was making a series of farming programmes for A.T.V. He was inquiring if we would allow him to make a film of hop-picking. They spent a day doing this, then about a week later I was asked to go to the Birmingham A.T.V. studios to do a live commentary on the film. On arrival at the reception desk with my sister Kate, who accompanied me, we were astonished to behold a receptionist with brilliant orange hair, which in those days was quite an unknown sight in our rural area.

During the rehearsal, there were a vast number of people working in the studio, some of whom were hammering and making a great deal of noise. My instructions were to talk about the film, which I saw for the first time while doing so. As this proved to be to Leslie Thomas's satisfaction, we had tea then I went to the make-up room to be made up, ready to appear on the programme, which was to last about 20 minutes. After Leslie Thomas introduced the programme, I did my live commentary again without any script, surrounded by about six cameramen and technicians. At the end of the film, I was much surprised to find that I was looking directly at myself on the screen, which was quite an alarming experience. Some time afterwards, I was told that this was judged to be the best agricultural film of the year in the U.K.

At the time we purchased our first hop-picking machine, Philip was very ill with pneumonia, from which he was failing to recover until the doctor and consultant discovered that he was very short of iron and probably had been from birth, as Pam was also. After very painful iron injections for Philip and medicine for the two of them, they recovered well. Then unfortunately I got my arm caught in the hop-picking machine and it was so severely bruised and painful that I had to stay in bed at the same time as Philip. My arm was not broken, but it was in a sling for nearly three months.

That year, we entered the Brewers Exhibition again and, to our surprise, we won first prize in the Herefordshire & Worcestershire class for Goldings and the gold medal for the best sample in the country.

Hops had been grown in the old hop-yard since, probably, 1740 and the first wire-work was erected in 1912, replacing the pole-work on which hops were grown in the olden days. This wire-work was only 11 feet high and by 1950, instead of having individual plants, these old Fuggles plants had spread outwards, thus becoming almost continuous plants. It was very expensive and difficult to train the resulting small weak shoots to climb up the strings and, in addition, the wire-work was so low that in wet years the crop became far too thick. Also, there were a lot of gaps in places due to disease, so Father decided to take the hops out after the crop in 1952 and thereafter we grew oats, mixed corn, beans and mangolds, until 1957 when this old hop-yard was replanted with Fuggles on new, higher wire-work which was 15 feet high. The Fuggles that had previously been in this hop-yard were the traditional old Herefordshire ones, which had a relatively small hop-cone. In their wisdom, the plant breeders had decided to breed new strains of Fuggles and the one we planted was called Clonal N. This produced a completely different shaped cone which could be anything up to two

Winston sheep-dipping

inches long, but the plants produced very disappointing yields. When eventually we started to machine-harvest, these cones shattered; therefore changing the form of the traditional variety had proved to be a disaster, and we replanted this yard with five different varieties of Golding hops.

One interesting fact was that when we took the wire-work down, the poles, which had been boiled in tar in the traditional manner at Stoke Edith station to preserve them, were still 90% sound after having been in use for over 40 years, and we used them to make a pen, in which to house the ewes at lambing time.

PHILIP DAVIES

John Jones, who was stock-man at the time, sometimes helped in the kitchen garden in the evenings. When Philip was a toddler, he used to love to help him and it was very difficult to get him to go to bed. Once, when John was planting broad bean seeds, Philip followed behind, apparently thinking he was helping by picking them up again. He used to love to come and help me to feed the ewes and the baby lambs. He also thought helping John Jones to feed the tiddler lambs from the bottle was great fun.

Top left: Philip gardening with John Jones

Top right: Peter and Philip in the hay field

*Left: Hop picking. Miss Gladwin and
Mrs Byard with Philip*

When Philip was old enough, we gave him a pedal Land Rover for Christmas. He was thrilled with this and, in due course, he was given a trailer. As there was no hitch on the Land Rover, I asked Mr Wargent, who owned the blacksmith's forge at Stoke Edith, if he could make one. He said that if we took it across he would get the blacksmith, Bill Evans, to do this. Philip explained what he wanted and a few days later we collected the Land Rover, fitted with a super little hitch with a dropper pin. I enquired the cost and Mr Wargent said he would send Philip a bill, which when it arrived gave the details of the job but stated 'No Charge'. This was very good of him.

Philip started his education at Hereford Cathedral School pre-prep when he was five, going on to the preparatory school

Top left: Michael Skittery in Philip's land rover with Philip on the tricycle

Top right: Philip putting hay in the sheep rack

Right: Philip feeding tiddler lamb with John Jones

and leaving when he was eight to go as a boarder to Aymestrey School in Rushwick, near Worcester. He was very happy there under the excellent leadership of the Headmaster, Dan Asterley, whose father had taught my father when he was at Lucton School in Aymestrey parish, north of Leominster.

After leaving Aymestrey, Philip went to Malvern College, where he sang in the choir and played the trumpet in the 2nd orchestra and in the brass band. He loved swimming, at which he trained hard, representing the college team for three seasons. He equalled the backstroke record for the college, but he was very disappointed not to be awarded his swimming colours.

In 1959, we ceased renting the hop-yard from Mr Godsall at Eastwood as by then we had the Marden hop-yard in full production. In the same year we bought our first oil burner. This was a tremendous step forward in hop-drying because it eliminated all the manual work, not only of hauling coal from the station but also of having to fill the hoppers for the automatic stokers. It was also a much cleaner method of hop-drying, eliminating the build-up of clinker which previously had to be removed from the fire at the end of each load. Another problem with the stokers was that the auger taking the coal to the fire got jammed if an odd bolt or stone fell in. This would snap the safety device, so preventing damage to the auger, but the coal hopper containing several hundredweights of coal, then had to be emptied to enable the cause of the jam to be removed – a very dirty and laborious job.

We acquired our second hop-picking machine in 1960, but were getting very worried about when it would be completed and in fact it was not until about midnight prior to hop-picking commencing the next morning that it was fully up and running. I remember Mr Brookes from the Bruff manufacturing company said that, in his experience, it would take a long time for us to organise the labour force in order to pick twice as many hops with two machines as with one. It actually only took three days! That was the first year that we picked all our hops by machine and we won both the gold and silver medals (Champion and Reserve) for the whole of the U.K. with machine-picked Golding hops and also the Silver medal for Fuggles, which were in the same class as the hand-picked hops.

John and Gwyn Pritchard pessing hops in the old cooling room

When Father had started increasing our hop acreage in the 1940s, he purchased the roots from what were considered to be the best hop growers. This he was doing, little knowing that it introduced a disease known as Nettlehead to the hops at Claston. This disease eventually became widespread in the West Midlands. East Malling Research Station had, by 1967, discovered that Nettlehead was caused by two viruses, one in the plant which was not noticeable, but the second was carried to the plant by a strain of eelworm infected with another virus, causing Nettlehead. This disease stopped the plants growing any more than about 6 feet high and the leaves became very

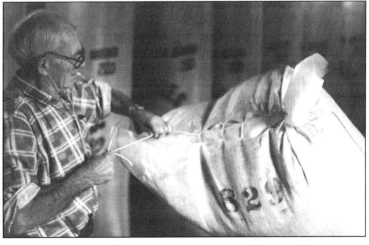

John Albrecht stitching up a pocket of pressed hops

similar to nettles. To overcome this, in 1968 and 1969, in conjunction with East Malling and Rosemaund, we did a number of tests involving fumigating the soil to kill the eelworm, before replanting with cuttings which we had propagated from our own virus-free plants. By this time Wye College and East Malling between them had found a method of producing virus-free plants and we then formulated a programme of grubbing an infected hop-yard immediately after hop-picking and leaving it fallow for the following twelve months. The next year, in late spring, we ploughed the hop-yard and devised a method of dribbling a chemical in the furrow to kill the eelworm. Then we re-planted the ground soon afterwards with plants propagated from cuttings taken from our own nursery of virus-free plants which we had planted in 1967.

Over the next few years we replanted the whole farm in this way. Since then we have not suffered any Nettlehead on the farm. This co-operation between a grower and the scientists to overcome the problems of a disease was very successful. To achieve this re-planting, we built two large greenhouses at Stanway in 1967 and 1968.

The following year we started loading the hops from Marden and needed 14 tractors and trailers to haul the hops the 8 miles to the Claston picking machines. I remember that one of John Turner's drivers used to deliver his first load, then he would take his second load to a local pub where he remained for several hours, eventually arriving at Claston in the afternoon with his long overdue load.

In December 1960 the rivers Wye and Lugg reached very high levels, causing grave concern that the 12 ft embankment at the Bunch of Carrots Inn at Hampton Bishop, known as the 'stank', might collapse, in which case the Wye would have flowed down the road from Hampton Bishop to Mordiford. There were small breaches of this flood bank and from one of these, due to the enormous pressure, the water was hitting an upstairs bathroom window at the Bunch of Carrots Inn. There was such severe flooding in Hampton Bishop that troops were brought in to evacuate the inhabitants of the village by boat and helicopter.

Inside the greenhouse

We continued planting hops to increase our production as our sales went up and in 1960 we planted the Garden hop-yard. Hop-roots were then being produced by specialist propagators in East Anglia, but these were very expensive. We discovered that a great friend of ours, the late Jim Knott, was producing his own hop cuttings in a greenhouse by taking green shoots from the end of April, through to early June. He put the cuttings straight into heated grit and supplied a mist to keep them damp. He then planted the rooted cuttings in individual pots. We very much liked this idea, so we put up our first small greenhouse in 1962. We quickly discovered that it would save a lot of time and labour, yet still be just as effective, if we planted the cuttings straight into 2$^{1}/_{4}$ inch Jiffy pots in a special rooting compost and placed the pots on the grit. We have continued producing our own cuttings in this way to this day.

The winter of 1962-63 was the coldest since 1740, lasting from mid-December till the thaw in early March. Heavy snow fell regularly, with strong easterly winds causing severe drifting, night temperatures dropping to -17°C and daytime temperatures seldom

70

reaching more than -4°C. The River Wye froze so hard that people could stand on the ice, and three of the water mains in Hereford were frozen. On the farm, the staff spent nearly all day thawing water pipes to provide water for the animals, feeding the cattle and sheep and in any time remaining they repaired and painted the farm machinery. When the thaw came in early March, there was no heavy rain as in 1947, so there were no floods.

In 1963 we planted our first hop-yard, which was the lower part of the Garden hop-yard really, with our own mist-propagated Earlybird plants. In the first year that we were producing the plants, we quickly learned how susceptible they were to fungal diseases. Although we were taking great care to spray the cuttings with fungicides, during a planting session in the Garden hop-yard to fill in some gaps, we left a tray of the plants in the hop-yard over the weekend, only to find that by the Monday or Tuesday every single one had succumbed to downy mildew. We rapidly overcame that problem by a more thorough method of downy mildew control in the greenhouse.

Geof Godsall on stilts tying down wire

In 1964, we purchased the 50 acres that we had been renting from Colonel Barneby at Longworth. We planted 14 acres with Fuggles, and two years later a further 21 acres, the remainder of the land being left to grass. Unfortunately, at the end of July/early August 1964, the hop-yard was struck by lightning and collapsed. The crop was a total write-off. We had insured our hop-yards against such an occurrence, but did not realise that this was what had happened because the collapse could have been caused by the very heavy rain during the storm, combined with the weight of the large and heavy crop. Our insurers asked whether there was a thunderstorm at that time and, as we knew

Geof Godsall putting an anchor block into the ground

there had been, they sent an expert out and he established exactly where the hop-yard had been struck. They then paid not only for the loss of the crop and compensation to purchase quota that we would have lost, but also paid to reconstruct the hop-yard.

John Albrecht stringing

In 1967, I was invited to join the Herefordshire and Worcestershire Joint Hops Advisory Group. This was a body of progressive and senior hop-growers from the two counties which met once a year. Also on that committee were scientists, people from Plant Health, hop advisers from Herefordshire and Worcestershire and personnel from Rosemaund Research Centre. I don't know if it ever achieved very much, but it was very interesting because we discussed, not political matters, but research and the programme for the hops on the Rosemaund Ministry experimental farm. I also got to know growers whom I had not met before.

In 1967, out of the blue, my father received a letter from Mr John Scott of Ansells Brewery and Brigadier Tetley from Tetley Walker, asking him if he would be willing to take over the running of the Tetley Walker hop-farms at Dormington Court. After much deliberation, thought and discussion, Father decided to take on the task. We realised that it would be an unpopular move from the point of view of other hop-growers, because they felt, or probably knew, that Father would make a success of it and they feared that this would damage their chances of selling their hops to breweries, which was complete nonsense because there was a shortage of hops at that time. When talking in later years to several hop-growers whom I knew had been very critical of what we were doing, I asked them what they would have done if they had been in our position, and they said that they would have done exactly the same. It was undoubtedly an opportunity not to be missed. I think Father really wanted to do it, as he was very upset that while we were producing good hops on similar land to that on the neighbouring brewery farms, they were producing hops of very poor quality. In fact, we discovered later that most of the 1966 crop had been burned by the brewery because the hops proved useless for brewing.

It was a tremendous undertaking because they were growing nearly 300 acres of hops on the Dormington

New two-tier kilns at Dormington

Court, Aldersend and Pomona farms. When Father took control, everything was run down, the staff were demoralised and the manager, when we came to meet him, was very uncooperative. It was an interesting challenge too because Father met all sorts of people in the brewing industry who used to visit the farms whilst we made visits to Burton which helped us a lot in our future hop-farming because they looked at hop-growing in a different light – we looked at it as a hop-grower, as most hop-growers did at that time, but the brewers thought of it as a purely commercial business operation.

There was an enormous amount of work to do to correct the kilns and to improve the hop-picking machines. The directors were keen that we should propagate new varieties of hops for their farms, because they realised after the first season that we were producing much better and cheaper hop-roots than they could purchase elsewhere. We then increased our propagation units dramatically to allow us to produce not only roots for ourselves but also for the brewery hop-farms.

It is amazing how one event such as being a member of a hop committee can lead to another, and in 1967 I was invited to be a member of the Association of Growers of the new varieties of hops, which was largely based in Kent, although there were some Herefordshire members. This was a very interesting body. Basically it was an association to promote the growing of the new varieties of hops which were coming on stream at this time. I think this started in 1950, but I'm not sure. We had two meetings per year, one in the Spring and one in the Autumn and also an interesting annual visit to a hop-grower's farm, mostly in Kent. In fact, I think there had only been one visit to Herefordshire and one to Worcestershire before I joined.

In 1968, we planted a 5 acre hop-yard at the Sheepcote with Bullion. This was our first venture into growing the next generation of hops that were produced by Professor Salmon at Wye College. Bullion was a very heavy yielder and had a higher bittering content than the older varieties. We called the hop-yard Smugglers because Pam, Philip and I had recently driven with some friends to Austria, for our first and only skiing holiday. At the start of my first beginner's skiing lesson, I was the last to get on my skis and when I stood up I accidentally moved off, knocking over all of the others in the class, who were mostly Germans and who were not at all amused. Mr Brookes of Bruff had organised our stay at Tettnang at a nice little hotel on our way to Austria, on the edge of Lake Constance, also arranging for a hop grower to meet us. When we did so, he invited us to go and have a look at his hops and to have a drink with him on our return journey. This we did and he insisted we brought some Tettnang hop cuttings back. We were very worried about this because we thought there would be problems bringing the cuttings into England, but we took a chance and got them back without any trouble. Hence the reason why we called the hop-yard in which we planted them Smugglers. Everybody thought we had named it after the dog we had at that time, also called Smuggler. The exercise proved afterwards to be a waste of time because the Tettnang hops were highly unsuccessful in this country, and never produced a worthwhile crop. Fortunately, as we only planted about 300 cuttings, it was not a great loss.

GOLDEN APPLE COUP

As a spur to improve management and production, Bulmers held their first orchard competition in 1968. This was limited only to orchards from which the apples were sold to Bulmers. We were fortunate to be the first winners of this Golden Apple competition. Then, in 1974, the seventh year of the competition, we were winners for the third time thus achieving a unique hat trick.

Peter and his father receiving the first Golden Apple award from Bertram Bulmer

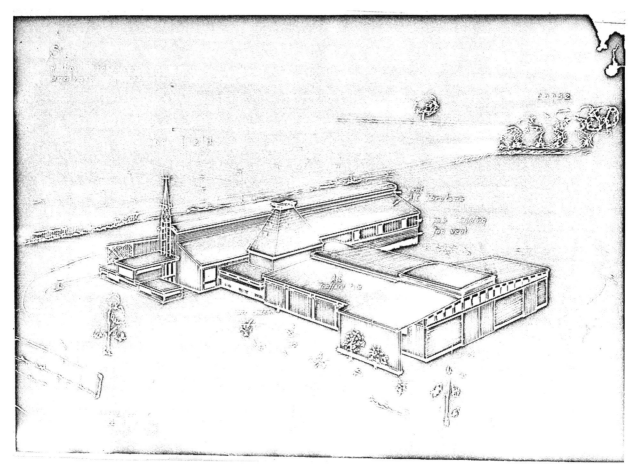

Plan of co-operative kilns

In 1969, a meeting of local hop-growers – Tom Bradstock, Andrew Foley, Philip Davies & Son, Dormington Court Hop Farms and John Turner from Kings Pyon – met to discuss the potential of a feasibility study on the formation of a hop-picking and hop-drying syndicate. This was agreed and the Central Council for Agricultural and Horticultural Co-operation agreed that they would pay 75% of the cost of carrying out the research. The plan was for the project to be up and running in 1971. The object was to have two hop-picking machines, one new and one moved from one of the farms to pick the hops from three of the farms, and a completely new set of kilns with the capability of drying 150 pockets per day for the five growers, working three six-hour shifts. There was to be space left in the building for future development such as the installation of a hop-processing plant to make hop pellets at a later date. This meeting was held on 10th March 1969. Another meeting took place on 24 March, to which Mr and Mrs Brookes from Bruff Engineering were invited. It was agreed that they should produce plans and costs for three-tier kilns to do 150 pockets a day and also to supply a new hop-picking machine and to move one existing hop-picking machine from another farm. It was agreed that we should ask Czechoslovakian engineers to come and discuss hop drying, because they had got some fairly modern plants in their country. Another meeting was held in May, when it was agreed to appoint Mr J.B. Weller, an architect from Biddestone, Suffolk, to design the buildings and roads, for which his fee would be 4$^{1}/_{2}$% of the build cost, together with 1% of the equipment cost because he would obviously be involved in that, plus his travelling costs. Mr Brookes arranged for the Czechs to attend a meeting at Rosemaund on 15 July where the Rosemaund officials were unnecessarily arrogant, saying the Czechs had little to offer. It was agreed with Mr Foley to do an independent exercise at Perton and we agreed a fee for them to bring the equipment over, also for engineers to come and install it and for their accommodation, as well as doing test trials during hop-picking. They installed the plant in the Perton Court kilns, but before the trial could be completed, the Russians invaded Czechoslovakia and they immediately rushed back to their country because they said some of the family were strong protesters against this impending invasion. However, the plant worked very well and the samples from this plant were satisfactory. The idea was that in the final part of the drying you put damp air into the kiln so that you got more even moisture content in the dried hops throughout the kiln, as opposed to the traditional drying, during which the bottom hops became a bit too dry and the top hops not quite dry enough. We had got all the plans and costs and planning permission but one stumbling block was that Mr Foley said that he would grant us a 99-year lease but he would not sell the land, although later he did consent to sell it. We all previously agreed that unless we could own the site it would be a risky project to undertake. Also, our final conclusion was that the costs of £180,000 were too high for the production of hops from 300 acres. It was a pity because the potential was enormous, but I agreed at the time, as did all the others, that at that stage, the costs seemed very prohibitive. On today's figures it looks ridiculously low. However, I also think, with hindsight, that if we had gone ahead with it, at the outbreak of wilt at Claston in 1974 there could have been very serious problems to resolve.

Peter and his father with the first 1,000th pocket produced in a single season

In 1969 we planted another six acres of Bullion at Tidnor, in the field next to the Smugglers hop-yard. Both of the Bullion hop-yards were very successful, although as the plants got older they became more difficult to manage and, especially, to harvest. Although we erected extra high 18 feet wire-work because we knew it was a very vigorous variety, the bines still became very thick and wiry which made them difficult to pick. We discovered some time later that Tidnor had actually been a hop-yard very many years before this.

Sadly, although Bullion produced very high yields of beautiful high-alpha hops, it never became popular with brewers because of its very unusual aroma and so, in time, these hops were taken out.

The 1969 harvest also brought about another landmark in the history of Claston when it was the first time we grew 1,000 pockets.

We planted the last new hop-yard in 1970 – an 11 acre field at Longworth which we took out of grassland and put into Challenger hops. There was a tremendous amount of preparation to be done before planting this field, not only because two or three mature trees had to be removed but also because there was a massive drainage problem. Fortunately at that time the Wye River Board had done a huge amount of flood restriction work and had built a large bank to stop that area flooding, so we were able to deepen all the ditches and utilise that flood alleviation scheme to make this a very successful hop-yard.

PHILIP DAVIES

Philip left school in July 1971, having refused to go back to Malvern College for the next term. He would not give any reason for this but later, when Matron wrote returning his medical card, she said that perhaps he was wise not to return, as the other four boys in his study were on drugs and some had been expelled. This must have put him under enormous pressure and been very stressful during the previous term or two. He then went to the Sixth Form college in Hereford, to study accountancy, economics, biology and physics for twelve months, after which he came to work on the farm.

Laddie Godsall taught Philip to shoot, instructing him in all of the necessary safety rules, and he became a very good shot. Later, David Hughes from Moor Mills managed a small pheasant shoot for Philip and his friends on the farm. We planted a small wood by the river and allowed other odd corners to become overgrown to encourage wildlife.

Philip attended four week-long residential hop-growing courses at Hadlow Agricultural College in Kent with Robert Lane, a school friend. He also went to four residential 'man management' courses conducted by the Royal Agricultural Society, at Stoneleigh, which he found very interesting and instructive. It was here that he

acquired the ability to put across his point of view and to secure the respect and trust of the staff on the farm. As well as keeping the staff informed regarding our weekly plans, he was always prepared to listen to their point of view. They would, in return, tell him of any problems that they had noticed while at work and knew that he would respond immediately. Under his management, Claston had become a very happy work place.

When the International Hop Growers Convention was held in Czechoslovakia, Philip and Graham Skittery attended and Philip became friendly with the girl who was the interpreter for the English delegation. She later came to stay with us at Claston and soon after she came to work in the Czech airline office in London. As a result of this friendship, Philip was asked by MI5 to work for them part-time. After about two years, they managed to catch the foreign agent who they had been looking for. During this time, Philip was helped by Jim Vakakalia, who was in the SAS and was married to my cousin Susan. When Philip discovered that many of the MI5 members were on drugs, Jim advised him on how to cease this work.

Left: Philip and Henry Weston shooting

In 1972 we made our last change-over from Fuggles to Challenger in the Greens hop-yard, which was to come into production in 1973. This change-over involved the completion of re-draining, new wire-work and planting with virus-free plants over 125 acres.

Ours was the fifth farm in Herefordshire to have a Farmplan computer farming programme, which was very satisfactory. Both Philip and my secretary, Jenny Jones, became very competent at using it. Some time later, Farmplan produced a proposed update of their financial programme, asking users to comment and make any improvements they thought necessary. Philip did a vast amount of work on this and as a result of his efforts he was presented with the new programme, which was worth £2000.

During 1972, I was invited to become a member of the NFU Hops Committee for Herefordshire. This was quite a surprise as I did not think we were terribly popular having taken on the Allied work, but it was an interesting committee to be a member of as we discussed not only research and things of that nature, but also the political side of hop-growing. At this time, the beginning of queries as to the legality of the Hops Marketing Board started. To my surprise, in a very short while I was elected to be one of the two members (Dennis Thompson being the other) to represent Herefordshire on the National Farmers Union Hop sub-committee and this opened the door to all sorts of other avenues.

On Father's and Mother's Golden Wedding anniversary we suprised them by having a steam engine driven threshing box working in the paddock. They were delighted as by a strange coincidence on their

A traction engine at Father and Mother's Golden Wedding in 1972.
Peter, Kirsty Gardner, R. Steadman, (engine driver), Philip, Father, Mother,
Tom Barnes, Jim Read

wedding day in November 1922 Townsend's machines were threshing both at Claston and at The Hyde, Woolhope, where Mother's family were farming

Father took me to watch my first Hereford United football match in 1933, when the school were given the afternoon off to see Hereford United play Tottenham Hotspur in a friendly match. However, I did not see many more matches until after the war, the first important match that I can remember being an FA Cup match against Sheffield Wednesday in 1958 and I still have a programme of that match. There were a number of memorable cup victories before, in 1971, I became involved with seating work in the stands. With a team of men from Claston, Dormington Court and Morris Wargent and Wilde, we fixed the seats in the first two sections of the main stand and all of the seats in the new Len Weston stand. The winter of 1971-72 was extremely wet and I took a team of Claston and Dormington Court men to help prepare the ground for the famous cup matches against Newcastle United and West Ham. My secretary, Jenny Jones, helped in the ticket office for these matches and I remember going in at 10 a.m. on the Sunday after the Newcastle victory, when tickets were to be sold for the West Ham match, to find a queue of people six wide all around the ground.

CHAPTER SEVEN

Disaster Hits the Farm : 1973-1981

THE START OF PROGRESSIVE VERTICILLIUM WILT (PVW)

When walking to inspect the hops in early August 1973, I found a hop plant in the north-west corner of the Greens hop-yard which was looking very strange, with discoloured leaves, I had never seen a plant in this state before. I was very puzzled and called in the ADAS (Agricultural Development & Advisory Service) hops specialist, who had a look and, unbeknown to me, took some leaf samples to send away for testing. He hadn't told me that he had suspected that it might be verticillium wilt. He said very little in fact, which was a disastrous mistake, as I will now explain. What he did not know, and I was not to find out until many years later, was that there was unreported progressive verticillium wilt at Perton in 1972.

PHILIP'S VISIT TO TASMANIA

On 7 January 1974, Philip and a friend of his, Andrew Powell, went with Albert Jeans and Henry Merrick from the Bruff Hop Manufacturing Company to Tasmania, to assist in installing one of three hop-picking machines, two others going to farms in Tasmania and Victoria. Philip and Andrew stayed in a pub at a place called Winnalia, which was a short distance from Ian Farquhar's three farms where they were working. The Farquhars farmed about 500 acres, with 30 acres of hops which were irrigated by trickle irrigation. They also grew parsnips, onions, carrots, silver beet which was grown for seed, and kept cattle which were left to roam on the bushland. The boys started work at 8 a.m. after a cooked breakfast, often consisting of eggs and very tough steak from cow beef. Work ceased normally at 5 p.m. The Farquhar's machine was nearly finished by 30 January, after which Philip and Andrew worked on the farm. Their first job was cutting thistles in the young hops with a hedge-bill, which they found exhausting as it was 95°F in the shade and at least 120° out in the open.

Their next job was filling bags with cocksfoot grass seed and then parsnip seed. They had problems with dust in the cocksfoot and thousands of earwigs in the parsnip seed. Other jobs which they did were pulling wild grass out of the parsnips by hand, picking up stones out of ploughed paddocks, pulling ryegrass out of cocksfoot grass which had been left to grow for seed and cutting fern blackberries and redberries from the edges of the boundary fences.

They finally completed installing the hop-picking machine in early March, when Albert Jeans returned having completed the machine in Victoria. During the hop harvest, Philip and Andrew worked on the picking machine in the day time and then had to take the sacks of picked hops on a lorry to Harold Davy's kilns in Scotsdale to be dried. This means that they worked very long hours, not getting back to Winnalia until 11 p.m.

On one occasion, the boys went to a beach at Tomahawk to go net-fishing, having been told that they would need a change of clothing as they would have to swim in the ones they were wearing to keep warm. They dragged the net out five times, Andrew and Philip always being made to go farthest out to sea, which was twice as hard work as for those nearest the shore. They caught about a hundredweight of fish, consisting mainly of garfish and Tasmanian black fish, and both enjoyed the swimming.

Towards the end of their stay in Winnalia, the landlord of the pub told them that he was going away and asked them to run the pub for the weekend. Knowing that the pub should be closed on the Sunday, they were persuaded by the locals to open, while they provided look-outs at each end of the street to warn them if anyone in authority approached. They then sold every drop of beer in the pub. When the landlord returned on the Monday, he was amazed to find that there was no beer left, but no questions were asked. When hop-picking was finished, Philip and Andrew spent a few days touring Tasmania before returning home towards the end of March.

WILT IS CONFIRMED IN 1974

In early August 1974, we received an unexpected telephone call from Plant Health to say that the plant Mr Vevers had sent for testing was infected with PVW. Now verticillium wilt to a hop-grower is like foot and mouth to a livestock farmer. It is a fungal disease which stops the flow of sap and kills the plant. It would be very easy to kill the fungus were it not for the fact that there is no known systemic fungicide that will go against the sap flow to kill it in the root, which is where the infection starts. Once the leaves are infected they take on a striped effect of brown, yellow and green colours. If the infected leaves drop close to another hop plant that plant will have wilt the following year. Parts of these leaves can be blown in the wind, or can be carried by birds and animals and obviously can be carried by tractors and people too. Therefore it would have been much better if Mr Vevers had warned us of the possibility of it being verticillium wilt on his visit the previous year so that we could have removed the plant and several around it straightaway. There are also many garden and wild plants which can be infected with verticillium wilt – potatoes and strawberries, to name but two.

We were informed that senior people from Plant Health and their chief scientists would come down to assess the situation and within a couple of days we had a message to say that they were indeed coming. They arrived with their waterproof clothing, Wellington boots and disinfectant. They informed me that the infected plant was in the south-west corner of the hop-yard. I pointed out that that was not where the wilt-infected plant had been found, but they insisted that the south-west corner was the site of the diseased plant. They took no notice of my protestations, so we all headed towards the south-west corner of the hop-yard. Of course, all of the plants there were healthy. The visitors were completely bamboozled and put out by this discovery. I reiterated the fact that the infected leaves had been found on a plant in the north-west corner and they set out to have a look, leaving behind their disinfected spades and buckets and their disinfectant. We walked down the hop row and on reaching the area I had initially pointed out, we found several infected plants. There were also several other plants showing signs of infection. Now here was a dilemma for the visitors - all of their disinfecting equipment had been left in the south-west corner of the hop-yard. It would have been idiotic to walk from the infected area to collect their equipment, thus spreading the disease, so eventually after much discussion, it was decided that I should return to the farm, disinfect my boots and take a vehicle to collect their equipment, then take it back to them via the road so that they could take samples for further testing.

It was beyond belief that these senior scientists would not believe me when I told them in which area of the hop-yard the infected plants were. Looking back to this episode, perhaps it was not surprising that they later made such disastrous mistakes in the control of the disease in the West Midlands, especially as the same rules had failed to control PVW outbreaks in Kent years before.

I was told that we had a major problem and that I must take out eleven plants round each infected plant. These were to comprise the infected plant and ten others in a five-row block. I commented that I thought that was a complete waste of time and that we should remove a larger block, but the advisers insisted that the removal of eleven plants was sufficient. Nothing more was said and the advisers left. However, I knew that this action was wrong and I therefore instructed our men to assist me in fencing off, cutting down and burning a total of one third of an acre. The whole area was burnt, swept and thoroughly cleaned. We then concreted both the headland in that area and the entrance to the hop-yard from the main road, so that we could keep it free of infection.

The next morning I went out to have a look and seeing pheasants and other birds scratching about, concluded that we had wasted our time, because I thought there were bound to be bits of the infected plants which we had missed and which they would carry around on their feet. This later proved to be so. The Plant Health advisers were very angry when they learnt what I had done. I also informed all the neighbouring farmers that we had an outbreak of verticillium wilt and the scientists were even more enraged about this, saying that the information was secret and that they would write to growers advising that "a farm in the Lower Frome valley" had been infected with wilt. There were a number of farms in the Lower Frome Valley and all the hop-growers were very appreciative of the action I had taken. Looking at the minutes of a meeting of the hops advisory group in November 1974, I noticed that they had analysed seventy-nine suspect verticillium wilt plants, from thirty-one yards on twenty farms. Amongst these, there was one yard of Challenger hops, which was obviously ours. The tests confirmed that there were forty-two plants with verticillium aboatrum, fifteen with verticillium dalia, others were unidentifiable and five were not diseased. There are two strains of verticillium wilt: verticillium aboatrum is the virulent progressive wilt, and verticillium dalia is a less virulent form and can appear one year and not the next. It is therefore known as fluctuating wilt. When the further tests had been completed, it appeared that ours was the only farm with the virulent strain of verticillium wilt. At a meeting later in 1974, after our outbreak had been confirmed, a senior Ministry inspector, who had again looked at the hops, said there was no evidence to date that the infection had spread, which was in fact completely untrue because we had had a very substantial number of plants showing signs of infection in the infected hop-yard by the end of that summer. Other yards at Claston soon became infected.

Shortly after this confirmation, we had visits from BBC Radio and TV, both requesting interviews to discuss the problem. They wanted to know what effect the wilt would have on our enterprise, whether we would be able to continue growing hops and also how serious it would be to the supply of hops to the brewing industry. I explained to them that verticillium wilt had spread to practically every hop farm in Kent in spite of their carrying out the government's grubbing policy, which was supposed to control the spread of the disease but had, in fact, been totally unsuccessful. When I told them this, they were astonished that we were instructed to carry out the same grubbing policy, as this had failed so dismally in Kent.

This was the beginning of a long and traumatic struggle to obtain a licence to plant Wye Target on our farm, this being the only variety that was, at that time, tolerant to verticillium wilt. Little did we know how bitter this battle would be and although I had about five growers in the West Midlands who supported me, I had to fight the Hops Marketing Board, Plant Health, the Ministry of Agriculture and other bodies who were all against the tolerant variety of hops being planted. I suggested we take out the whole of the infected hop-yard and re-plant with Target after a two-year break, but they claimed that Target harboured the disease without showing symptoms and then it could be spread to other farms. However, this had not happened in Kent, where wilt had been prevalent for many years and growers who had planted Target after a two-year break found that this reduced the incidence of wilt. We were the only hop-growers in the West Midlands who had ever reported an outbreak of verticillium wilt but had decided to continue hop-growing. This was because we had just completed draining, treating the soil against eelworm, re-planting with virus-free Early Bird, Northdown and Challenger, and renewing the wire-work where necessary on 125 acres, which was a very costly business and was carried out prior to the

The effect of PVW

discovery of wilt on the farm. We virtually became outcasts but I ignored this although Philip and Pam found it very difficult. Philip was not welcome in the Young Farmers Clubs and even Pam found that the wives of other hop-growers were crossing the road to avoid her. Little did we know that it would take over eight years to get a licence to plant a tolerant variety of hop.

The following year, the hop-yards were inspected by a team from Plant Health, who came with a senior Plant Health officer and the local Plant Health inspector. Students from one of the universities, and other ministry people, who knew nothing about hops or wilt, also came and spent a few hours walking in the hop-yards where they were shown the infected plants as they were found. Once the students were considered competent to recognise the infected plants, they were allowed to walk and inspect on their own. This worked reasonably well, but after the wilt really started to spread rapidly I very seldom went into the hop-yard, immediately after an inspection, without finding an infected plant which they had missed.

During this time, beer sales were buoyant, resulting in high prices for Northdown and Challenger which, unfortunately, were the varieties which were rapidly becoming infected, and we were forced to take out. As a result of this, we lost well over £1,000,000 worth of sales by the time we were able to replant the hop-yards.

Extensive records were kept of the wilt, both at Claston and later Dormington Court, which became infected in 1976. We had a scaled plan of every hop-yard with each plant marked on it and when an infected plant was found it was marked on the plan, and the grubbed space around also recorded. It quickly became obvious that the greatest danger of spread was down the alleys from tractors, sprayers and cultivators working in the yards.

THE NATIONAL HOPS COMMITTEE AND THE HOPS MARKETING BOARD

To my amazement, in March 1975 I was made Vice-Chairman of the National NFU Hops Committee in London. The following year, the Government decided to hold a public enquiry into the legality of the Hops Marketing Board. The enquiry lasted ten working days, eight days covering the Board's case and two days for the objectors. The latter were objecting to amendments to the Hops Marketing Board's constitution. These were urgently needed because the Board was formed in 1932 when hop prices were at rock bottom and hop-growers were going bankrupt. When the HMB was formed, the agreement with the brewers was that they would take all the hops they required from English growers, each grower having been given a basic quota for their farm which was based on the average of several previous years' production. In January, the brewers would say how many hops they wanted for that year, so they were really buying hops on the spot market, and then, depending on their requirement, growers were allocated a percentage of their basic quota. Growers could trade in annual quota which was just for one year's crop, between a grower who was short to a grower with a surplus for that year. A grower who was giving up hop-growing could sell his basic quota. I believe there was a serious flaw in this arrangement with the brewers, because they demanded all the best quality hops so any hops surplus to their requirements would have been of poor quality. This meant that there was little chance of building up an export market.

The brewers now wanted to make forward contracts, because it had become a worldwide system of marketing and they could buy hops more cheaply from the continent. This was because the English price was an average annual cost plus profit; therefore growers had become uncompetitive in the world market. In the early 1960s, West Germany and the U.K. were growing about an equal quantity of hops. However, the Germans adopted a vigorous export strategy, largely by making agreements with brewers worldwide to brew German lager beer, but using only German hops. Sadly the HMB never changed the original marketing agreement with brewers, and by the 1990s the German growers were producing six times as many hops as growers in the U.K. This was helpful to their growers who could plan their forward production. So the objectors wanted the Board to change their new marketing amendments. I won't go into detail about it because it was a very complicated, legal argument.

The Chairman, Vice-Chairman and Secretary of the Hops Marketing Board gave evidence at the enquiry, the Chairman and Vice-Chairman both being growers, and the Chairman and Vice-Chair of the NFU also gave evidence. As Vice-Chairman of the NFU Hops Committee, I was therefore expected to give evidence, but had not been to a public enquiry or even to a court case in my life before. Unfortunately, no other hop-growers were prepared to give evidence in support of the HMB. I ended up having 4½ hours in the witness box and it was a very interesting experience which I thoroughly enjoyed. I was amazed, however, that when, on finding I was shortly to give evidence, I asked the Board's barrister for guidance, he said he did not think this was necessary although he really had no idea if it was the case. I had a lengthy battle with Christopher Bellamy, a very able and knowledgeable European law barrister, who represented the objectors. During the questioning, I thought I had worked out Mr Bellamy's line of thought and gave my answers expecting him to come up with a follow-on question. This he did until the end of the 4½ hours when he asked me a question which I answered, anticipating a further question. He then said he had no more questions which gave a very false impression, thus damaging the case I was putting forward. It was, however, a friendly enquiry although the Chairman, Mr Vick, did not talk much to anybody, but the barristers and the growers on opposing sides did talk to one another and it was all very amicable. At the end of that day, Mr Bellamy came across and congratulated me on how well I had put my case, despite having lost in the end.

Following that case, sadly the Chairman of the NFU Hops Committee, who had been in office since 1948, resigned his position through ill-health and muggins was made Chairman. I suppose that my Chairmanship, from 1976 until 1982, was probably the most hectic in the life of the NFU Hops Committee, because it was after the enquiry that the European Union challenged the legality of the Board and so we had numerous meetings with the Government on the way forward. In addition to this, there were many meetings with Plant Health regarding the wilt situation in the West Midlands.

Looking back it was quite amazing really because at the end of a meeting, probably with the Minister and senior officials, or maybe just with senior officials at the Ministry, to discuss various problems and ideas, they would inform us that another meeting would be held shortly. You would then hear nothing for a number of weeks before being summoned to a further meeting at very short notice. It was all very interesting however, especially when Peter Walker was Minister for Agriculture. He was very friendly and always enquired at the end of a meeting about our wilt situation and what was happening on the farm. I remember one meeting in particular which was similar to the TV programme 'Yes, Minister', although Peter Walker was much more ruthless and intelligent than the portrayal of the Minister in that programme. He had previously asked a feared lady from MAFF, Jean Archer, three questions to which she did not know the answers and at the next meeting he expected a response. Peter Walker asked her the first question to which she still had no reply and he was naturally quite cross. Later he requested the answer to the second question and when she did not have this either he became very cross, but when she did not have the third answer, I have never heard anyone, without swearing or raising his voice, deliver such a dressing down as Peter Walker gave her. She must have felt very small. She was never seen or heard of again at those meetings and I do not know what happened to her, but it indicated how ruthless Peter Walker could be if necessary.

I always took my Vice-Chairman, Richard Coleman, who was a Kent hop-grower, to those meetings, because when I held that role I was not taken to any meetings at the Ministry and therefore when I became Chairman it was all completely new to me, which of course was a great disadvantage, and I did not want my Vice-Chairman to have the same problem. It was owing to the verticillium wilt that I ceased to be Chairman of the NFU Hops Committee, as I will explain later on.

In 1976, the NFU advised me to join the Farmers' Club so that I had a base in London from which I could attend meetings, where I could always get a room when they booked it for me, at short notice. Also it was a much pleasanter place to stay overnight, the food was excellent, the rooms were good, it was much cheaper than hotels and there were often people that I knew or farming people I hadn't met before who were happy and keen to talk.

By 1977, Father had greatly rationalised and improved the hop-growing at Dormington Court and Pomona, although sadly Dormington Court had suffered verticillium wilt in 1976, as previously mentioned. Father had before then re-drained most of the hop-yards and then re-planted them with virus-free plants, mostly Wye Challenger and Northdown. The kilns at Pomona were closed and the kilns at Dormington were enlarged and modernised to dry the hops from both farms.

DORMINGTON AND MORDIFORD PARISH COUNCIL
SOUTH HEREFORDSHIRE DISTRICT ASSOCIATION OF LOCAL COUNCILS

In 1976, I became a member of Dormington and Mordiford Parish Council and it is interesting when looking at the records to note how, over the centuries, the same topics seem to come up from time to time. One of the major problems we had when I first became a member was the management of the three commons – Checkley, Swilgrove and the Cockshoot. This had been going back a long time, I have a note here on this subject in the Commons Act 1899 and another one in 1908, signed by my grandfather when he was Chairman of the Rural District Council. These management problems seem to keep recurring. The commons are owned by the landlord, Mr Foley in this case, and the rights that various people in the parishes have on the common land vary greatly. On Checkley Common, which is the largest common in the joint Parish Council, one person had the right to graze ten sheep and two cattle, another person one pony or two sheep, another one fifteen sheep, four cattle and two ponies, another five sheep and another two sheep. On Swilgrove Common, one person had the right to graze thirty-six sheep, six cattle and one horse, another person two sheep or one pony, another five sheep and another only one. Many problems were occurring because in these modern days people did not need the grazing, except on Checkley Common, which some people used. The other commons became wild because they were not grazed. The Lugg Meadows are commons and those are still farmed properly but on a larger scale, so that it is a practical proposition to do so.

Another recurring problem has been footpaths, largely, I think, because after the 1951 Ordnance Survey a large number of footpaths were eliminated as people were not using them. Originally, footpaths were major routes for people who had no other form of transport to walk from their dwellings to one of the mills to get their wheat-flour, or to the doctor or to the church or school, but of course this is no longer necessary. In 1977, a Commons and Footpaths Preservation Society, which the Parish Council agreed to join, was formed and they became members for the sum of £2.

Planning was another major problem all the time that I was on the Council, in fact, the only times when any number of the public came to Parish Council meetings were when there was a controversial planning application. One of the more difficult things in planning was caused by newcomers coming into the parishes, buying old cottages then wanting to modernise them and, in many cases, enlarge them considerably. Also, there was the problem of barn conversions and new houses which needed to fit in with the surrounding landscape.

Soon after joining the Parish Council, I was asked to represent Dormington and Mordiford Parish Council on the South Herefordshire District Association of Parish and Town Councils, and I agreed to do so. This was quite an interesting body, but eventually it created a lot of work for me. South Herefordshire Association of Local Councils (SHALC) consisted of representatives of all the Parish Councils in the South Herefordshire area and the Clerks of the Councils were also entitled to attend. Normally, there were about thirty, sometimes forty, people present and there were good discussions, always with a speaker, either from the Council or from other bodies.

One thing that we did in the early days of my membership of SHALC was to organise regular meetings with South Herefordshire District Council. At those meetings about six of us, or sometimes one or two more, met at Brockington where we would, in discussion with the Council, decide what subject we were going to debate at the next meeting. It may have been planning or any other Parish Council matter. The Council would always arrange for Councillors to be there, also the officer who was responsible for whatever subject was under discussion, such as the

INTERNATIONAL HOP GROWERS CONVENTION
VISIT TO AMERICA – DEATH OF FATHER

There is a body known as the International Hop Growers Convention which holds an annual congress in different countries, and in 1977 this was to take place in Yakima which is in Washington State in America. It was decided that I should go, although Father was not at all well.

Whilst Philip was taking me to the airport to go to America, a cowboy firm of road repairers apparently called at Claston wanting to tarmac the drive. Father signed the contract to have the work done but omitted to agree a price. This put Philip in a very difficult position as they could have vastly overcharged us. He was only 22 years old at the time and on hearing about this on his return from the airport he was very worried. He rang our solicitor, Bill Masefield, who came out and assisted Philip, when the contractors came to start work the next day. After much argument with the repairers, they agreed a price to do only part of the work.

It was very interesting, seeing a different approach to hop-growing in a completely different climate and soil, this was alluvial soil from the volcanoes, and on my return we actually flew over the volcano, Mount Helens, which erupted again several years later. Several thousand acres of hops are grown in the Yakima Valley, all in one block. There are no hedges and because the hops are grown right up to the little used roadside, the roads are used by the tractors to turn into the next hop row. During the first night that I was staying there, we had a violent thunderstorm, which caused a number of hop-yards to collapse.

Because of the very high temperatures, 100°F when we were there plus very little summer rainfall, it was necessary to irrigate the hops. This was largely done by pumping water from the Yakima River into large underground pipes along the roadside. These pipes were fitted with taps which were turned on for each hop row as needed. The land was very flat before the hop-yards were planted, making it easier to grade the land, so that when the taps were turned on the water flowed very slowly down the hop rows. This is known as flood irrigation.

The wire-work was much higher than in the U.K., mostly 23 ft against an average U.K. hop-yard height of 15 ft. The hop rows were much wider, enabling them to use bigger equipment. Because of the climatic conditions, two-spotted spider mite was their major pest, although during our visit they were spraying against the hop damson aphid. Powdery and downy mildew were not a problem in Yakima, although downy mildew had caused growers to abandon hop-growing in New York State. However, powdery mildew has become a major problem over there in the last few years, with strains of the fungus adapting themselves to the American climate.

We discovered that the Americans were attempting to grow hops on a 6 ft high hedge. Dr Neve, head of Wye College Hop Research Unit in Kent, two hop growers, John Blest and Jim Worley, and I located this small, trial hop-yard. It looked like rows of Beechers Brook Grand National fences, being solid with leaves but with very few hop cones. This was because these were traditional varieties of tall hops, which were being grown on 6 ft high wire-work instead of the usual 23 ft in the American yards. We could immediately appreciate that there was great potential in this lower wire-work for hops with a dwarfing growth, which would make it possible to use a mobile harvester in the hop-yard, thereby reducing the

Dwarf hops in America

labour force dramatically. I could also see that lower spray volumes would be needed, thus benefiting the environment. Dr Neve remarked that in his breeding programme he was producing plants which had a dwarfing habit but had thought that they were of little use. We all agreed that confidentially he should utilise any dwarf plants still available to set up a dwarf hop breeding programme. This he did at Wye College and in 1992 he was able to release three varieties to six growers.

While we were in America, we had one day free and a friend of mine, William Alexander, and I decided to hire a car and go up the Yakima valley to look at the fruit growing area and get to the edge of the great Corn Belt. No car was available for hire, but the boss at the local travel agent offered to lend us his car, if we provided the petrol. William drove on the outward journey and I was to drive back. He drove to the petrol station, pulled up at the pump and when the attendant came out, he rashly said 'Fill her up'. To our amazement the tank took 25 gallons! On reflection this was not surprising, because it was such a very large car that when sitting in the front of it you seemed to be as far from the front end of the bonnet as when sitting in the back of an English car. We proceeded up the Yakima valley and as soon as we had left the hop growing area we came to a very large and intensive fruit growing region, also irrigated by water taken from the Yakima River. We called at one fruit farm where they were loading a lorry with red delicious apples which were to go to the city of New York. The grower remarked that this journey would be farther than from New York to London.

We continued climbing to the top of the valley and suddenly we came to the great Corn Belt. Stretching as far as the eye could see there was a vast expanse of corn. Driving back on another route, we came across a vast beef lot which was quite an impressive sight – these fabulous, huge cattle in wonderful condition were enclosed in a sterile area. There was no grass and there were no trees for shade, but there were large banks for them to lie on if it was wet, and I believe they were mainly fed maize silage. There were hundreds and hundreds of animals in this lot; in fact we could smell it long before we arrived there. The temperature was 100°F that day and because there was no shelter a tractor was continuously driving up and down 'the lot', spraying the cattle with a huge jet of water to keep them cool.

Father had been very poorly before I left for America, but I had a terrible shock two days after I had arrived when Philip phoned to say that he had died, because I had not expected this so soon. In fact for him it was a wonderful end, because he had been looking at the hops at Dormington which he loved to do, with Dr Howard and Geoff Bridges, who was the manager then at Dormington Court. They had inspected the hops and were entering the kilns to look at some new electrical equipment when Father said he would go back to the car. Dr Howard and Geoff replied that they would not be many minutes. When they emerged, Father was sitting on the seat of the car with one leg inside and his hands on his other leg ready to lift it in, as he had done for some time because he had a problem to move it following a break many years earlier. They found that he had died, which was a tremendous shock to everybody.

Following Father's death, I had to return home as soon as possible and the local travel agents were most helpful in organising my return flights. The telephone call had come at breakfast-time on the day that we were due to visit Yakima Golding Farm. The travel agents, when advised, said 'Go and enjoy your day at the Farm and we will organise your air tickets for you to return tomorrow', which they did most efficiently.

That day, while my return flight was being organised, we visited the 750 acre Yakima Golding farm, where we saw a fabulous crop of hops; the whole crop was picked by one giant hop-picking machine, and was then dried on a massive set of kilns. In the evening, we had some delicious roast beef which had been cooked in a most intriguing manner. In the garden, a large hole several feet deep had been dug and the bottom had been covered with a deep layer of charcoal. This had been lit and sheets of metal punctured with holes were placed over it, with a metal chimney in the centre of the hole. Large joints of beef wrapped in foil, with wire loops around them for easier retrieval, were put on top of the metal sheets. The hole was then filled with earth and left for a number of hours for the beef to cook. There were two or three of these 'ovens' and we had been rather puzzled by the apparently newly dug graves, complete with chimneys!

Several hundred of us then watched the ceremony of digging out the joints, with much showmanship, which was most entertaining. The huge joints of beef were superbly moist, tender and full of flavour, but sadly the sweet corn which was served with it was rather old and mealy. However, it was a splendid evening of American hospitality.

During the short flight from Yakima to Seattle the next day, at the start of my journey home, we not only flew over the Mount Helens volcano, but also flew round three thunderstorms. On arrival at Seattle airport, I was unable to pay for my air tickets with my travellers' cheques and was told to change them for dollars, but unfortunately the desks were all closing and it was not until I got to the very last one that I was able to do so. This took some time, but I just managed to catch my Pan-Am flight to London, being the last passenger to board. I was very lucky, in that I had the front three seats to myself, near to the First Class area, and was able to stretch out across the seats and go to sleep after dinner and three large gins, an almost unheard of event for me. On waking up some time later, I went to the nearest toilet but a voice said, 'You cannot go in there Sir, it is the First Class toilet'. When I asked why, the stewardess said, 'There will be a queue and everyone will want to use it if you do'. I commented that everyone else was asleep, to which she said, 'You can use it just this time, Sir'.

FROM STANWAY TO CLASTON

About four months after Father's death it was decided that Pam and I should move down to Claston, as Mother had become an invalid and was then living there on her own, apart from an ex-German prisoner of war who continued to lodge at Claston, not wishing to go home at the end of the war. It was agreed that we would convert part of the house into rooms for Mother and a companion. Mother was thrilled with this idea, but my sisters were unhappy with the proposed alterations to the remainder of the house, which were designed to make it more economical and convenient to run. Before the alterations, there was a journey of 33 yards from Father and Mother's bedroom to the bathroom and toilet, and the kitchen was a similar distance from the dining room and drawing room. The plumbing, heating and electric wiring were in urgent need of renewal and the alterations involved a huge amount of demolition work. In fact at one stage after we had started the alterations, it looked as if a bomb had exploded in the house. The main bathroom and kitchen were moved back to the middle of the house, which centralised these areas of activity, but also involved work in the old kitchen to take out a very large bread oven, from which about three trailer loads of rubble were removed.

The old kitchen was converted to a toilet for Mother and also a sitting room, with a large bay window low enough for her to see the garden from her chair. In the corner of this room we uncovered an egg-shaped well, 13'6" deep with six feet of water in it, over which the old kitchen pump and stone trough had been situated. In former years these had supplied water for the house. The well was beautifully made and in perfect condition. I can remember the pump and stone trough when they were still in use during my childhood. The large old bathroom, airing cupboard and toilet above the old kitchen were made into a bedroom and bathroom for Mother.

Claston from the air in the 1960s.
The gypsy camp is in the right corner; Claston Cottages are in the foreground

In the sitting room, which was made into the new kitchen, the fireplace was removed to reveal the original old stone open fireplace, which was part of an enormous chimney, complete with stepping stones, for the chimney sweep boys to climb up years ago. Here we installed a hob unit, with cupboards below. We employed Honey's of Hereford, to do this work. Most of it was done by local craftsmen employed by the firm, Alan Beavan, who was a carpenter from Bartestree, and a mason Roy Cooper from Checkley, our own staff doing a lot of the demolition work. Alan Beavan made the new kitchen units under the hob from beautiful old boards which had probably been the back of an old seat in the corner of the room. This must have been the kitchen when the house was built.

During the demolition, some of the ceiling plasterwork was damaged and to our delight some lovely old beams were revealed. We then decided to uncover the beams in the kitchen, back hall, office and part of the upstairs landing. This, together with the demolition work, unfortunately created a vast amount of dust, and also uncovered many rat and mouse skeletons.

We moved the front entrance from the west side of the house to the south side, where the back door used to be, and Alan Beavan made us a new front door using the 300 year old oak floor boards from the old front hall. He put hurdle nails from the race course on the outside of the door for effect, also transferring the beautiful antique brass door knocker from the old front door.

Some years later, we took out the fireplace in the dining room to reveal a lovely old stone fireplace which formed te other half of the enormous 11 ft 6 ins deep chimney in the kitchen. The stone work, which was plain and simple, was in perfect condition and, with the original large oak beam above plus stone slabs below in the grate, it really was most attractive. We also revealed the oak beams in the ceiling and built a new double-glazed window on the north wall to provide more light, as the room had always been very dark.

A firm from Manchester was engaged to put in the central heating system, which proved to be extremely efficient, probably due to the fact that large pipes were used instead of the usual small copper ones which are used in modern houses. We had only one problem with this firm, this being that they sent an engineer before the installation began to make marks to show where holes were to be bored for the pipes to go through the walls, but when their plumbers came to do the installation work, they said that some of the holes were in the wrong place and the engineer said that the marks were only approximate. As most of the holes had been bored through 22" thick walls by the builders in readiness for the plumbers, a furious row ensued ending with the builders telling the plumbers what they could do with their holes.

In late summer, the estate agent whom we had asked to let Stanway informed us that he had prospective tenants – the man was the engineer in charge of building the electricity generating plant at Bulmers cider factory and needed to rent a house urgently. He was prepared to pay a very good rent for a 2-year period. We decided that it was too good an opportunity to miss, but this meant that we had to move to Claston well before the alterations were completed. For the first few days after moving, there were at least four workmen in the house and we had only one cold water tap and one toilet between us. To get to the first floor, we had to climb a ladder and there was a mass of dust to clear up after the men had finished work each day. There were also floor boards taken up on the upstairs landing and electric wiring left loose over the gaps, which made it a very hazardous journey when going to bed, with only partial lighting. The alterations were almost completed just before Christmas 1978 and Pam and I were delighted with the end result.

CIDER SYNDICATE

In the Autumn of 1978, we formed a syndicate of five cider fruit growers to harvest their fruit mechanically, and purchased a Tuthill mobile apple harvester. Philip ran the harvesting operation which was a great success. We had problems to start with because the machine hadn't been made strong enough, but the Dormington fitter, Ray Russel, spent a lot of time rectifying this fault. We started harvest about the middle of October, and by the end of November we had collected 1000 tons. It was a huge success but that year Bulmers were not paying a very good price for their cider fruit, so I went and saw the Chief Executive, Brian Nelson, and discussed this low price with him. This was before Bulmers started making

Somerset apple harvester

contracts. I had already found out after a visit to Somerset that I could get a lot more money from Thatchers. When told this, Brian Nelson replied that if I could get more money, Bulmers would be happy for me to sell my fruit elsewhere, although they would be disappointed to lose it, but when I thought their price was satisfactory I could go back to them and they would welcome me with open arms. This is what happened a few years later, although we have sent some of our cider fruit to Thatchers Cider Company ever since. A few years later the Tuthill harvester was replaced by a tractor-mounted machine which had a greater harvesting capacity.

ALLIED HOP FARMS – BRIERLEY COURT

After Father's death, I was appointed Consultant to the management of the Allied hop farms. In the Spring of 1978, the Chairman of Allied decided that because of the shortage of UK hops they wanted to buy another hop farm, and they asked me if I could find a farm suitable for planting 125 acres of hops. I was fortunate that a very short while after that Brierley Court came on the market, a farm of over 400 acres situated near Leominster, 16 miles from Dormington. I informed Allied that there was suitable land available there to plant 240 acres of hops if they so wished, and they were very enthusiastic. They asked me how much the farm would make, to which I replied "£1,000,000". It actually made £1,050,000, being the first farm in Herefordshire to make one million pounds.

Allied asked me to prepare a budget for planting 240 acres of hops at Brierley. This included draining the land, planting the hops, erecting the wire-work and building a new set of kilns, as there was only a very small set currently there, also sufficient picking machinery to harvest the crop. Allied asked me to do this within a fortnight and three days later they rang to enquire how I was getting on and whether the budget was complete. They were very surprised to learn that I had actually finished the task, not knowing that we had done a lot of similar work earlier when looking at ways of building new kilns for ourselves, and I already knew how much it cost to plant and put up an acre of wire-work. While doing these costings, I also enquired into the cost of multi-tiered driers in Germany. I reached the figure of £1,750,000 which was accepted, and it was agreed that I should go to the Hallertau hop-growing area with two engineers to look at this hop-drying equipment.

They then altered the structure of the company, changing the name from Dormington Court Hop Farms to Brierley Court Hop Farms, and the office was moved to Brierley.

PHILIP MOVES INTO BEEF PRODUCTION

The new cattle sheds at Claston in 1984

Cattle at Claston

Philip with his grain cleaner

It was at this time that Philip decided to expand our beef production, to a Friesian cross bull beef system, in conjunction with a friend of his who bought baby calves and reared them for three months. We then took them on and fed them through until they were between 15 and 18 months old. To achieve this, we rented some extra land to increase our cereal acreage to 300 acres and installed a grain cleaner, Blanche Dryer, storage bins and a grain mill and mixer. These animals were fed on the silage and cereals which we grew ourselves. The only items we bought were minerals to supplement the feed and molasses to make the food much more appetising. This was very successful until the advent of the Holstein strain of Friesians. These were Friesian cross Hereford bull calves but once the Holstein came in, they produced calves that were very difficult to distinguish from the true English type Friesian cross when young. As they grew older, the proper Hereford cross Friesian grew into good beef animals, whereas the Hereford cross Holstein just grew and grew but it was virtually impossible to get any flesh on them so that the carcasses were only suitable for processing. We had also increased our numbers of breeding ewes and they were also fed silage, the grass for which was mostly grown in the hop-yards and on the river land.

Although Philip had no training, he became a very competent design engineer. As well as the bine track on the hop-picking machine which I have already mentioned, he produced a very efficient grain cleaning, drying and handling system. None of us could understand how he had calculated the volume of air needed to blow the grain from the dryer to a cattle shed. This meant lifting the grain about 15 ft up a pipe and then blowing it another 60 ft. Provided the blower was allowed to get up to full speed before releasing the grain from the dryer, it never got blocked.

Taxing the Casual Workers

In 1978 we had a visit which had been arranged by George Johnson, the Secretary of the Herefordshire NFU, from the special branch of the Inland Revenue from Birmingham. The Inland Revenue was saying that all hop-picking casual workers should pay tax. This was very difficult, because we would have had to break the law by paying their tax for them or we would have been unable to get sufficient people to pick the hops, as they would not work at all if forced to pay the tax. We took an Inland Revenue inspector to the hop-yard and introduced him to our roughest and toughest casual workers, mostly travellers, and then we had lunch, after which he said, "I can see you have got a case for a better tax system for casuals" and he told me that he would come back to us. Early the following year, we received a letter from him, saying that he thought it would be sensible if we paid 8% tax on all casuals. There was a very simple form to fill in, all that we had to say on the form was that we had spent £x000 on casual labour during the year, and enclose a cheque for 8% of that amount which had to be paid by the end of October each year. It was a brilliantly simple answer to the problem – no book-keeping, except for a record of the amount of money spent on casual labour for the year, and the Chief Inspector of the Hereford tax office was very pleased because he had nearly £50,000 in tax that he said was a bonus. Unfortunately, the NFU headquarters Horticultural Committee did not approve of this simple scheme and it failed a few years later, because a few unscrupulous growers smartly increased their casual labour bill on which, under the new scheme, they only paid 8% tax instead of over 20% on what would have been their larger profit, so after a few years, the scheme was withdrawn to the detriment of all employers of casual labour.

Brierley Court Hops

In the autumn of 1978, we started planting hops at Brierley. One amazing thing was that when I asked the directors which variety of hops they wanted me to plant, expecting them as brewers to know which hops they required, they left the decision to me. I immediately advised planting Northdown and Challenger, as well as a large area of Target because it was perfectly legal to do so if you had no wilt on the farm. Allied told me that they could not possibly plant Target, as they feared it would make them outcasts amongst their fellow growers who were still against planting this variety in Herefordshire. We therefore planted only Northdown, Challenger, Bullion and Zenith. It was agreed that we should get full costings for a drying plant from Germany to dry sixty bales a day. On receiving their figures, we agreed that this would be the most efficient way to dry the hops and I was sent to Germany just before Christmas with a team of two engineers and an interpreter to finalise the details and order the equipment. While there, we were taken to Munich one evening to have dinner and to look at the Christmas lights in the centre of the city. It was really beautiful, like being in fairyland, with millions of white twinkling lights, but no coloured ones at all.

At this time I was in a strange position, being Chairman of the National NFU Hops Committee, because the Herefordshire NFU Hops Committee, Plant Health, the Hops Marketing Board, various other bodies and practically all growers were still against me being allowed to plant Target. It was a very difficult battle and if we didn't win we would have to go out of hop production at Claston and other infected farms would also have to do so. We had numerous unhelpful meetings with Plant Health, as by now all of the hop-yards at Claston and a number of the Dormington yards were infected with PVW. Because of this, we had either taken out large areas or even whole hop-yards and planted them with grass. We decided to use this grass for silage and were therefore able to increase the number of cattle that we held.

During the problem of verticillium wilt, we always managed to produce the quantity of hops required to honour our reducing contracts. Wilt had become a way of life now for many hop growers, and people were getting more and more worried because it was spreading fairly rapidly. There were a number of farms in the Lower Frome Valley which were infected and the disease was beginning to spread to other areas, but still the Ministry refused to change the system. I do not know why they would not do this because the Kent

The new hop-driers at Brierley Court

growers, who had been living with wilt for many years, were planting Target and there was no evidence to show that it caused the spread of disease. In fact, the Kent growers had solved the problem, saying that once you planted Target it helped to reduce the incidence of wilt. Eventually wilt spread to Worcestershire and everybody was getting very frustrated as Plant Health still insisted that they would not change the rules, although by this time many growers realised that this was the only way forward.

The kilns which we decided to construct for Brierley were revolutionary. Following my visit to Germany in August 1978 to inspect their latest kiln designs and after seeing their multi-tier driers, I decided that perhaps this would be the best and cheapest way to dry hops at Brierley, as they were so fuel efficient. The problem was that at that time, English hops had to be sulphured. To do this, sulphur was burnt and the fumes allowed to pass through the hops to bleach them. It was a horrible job which no hop-grower liked because it made all the machinery go rusty, as well as being unpleasant for the staff. However, we had to design the kilns with a sulphur chamber as required, which added considerably to the cost. A further problem was that nobody had ever moved green hops in conveyors in bulk and to make sure that you loaded the kiln continuously, because the whole system was automated, you had to be able to reverse these conveyors. The whole system was nine feet wide and John Rowlands, an engineer in Hereford whom I employed to design the kiln, evolved a very ingenious way of making sure that you could reverse the conveyors as well as moving them forwards without leaving any gaps. The conveyor consisted of a large number of pieces of metal about 3 inches wide and the engineer curved both edges of these pieces of the conveyor so that it fitted over the next one. This meant that as it turned the corner, where, if they were flat you would normally expect a gap to appear, these curves opened and closed and the conveyor was sealed all the time. It worked extremely well and we never had any problems.

Unfortunately, by the time we started construction, the brewers had decided that the sulphur was affecting the hops they used for lager, whilst unsulphured foreign hops were acceptable. They therefore told growers to stop sulphuring the hops. We then made use of the proposed sulphur chamber to blow cold air through the green hops, as when the hops were picked on a hot day they were quite warm and would heat very quickly on the storage conveyors, causing them to sweat and go discoloured. By blowing cold air through them we were able to cool them down and they then kept perfectly until it was time to load them onto the kiln.

The kiln itself consisted of three 9 ft wide and 47 ft 6 ins long conveyors and the hops were automatically loaded about 15 ins deep on the top layer where they were dried for about two hours. Then the conveyors were started up and the top layer dropped onto the second conveyor. While that was happening, green hops were re-loading on the top conveyor, and after another two hours this process was repeated, at the end of which the three tiers had been loaded. From then on you had a continuous drying process and the hops could be dried in about 6 to 7 hours as opposed to 9 to 12 hours in a traditional kiln. We had problems in having too much moisture to start with because a traditional kiln was loaded to about 2'6" – 3' deep and the hop-dryer had to strike a balance between the hops nearest the floor, which would be a lot drier, and the ones at the top, which were more moist. On our new dryer, they were all the same dryness and we were tending to take them off a little too soon. Fortunately, because I had seen this system working in Germany, I had foreseen the problem and so was able to resolve this. There, they dried the hops too much and then used a conditioning kiln to blow wet air through the hops in order to bring them back to the required moisture content. We had designed a very simple conditioning kiln that was half the length of the dryer with a wire mesh floor, on which the hops were conveyed after they left the kilns. The hops were loaded 3 ft deep on this kiln, and we had a burner there so that if they were under-dried we could dry them a little more, but if they were a bit too dry we could blow cold air through them. The hops then went by conveyor to storage conveyors and when they were cool and ready for pressing they automatically went into a baler hop press. It was a very efficient system and by working two shifts a day instead of an eight hour day, as we had planned, we only needed two picking machines instead of four, saving £250,000. We would start picking at 6 a.m. and that shift worked

until 3 p.m. then, after servicing the machines, the night shift started at 4 p.m. and worked until 2 a.m. Therefore, instead of my total budget of £1,750,000, we actually completed the whole task for £1,500,000.

It was the first time that bales had been used on a hop farm in Herefordshire, although they had been used on one or two farms in Kent. They were copied from an American bale which was palletised, putting six or eight bales on each pallet. When the lorry came to collect the first load, the pallets should have been lifted mechanically onto the

Using bales for hops

95

lorry, but the driver told us that they were too wide. Therefore we had to manhandle all the bales off the pallets and onto the lorry, which was unacceptable, so I worked out that if we had a bale that was 4 ft by 2 ft by 2 ft, which gave the same volume as the traditional hop-pocket, it would then be possible to get 18 pallets on the lorry. We produced this baler and the Hops Marketing Board told us it was illegal. By now there were eleven other balers, two types, in use on farms with two different sized bales. I suggested to the Board that they paid £1000 to each grower with a baler, which is what it had cost to modify our baler, and it could then be adapted to our system, but they refused. As all of the Brierley hops were going to the Allied breweries, we took no notice of the Board's decision.

We started work on the kilns in the middle of February, the plan being to start hop-picking on 15th September 1979, and we actually started on the 16th. I remember the brewery people who came to visit during the building process were amazed to see how everybody working on site, including the barn builders, electricians, hop-picking machine fitters and those working on the kilns, all worked together to overcome any difficulties. This was something which did not happen in a brewery, apparently – in fact, it would have caused strikes.

During my visit to Germany, mentioned previously, I was able to visit several farms where they had started hop-picking and saw them loading their trailers with an automatic Wolfe bine loader. This was working so efficiently that we decided to purchase one for Brierley, which was equally successful.

LONG SERVICE

In June 1979, Bert Gwilliam, who had served at Dormington most of his life, was presented with his long-service medal at the Three Counties Showground. He actually started working for my grandfather, before the First World War in 1914, at the Pigeon House, then served in the army throughout the war and afterwards started work at Dormington Court.

At the same time Bert Green, who was a very skilled member of our staff at Claston, was also presented with his long service medal. Bert taught me how to do many of the jobs on the farm, including hop-drying.

Bert Green and Bert Gwilliam

INTERNATIONAL HOP GROWERS CONVENTION

In 1979, the International Hop Growers Convention was held in Canterbury, Kent and I was amazed to be asked to give a paper, which was very well received, on how we grew hops at Claston. It was a very good congress, although unfortunately on the day we visited Tony Redsell's hop farm there were several thunderstorms which rather spoilt the potentially interesting visit. When we held the final meeting, to my great surprise I was awarded the Order of the Hop, which is an ancient European Order, dating back to the

16th century, complete with badge and certificate. One other hop-grower from Herefordshire, John Cotton, was also made a member of the Order at that Convention. I, as Chairman of the NFU Hop

John Cotton, Peter Davies, Edward Lane and 2 others at Eastbourne

Committee, and Pam were to sit at the top table for the final banquet and I remember that the speaker, at the last minute, was unable to attend. A German hop-grower and brewer, Leo Hoefter, was asked to stand in. I knew him quite well and we were good friends. He approached me at teatime and asked my advice about how to address the President. Edward Lane of Bosbury was President of the International Hop Growers then, and all the American hop-growers called him Ed. I told Leo this and, to my amazement, he commenced his address 'Mr President, Mr Davies said I am to call you Ed', which brought the house down, but Edward was not amused. However, the Congress was very successful.

DORMINGTON AND MORDIFORD PARISH COUNCIL

In 1980, I was elected Chairman of the Parish Council and the first thing I did was to get the rest of the Councillors more involved with the work of the Council. To achieve this, with the agreement of the Council I set up a number of committees with two or three Councillors on each. These committees were Planning, Footpaths, Finance, Social Services, Transport and Communications, District Council reports, Mordiford Churchyard and one for the school. The Parish Council did all that they could to help with any improvements needed for the school, one of the Councillors, John Harris, having represented the Council as a School Governor for many years. I think my committees worked well and some still continue today. It meant that at nearly every Council meeting every Councillor had something on which to report.

At the October 1980 Parish Council meeting, we had a letter from the District Council on 'the maintenance of roadside ditches'. The Council had said their only responsibility was to clean the ditches if they were full and flooding the highway. I remember that I had spoken to the Council about this, suggesting that they wrote to farmers telling them that it was their responsibility to keep the ditches clear. I could not understand why farmers were not doing so because, on our farm for instance, many of the land drains emptied into the roadside ditch, so it was in the farmer's own interest and vital for the farm land that the ditches were kept clear.

THE AUSTRALIAN CONNECTION

With the advent of Allied joining in the amalgamation of the Australian brewers, Castlemaine and Tooheys, and agreeing to plant up 400 acres of hops, the Australians seemed interested in our new drying plant at Brierley. To our amazement, they sent a scientist over to inspect this. It was agreed that they would install one of these German driers for the 1982 crop.

In 1979 I was made Managing Director of Brierley Court Hop Farms, which was an interesting promotion. They had paid me a certain amount to design and plant up the farm as well as my salary. I had been going to meetings in Burton both with Father and on my own after he died and we always had lunch afterwards. It was interesting to note how the venue for this meal changed as you crept up the ladder. When we first started, I had a very good lunch in the various company canteens, then when I became Managing Director we had lunch in a house a little way down the street from the brewery. We had a glass of beer after the meeting in the morning, then down at the house the brewers would consume a couple of shorts, gin for example, before lunch, and there was always plenty of wine during the three course meal. It was a real four-star affair, with waiter service. There were often only six or seven of us and I would never know who I was going to meet. There was port with our coffee after the meal, but I drank very little during these lunches as I had to drive back home afterwards. The others all did, though, and I can't imagine how they managed to do any more work that day, but I suppose that if you were drinking like that on a regular basis you would become accustomed to it.

In 1981, the Chairman of Allied Lyons, then Keith Showering, told me that the company thought they ought to buy a hop farm in Germany for which I should be responsible. I replied that that would be impossible as I had quite sufficient to do in managing their farms in this country, as well as our own, making 600 acres of hops in total. The brewery gave up that idea, but I suggested that if they wanted to buy another farm it would be more sensible to consider a farm in Australia, because the hops would be harvested in March, as opposed to our September harvest. This would mean that the brewery could purchase hops twice a year and need only keep stocks for six months rather than twelve. To my amazement, a while later they did just that! At this time, two of the major breweries in Australia, Castlemaine and Tooheys, joined forces and one of them owned a small hop farm in the north of Tasmania. Allied joined this venture and decided to build it up to 400 acres at Forester River farm.

PROGRESSIVE VERTICILLIUM WILT AND WYE TARGET HOPS

Progressive verticillium wilt continued to spread and it is interesting, looking through the records, to find how the situation in the West Midlands was following that in Kent. The first lethal wilt was found in Kent in 1924 when it killed the variety, Fuggle. By 1939 there were 27 farms infected and by 1948, 109 farms. In 1950, infected farms totalled 146 and by 1956 the figure had risen to 252 farms. By 1961 there were 323 farms infected, 17 of which were in East Kent and 18 in Sussex. Then eventually they decided that no control should take place in the Weald of Kent because virtually every farm had wilt, so in fact they gave up the controls, but the other areas they counted as eradication areas. However, by 1971 out of the 40 farms in East Kent, 17 had become infected and by 1981 there was a reduction of 10 farms and 27 of those 30 had PVW. They now called it a containment area and allowed three farms to have a licence.

There had then been three farms infected in Herefordshire. This was in spite of the controls of the 1965 wilt order. In 1981, there were 11 cases in the immediate Herefordshire area and this was the year that we really decided that we had to take more drastic action. There were various meetings, one of which, in Malvern in the Spring of 1981, was attended by a lot of growers. It was a very bitter meeting and it was on the way to that meeting that Philip and I had decided that the wilt situation had become so serious, so many hops having been taken out at Claston, that we would stop hop-growing in an effort to halt the spread of the disease. However, it was such a horrendous meeting and I was attacked so vigorously that I was very upset and coming back Philip, out of the blue, said, 'Dad, we're not giving up, we're going to beat them'.

So we then decided to see what we could do about it and, talking to Dormington Court Hop Farms directors, they decided that the only action which might bring it to a head would be to plant some wilt-tolerant hops at Brierley Court. It was perfectly legal to do this because there was still no wilt there. This was done and at the AGM of the Hops Marketing Board I informed the then Chairman, Lord Selbourne, of our action. He was very angry and everybody at the meeting was completely shattered. In the afternoon, we had an NFU hops meeting, which one of the Hops Marketing Board directors always attended and Lord Selbourne came to that particular meeting. I was still Chairman then and when it came to verticillium wilt I vacated the chair and my Vice-Chairman, Richard Coleman, took over. One of the items on the agenda was a letter from Plant Health concerning the grant of licences for the planting of wilt-tolerant varieties in the West Midlands. This indicated that the Minister was not prepared to grant such licences at that time but would study further the situation over the next few months, after which the policy would be reviewed. It was reported, obviously, about this planting of Target at Brierley and also another farm in the West Midlands where it had been done. The Committee was very angry about this but they had warned Plant Health in April that if they didn't get on and grant licences, this is what would happen. The sub-committee was in disagreement with the action and agreed that a letter should be sent to growers, asking them not to plant wilt-tolerant varieties as it was against the policy of the Hops Committee and what the industry had been attempting to achieve.

Growers were so angry about our planting the Wye Target that the Ledbury branch of the NFU called an emergency meeting, at which they passed a resolution that I wasn't a fit person to represent them in London. This resolution went to the Herefordshire Hop Committee meeting where a great friend of mine, Peter Turner, who was supporting me, was chairing the meeting and there was a long debate about the Ledbury resolution. With hindsight, there should have been a secret ballot because when it came to the vote it was quite obvious that everybody seemed reluctant to vote for the resolution, but eventually one raised his hand and then they all followed. It was then passed that I should not represent Herefordshire any longer on the National NFU Hops Committee. I thought that I had a lot of friends on this Committee and the situation reminded me of Mother Theresa's words 'When you're successful you win some unfaithful friends and some genuine enemies'. Legally, I could have gone on until the end of the year because I was elected Chairman for the year. This resolution went to the full Herefordshire NFU Committee who were apparently very angry about it and really did not want me to be sacked. However, it was passed and I decided that rather than go to the next meeting in London I would resign from the Committee and it was very soon after that I had a letter from the NFU President, Sir Richard Butler, saying how sorry he was and thanking me for all the work I had done. I also had a letter from Peter Pearson, who was the Chairman of Central Horticulture, saying that he regretted my decision although he could see why I had done it and he accepted my resignation. Talking to lots of hop growers afterwards, they all said that if they had been in my position, they would have planted Wye Target much sooner. I was very disappointed at the time, because I had put a lot of time and effort into NFU work in London, but after a while, on reflection, I realised that perhaps it was a good thing because, being Chairman of this committee in London was taking up too much of my time. It wasn't just the hop meetings that took time, but I was automatically also a member of the Central Horticultural Committee and of the Education Committee, and so had all the paperwork from these committees to study before meetings, then once a year all the Chairmen were invited to a meeting of the Council of the NFU, to which the Minister of Agriculture came. It was quite interesting then because I was practically the youngest there and most of them were fairly elderly gentlemen, who I thought looked like professional committee men. They had served the NFU well but I felt that there was a lack of younger people with new ideas.

In August we had a visit from the head of Plant Health, Mr Bodrell, who, after going around the farm and looking at the situation, could see that things were pretty desperate. In fact we had one hop-yard that was riddled with wilt and we had a lot of tests done which came back saying it wasn't wilt, which was absolute nonsense so it took away all credibility of the wilt tests. During tea, I said to Mr Bodrell, 'If you were a neighbouring farmer who hadn't got wilt and you wanted to plant a yard up with hops, what variety would you plant?' Without batting an eyelid he replied, 'Wye Target'. The Chief Scientist was with him and he was so shocked that I thought he was going to fall off the chair! It was quite interesting that at least the new head of Plant Health was aware of the situation.

In April 1981, I was asked to chair a meeting in Bromyard by John Hill Hops of Ledbury. This was a hop growers' meeting and they had invited a number of representatives from different chemical companies to update people on new developments and different ways of treating pests and diseases. I remember there was a new chemical called Alliette which was a downy mildew fungicide which everybody was very excited about, but when the speaker had concluded his presentation it was obvious that he didn't really know much about it and that it wasn't going to be available for a while. After several questions, another question was asked and when I looked up, expecting a reply, to my amazement he had gone. It is the only time when I have ever chaired a meeting from which the speaker has just disappeared!

THE DORMINGTON CHURCH DOOR-KNOCKER

We were shocked to find in March 1981 that the Dormington Church door-knocker had vanished. We weren't sure exactly when it was stolen, because we weren't in the church every day, but when we discovered that it had been taken, we decided that the only possible chance of getting it back would be to persuade both the local and national press to write a piece about this. Luckily, every national newspaper and all the regional papers included a little article about the theft and it was because of this that it was returned to us. Apparently the thief had broken bail from Portsmouth court where he had been arrested for stealing items from churches to be exported to America, which apparently was his way of making a living, and he took our small bronze knocker which is of late 12th century date and is finely worked to represent a devil's bald head sinisterized with a large ring hanging from its grimacing mouth. Little is known of the

original artist, except it is thought that he was influenced by the Hereford School of Romanesque sculpture. It is only one of two in Europe and the thief didn't know its value, so he took it to an antique dealer he knew of in Stratford who said that he couldn't value it, but if he left it with him he would take it down to London to an antique dealer whom he was sure would know the value. This he did, but the dealer said he was just going on holiday for a fortnight and he would leave it in his safe to value it on his return. When he came back, he saw the articles in the press about the stolen knocker and realised that this was it, and so it was returned to us. By chance, when the thief had his car stolen some time later in London, he went to a police station to report the theft and as they shrewdly realised who he was, he was re-arrested. Some time later, when there was an exhibition in London, they enquired if they could have our door-knocker and we agreed, provided it was insured. They replied that they realised it was valuable and that it would be insured for £10,000. In the meantime, we had an idea that perhaps replicas of this door-knocker, which is quite small, could have a market in America as house door-knockers. We therefore had a bronze replica made, which in fact I think looks better than the original. However, it was quite expensive to have these replicas cast, costing about £250 each providing we had about a dozen, and we decided in the end that perhaps it was too big a gamble to take with church money. We have a copy on the door now and the original is safely stored in Hereford Cathedral, along with other church silver.

Some years later, we had another enquiry to borrow the knocker for an exhibition in Rome and once again we agreed provided it was well-insured, and they immediately told us that it would be insured for £100,000. We were absolutely staggered at this and I suggested that, if it was so valuable and as we had got the super replica on the church door, it might be better to sell the original because even if it didn't make £100,000 it was obviously going to make a lot of money which could put our church finances right for generations to come, but nobody really agreed with my idea so it was abandoned.

CHAPTER EIGHT

A Breakthrough & a Tragedy : 1982-1991

WILT AND TARGET HOPS

By the end of 1981, it was obvious that the Ministry would have to do something about wilt in the West Midlands. I was getting no help from anyone, but then decided to have a word with Peter Temple-Morris, the MP for North Herefordshire, Leominster Division, and explain the situation to him. I had already talked to our MP, Colin Shepherd, but this hadn't borne fruit.

When I explained the situation to Peter Temple-Morris, to my amazement he said, 'Well, that's not what I've been told by other hop-growers' and so we went into great detail about this. He realised that something had to be done about the problem and said he would talk to the Minister. I hoped that maybe something would happen at last.

Philip with staff planting the first Target hop plants

To my surprise in a very few weeks we learnt that the Ministry were thinking of changing their attitude and would now allow wilt-tolerant hops to be planted. Having heard this, I thought I would take a gamble and asked a friend of mine in Kent to buy some Target roots for me. He agreed to keep them in a cold store in Kent and if we obtained a licence we would plant them, but if not he would destroy them although I would still pay for them. This he did and in April 1982 we received a telephone message to inform us that we were to receive a licence. Immediately I rang my friend in Kent, we prepared the ground and Philip and Winston Price, one of our men, made two journeys of about 760 miles in total in one day to the south-east to collect these hop-roots. We started planting the next day and planted 10 acres over two days. We didn't have quite enough plants to plant round the edge of the hop-yard underneath the anchor wires, so I decided to propagate some plants myself for this area, which we later planted. Out of the blue, we heard that one of the Ministry Plant Health officials was coming to have a look at the farm. We had not, at that point, actually had a written licence to propagate and I knew we would be in trouble if the official saw these misted plants, so we had to go around and dig them up again. I think there were about 2,500 plants in total. The official came and inspected the yard we had planted and reminded us that in the eyes of the Ministry these plants did not exist. I explained that I had received a telephone message saying that we would be getting a licence but he said that the Ministry had no record of that and advised that we would probably have to dig them up. I replied that there was no way that we would be prepared to dig the plants out, but the official said the Ministry would ask a contractor to come and do it. I told him that we would not allow contractors on the farm, particularly bearing in mind the wilt precautions. The official departed, we heard nothing and we replanted the hops around the outside of the hop-yard. I am positive that this pompous official knew all along that we had had a verbal agreement to plant, but was anxious to exert his authority simply because we had not got the necessary papers at that time. In July, we received a written licence and we actually grew seven zentners to the acre on those Target roots in the first year.

It is quite unbelievable that it took eight years to get a licence to plant tolerant varieties, by which time the spread of wilt was beyond control in the West Midlands. That the Plant Health officials did not acknowledge the fact that their policy had failed in Kent, and insist that either whole hop-yards or at least several acres were grubbed immediately an infected plant had been found, as I had suggested at the outset of our outbreak, I find absolutely unpardonable. However, it was not surprising, as I later found out that the heads of Plant Health and their officials were infamous in failing to make positive decisions, or to accept that a particular policy was not working.

VISIT TO AUSTRALIA

After their Australian scientist visited Brierley, Castlemaine/Toohey brewery installed a Wolfe drier similar to the one we had at Brierley and it was decided that I should go out to Australia in March 1982 to have a look at this plant as they were having problems. It was agreed that I should spend three weeks on the farm. This was the first time that I had been to Australia and I must say it was a very interesting experience. I arrived in Sydney pretty shattered after the 27-hour flight and was met by one of the secretaries from Castlemaine breweries. We had a quick look round and went to their headquarters, then I went to my hotel and went to bed. The next day it was agreed that they would take me on a tour of Sydney.

We had a super day, going on a boat trip from Sydney harbour down the river, which was interesting. We saw very many expensive houses right on the riverbank which had either a staircase or a conveyor system to take the people down the steep bank to the houses, because they were so far below the level of the road. We then went to the famous revolving restaurant in Sydney for lunch and I think it completed two revolutions whilst we were eating.

In the evening, I flew to Tasmania where the hop farm was situated. It was quite amusing because they had booked first class tickets for me, so I had a super dinner on the journey from Sydney to Melbourne and then I had to change flights to travel from Melbourne to Launceston. The stewards on the second flight were upset because, having already had dinner, I was unable to eat their meal.

I was met and taken to an hotel in Launceston that night. The following day we went down to the farm, passing through a forest where the year before there had been a fire which had destroyed all of the imported trees of similar age to the native eucalyptus trees, but the native trees had all survived. The farm, called Forester River, was in the north of Tasmania and I stayed in what they called a motel, but it was a pub really, in Scotsdale. I just looked in at the farm that day and, to my surprise, the hops were in a terrible state but I could see at once what the problem was. In their wisdom, they had installed the drier and a very super set of kilns, but they had forgotten about any place to store the green hops while they were waiting to go into the kiln. There was just a small storage hopper on the Wolf drier and when they brought the hops from the picking machines, they were stuffing them all in there and, as green hops heat very quickly and the temperature was in the region of 100°F, the hops went brown before they even got into the kiln to be dried. Obviously the end product was disastrous and I doubt whether you could have sold them in the U.K.

On arrival at the farm the following day I discovered that no other hop-growers were allowed to visit it and the only people who were allowed there were the officials from the marketing organisation in Australia and also Peter Versleu, who was the technical adviser to the hop growers. Peter and I became great friends, but we could not understand why nobody else was allowed on the farm because the other hop growers could probably have helped them. Another interesting thing was that the farm was run by a Maori man. He was a nice chap but didn't have a clue about hop growing, nor did the second in command, who was a recently-appointed former forester. The boss of the farm, Dick Watson, who was one of the directors of the company, was absolutely hopeless, he hadn't a clue and his daughter, who was the secretary there was doing the analysis but getting the results wrong. I discovered that she was quite a trouble-maker. They grew raspber-

ries on the farm, and she had caused a strike over pay by telling the workers that they were not being paid enough. They went on strike and obviously her father gave in, consequently they were all getting a much higher rate of pay than casual workers were normally paid.

I decided that I should make the acquaintance of the neighbouring hop grower, Stewart Ferguson. This was interesting because he was producing the heaviest crop of hops that I had ever seen. He had got the

Overhead irrigation of hops in Australia

Hop-yards at Forester River

biggest Bruff hop-picking machine possible, but they could only just manage to pick eight bines a minute as the cleaner couldn't cope with any more of these heavy bines. I asked him how he managed to grow this huge crop and he replied that it was fairly simple thanks to the brewery farm spreading their fertiliser from a helicopter. Most of the fertiliser landed on the wrong hops! I met several other hop-growers in the district who had all got very good crops, but I was amazed that they had thought it necessary to buy the German hop drier for Forester River because other farms had super multi-tier Australian driers which must have been very cheap to install and were run very efficiently.

On a tour of the farm it was quite astonishing to find that they had planted up huge acres of hops, because over there they use sheep for defoliation, and they had thought this could be done for baby hop plants also. We went to one huge hop-yard where there were hardly any of these young plants left alive, as they had mostly been eaten by the sheep. They had used plastic string to train the hops up and the sheep had broken this down, a number of them becoming entangled in it and unable to move. They were also cutting corners by not treating the poles properly against rot. They were just putting a tar paper around the base of the poles instead of boiling them in creosote. They were building one new hop-yard where a vast amount of earth-work was going on to level the site, which had been a wood I think. It was pretty poor soil so whether that ever became a successful hop-yard I do not know.

One of the neighbouring farmers, Mr Neville Williams, had an amazing set of kilns. It was the traditional Australian multi-tier system, but he had got a massive wood-burning stove to provide the heat, about which his wife was very worried. She said 'I'm sure it will blow up and burn the kilns down sometime'. Many years later apparently it did. I went to another set of kilns nearby and, to my amazement, met Julian Cotton working there. This was a very modern set up and they had actually got a pelleting plant on the end of the kilns so that the hops were never baled or put in pockets as at other hop farms, but were all pelleted and packaged in boxes.

At Foresters River there were so many things wrong that it was difficult to know where to start. To begin with, the staff were not interested, they were all pretty demoralised, the equipment had not been properly maintained, also they had got a new German hop-picking machine but nobody really seemed to know how to operate it. The through-put was appalling.

After about three or four days we managed to solve the problems when the hops were waiting to be dried at Forester River. They were loading them off the picking machine into sacks, so I made them store the sacks in a proper manner with spaces between so that they wouldn't heat, and to their amazement after that the hops were coming off the kiln the right colour. There was nothing wrong with the kiln itself, it was just the storage of the green hops which caused the problem. I was very embarrassed because after that the men were coming to me for instructions rather than to the management team and this put me on the spot. I suppose if you send a chemist to advise on the working of an engineering project these are the sort of problems you can expect.

Another problem was that they worked a night shift which was very badly organised in the picking machines and kilns. One morning I went in to find that the kilns were all empty and when I asked what was the matter, they replied that they had damaged the hop-picking machine. The conveyors on this German hop-picking machine were canvas with wooden bars to keep the canvas rigid and somebody had tossed some hop sacks on them, completely wrecking the conveyors. So that took a while to mend. They also had a very ancient Alleys hop-picking machine and I had talked to the chap running it who was very pleasant and a very good fitter. I asked him why he thought they had so many breakdowns and he replied that they were never allowed to do any maintenance during the winter, which is the very time when it should be done in preparation for the harvest. Going around the hop-yards, you'd find areas where there were no hops and these were what they called bog-holes. They were places where in heavy rain the water would stand and they were just filled with gravel so that they could get through with tractors, but they didn't re-plant the hops. They did give me a truck to drive round in, so I got friendly with some of the neighbouring hop-growers and I suggested that they should be allowed to come and have a look at the farm. So in the end a number of hop growers came to have a look and they gave me some background to the cause of all the problems that were there.

As I have noted, it was a very interesting experience and Peter Versleu, the Australian hop merchants' hop growing technical advisor, who was living on his own, knew of some good places to eat. He had found a very nice little restaurant in Bridport, which is about 3 or 4 miles away on the coast where you could eat very cheaply and super fish meals were served. So we quite often went there together for a meal. The meals where I was staying were pretty mediocre, including fish fingers for dinner sometimes. If it hadn't been for Peter it would have been a pretty grim and lonely experience.

Later, Dick Watson drove me down to Hobart where I spent a couple of days for a short break. It was an interesting journey and, to my amazement, I saw that all the Hereford and the Aberdeen Angus cattle were giant animals, just the reverse of those in the U.K. at that time. When we had nearly arrived at his house, Dick said that he had forgotten to tell me that he had a new woman since I had last met him, and when we arrived I was surprised to see her lying on a whole lot of cushions on the floor. It was a beautiful house, right on the bank of a river. I had two enjoyable days there and then I had probably the most interesting flight I've ever had; a scheduled flight from Hobart to Devenport in northern Australia, where the brewery owned another hop farm, this one being run very successfully. The plane was a twin-engine Cessna which flew at only 8,000 ft and there were just six of us on board plus the pilot. Travelling across, he was pointing out all the features on the landscape, especially some huge lakes full of fish which they were just developing to open up as a tourist attraction. The very large hop farm in Devenport was a super operation where they had got the traditional Australian kilns and probably better soil. The next day I flew back to Sydney where it had been agreed I should make my report on the hop farms. The major problem was Dick Watson who was in charge of the farm, and should have known either how to solve their many problems or obtained the help of a neighbouring farmer. It was most embarrassing to have to tell them this as he had looked after me very well, in fact he had arranged for the Chairman of Castlemaine and Toohey to take me out to dinner in Launceston one evening. At that meal, they invited me to visit at Christmas time and said they would entertain me when England were playing cricket against Australia in Sydney. I would have liked very much to do so but could not spare the time and was sure I could not have kept up with their drinking. I was astonished by how much they drank at that meal! Dick seemed a very able chap, having represented Australia in the Olympics in Canada at skiing, and he was boss of Medical Benefits in Tasmania, but a friend of mine Jim Shoebridge, whose farm I visited, said that he had never known a man enter a company at the top and work his way down like Dick. Anyway, in my report I said that he was the problem and that my recommendation was that they had a hop-grower to advise them, as Allied had in England. This is what they did and Neville Williams, who had the kilns heated by the wood-burner, took over to sort the farms out.

One thing that happened was a bit embarrassing – they asked me to test a load of bales, before they were sent to Melbourne. This I did and all the hops that I tested were alright; one or two were neighbouring on the limit of moisture, but they were O.K. as far as we were concerned in England. About three weeks after my return I had a letter to say that this lorry load of hops had gone on fire. There were lots of letters and discussion but nobody in the U.K. had ever had experience of hop-pockets going on fire. It wasn't until later that we discovered that you had to dry the hops drier when using a baler. In the end, they agreed that it was not my fault, but it was an unfortunate end to my time in Tasmania.

AUSTRALIAN FAMILY TIES

From Sydney I flew to Perth for a few days to see an uncle of mine whom I had met in 1974 when he visited England. He had emigrated with his sister in 1926 and was living in a bungalow a few miles outside Perth, so I hired a car and went to see him every day. It was very interesting to meet him again and he gave me a lovely book of photographs of Claston, which had been taken in 1902 and which he had taken out to Australia to remind him of home. I also went to see Auntie Gwen, his sister, who was 90 years old. Uncle Norman told me that she would not know me as she was very ill in hospital and was not expected to live for long. However, when I got to the hospital they said she was expecting me but they didn't think we would have much conversation. I entered the ward and there was this very frail old lady, as white as a ghost, sitting up in bed and we had the most wonderful talk, for about two hours. She told me all sorts of things about home, some of which I already knew but she told me in greater detail, foolishly I didn't write it down but I remembered a lot of it and Uncle Norman was absolutely astonished that she was able to converse in this way. It was only a matter of weeks before she died.

Perth was a lovely city but I found it very lonely in the evenings because I didn't know anybody, so I was quite pleased when it was time to come back home.

PARISH BOUNDARIES

A major problem the Parish Council had in 1983 was changing the boundary of Mordiford and Fownhope because, at that time, part of Mordiford which is on the Fownhope side of the Pentaloe Brook was in Fownhope parish. All the children, because their postal address was Mordiford, attended Mordiford School and went to Mordiford church. After much discussion, we had a meeting and it was agreed overwhelmingly that the boundary should change, but Fownhope did not want that. Eventually, it was agreed that the boundary should be put back to the original Ecclesiastical boundary.

LOCAL HOP MARKETING
WESTERN QUALITY HOPS LTD. (WQHL)

I invited a number of hop growers to a meeting held at Dormington Court hotel on 15 June 1983 at 6.30 p.m. Eleven growers, together with Bill Carghill, Jonathan Virdin and David LeMay who represented the hop merchants, and also George Johnson to act as secretary attended. I explained that the main objectives for inviting those present were to consider:

   a. concern about the future marketing of hops;
   b. the desirability of forming a local producer group of growers whose objective would be to improve the quality of the hops offered for sale;
   c. the possible advantages of having a producer group being able to offer, for sale through a merchant, a large quantity of assured type and quality of hops, bearing in mind the inability of Hops Marketing Board Ltd to contract with individual producers.

Jonathan Virdin then gave a proactive talk on the possible relationship between dealer and producer group. This stimulated a vigorous discussion, many present being astonished at some of his comments. Apart from an hour's break for a buffet supper, the meeting lasted until 11.45 p.m., when it was agreed to hold a further meeting on Wednesday 17 August 1983 at the Falcon Hotel, Bromyard.

At that meeting, Tony Redsell of East Kent Golding Growers Ltd was invited to explain how this society, formed under the Industrial & Provident Society Act 1965, worked. After much discussion, it was agreed to the formation of such a society on EKGG lines, acting in the first place as only a discussion group, but being prepared to move into a marketing role should this become necessary, and a steering committee was set up to convene a further meeting as soon as possible to report on their considerations of the steps necessary to form a producer group.

The steering group met on 1 March 1984. The committee consisted of R.M.O. Capper, J.H. Nott, J. Hereford, myself and also Vernon Hurst from 'Food from Britain'. At the meeting, it was decided that a co-operative society should be set up, to be called Western Quality Hops Ltd. (WQHL). Fifteen growers would be invited to be the original members and George Johnson agreed to be Secretary of the group. The first provisional members' meeting of WQHL was held in Bromyard on 28 June 1984, when fifteen members attended and there was one apology. A formal agreement was reached to form the producer group, the rules of the society were adopted and seven directors were elected. At the next meeting, on 30 July 1984, the main topic for discussion was the marketing of hops for the 1986, 1987 and 1988 crops. It was agreed that a decision would be needed very soon as to whether WQHL should prepare itself for a marketing function and, as a first step, to collect information from members of their production by varieties.

International Hop Growers Conference, Munich

In August 1984, Philip and I went to the International Hop Growers' Conference in Munich. One of the main things on the day that we had the farm visit was to look at the latest equipment for assessing the weather conditions and telling you when the fungal disease downy mildew was likely to occur. I had a look at this equipment and found, to my amazement, that it was made in the U.K. Being a bit cheeky, I told the lady professor who was doing the experiments and talking about it, that I was very interested in the equipment and asked her where she got it from. She wouldn't tell me, but I could see she was embarrassed, although she didn't know that I knew it had come from the U.K. The amazing thing about this congress was that the Germans are supposed to be so efficient, but the times of the meetings on different days were different for each language, for instance the English schedule may have said the meeting was at 9.30 a.m. whilst the German version said it was 9.45 a.m. I remember on the evening out when we were entertained in Wolsnach in the Hallertau, when the time came for us to go to have the meal we weren't able to do so for about two hours, because all the local hop growers who had got there first had eaten the food that had been prepared for the visiting hop growers, so we had to wait while they prepared more for us. The organisers were very angry. We weren't too worried though, because half a dozen of us went up to a very nice little pub in Wolsnach which I had stayed at several times, called the Hotel Schlosshoff and we had a very enjoyable session there.

PVW at Rosemaund

It was in August 1984 that Rosemaund, the Ministry farm, had their first progressive wilt. This was four years after planting the susceptible variety, Challenger, but they grubbed the whole hop-yard immediately, instead of the few plants which they had advised us to take out when we had this problem. This was just what I had always said should be done, but without permission to plant tolerant varieties no farmer could afford to take this step, although of course a government-funded farm could. Another interesting thing was that the Ministry said that we and other growers had to provide wheel baths for the tractors to go through, with the formaldehyde solution about one foot deep. However, they advised against Rosemaund doing so as they said it was too dangerous in case somebody fell in. Later I found out that this was considered confidential information.

The Association of Growers of New Varieties of Hops (AGNVH)

In 1944, a small group of growers in Kent had decided to form what was known as the Association of Growers of New Varieties of Hops. In their first year, they recruited 17 members. The objects of the Association were to promote new varieties and to help growers to produce better quality hops with better yields, to promote these new varieties to the brewing industry and to have an annual exhibition and competition for these hops. I joined the Association in 1967 and was made Chairman in 1984, a position lasting two years. In the first year of my Chairmanship, there were 189 members but by the second year it had

107

dropped to 166, owing to the gradual decline in the number of hop growers, which continued until, in 2006, there were only 50 hop growers left in the U.K.

During my Chairmanship, we had the second AGNVH farm walk to be held in Herefordshire at Dormington. Unfortunately, it was a very late season therefore we had not started hop-picking so, after having the normal tour of the hop-yards, we were unable to show people our machines picking the hops and the drying process or the kilns as was usual at the farm walk. Because of this problem, we organised a competition for the visitors to identify the different varieties of hops from over twenty green hop bines which I had obtained from several hop farms. After tea when we looked at the entries to find a winner, only one person had named them all correctly. This was David Samwells, a hop factor. Some of the answers were amazing, one brewer calling 'Bullion', which has a very strong distinctive aroma, 'Fuggle', which has a very old traditional English aroma.

The Association also had an Annual General Meeting when a prominent figure in the hop industry gave a paper on various topics. They produced an annual booklet, which was extremely useful not only to hop growers, but also to the brewing industry, because it gave statistics of the quantities of hops of each variety which were produced, also the acreages and other interesting topical facts about the hop industry.

Testing Hops

During the 1984 hop-picking, when Allied set up a laboratory at Dormington to test hops for their bittering levels, their findings were rather surprising. The results from these hops at Dormington were higher than the results of the Hops Marketing Board for the same hops, but they were similar to the results from the Scottish and Courage Brewery. This resulted in the Allied scientist having to go down to show the HMB where they had gone wrong. It was not surprising that no brewer ever complained that their results were too high.

Purchase of Prior's Court

In the autumn of 1984, Prior's Court came on the market and we thought it would be a good idea if we could buy some of the land and transfer the hops from Longworth, then sell the land at Longworth and have all our hops closer together. So we agreed with Michael Godson, a farmer from Bartestree who was also interested in buying the farm, that I should purchase Prior's Court. We would keep 100 acres and plant 50 acres of hops and roughly 50 acres of cider fruit, while he would keep the rest of the farm. We had a meeting with our solicitor, David Matthews, to agree the proportion that each one would pay. Michael was going to have more land than us but it was mostly hill-land, plus the house and the farm buildings, which were ripe for development, and also the bungalow. Anyway, when we told Michael what we thought the figures should be, and I can't remember but just as an example, say we had said we would pay 50% and Michael 50%, he said he couldn't agree with that and so David suggested he went out and considered what he should pay. Michael came back in and said he thought he should pay more than that, so we agreed, but he was worse off because he had paid a higher percentage for poorer land than we were actually to pay. When the sale came up, we bought it for £513,000 and planted corn for a couple of years. There was one field that was always very wet during the winter, part of it was nearly a lake, but when we cleaned out the deep ditch which ran across the middle of four fields, which were the 50 acres on the south side of the road, to our amazement we uncovered a 9 inch pipe which was blocked. When freed, the water which was draining down off the hill poured out and this had been soaking into the field. We then re-drained the 45 acres prior to planting the apple trees.

Western Quality Hops Ltd.

At the first general meeting of members of Western Quality Hops Ltd., held on 8 November 1984, it was decided that a display of hops produced by members was to be held in March 1985, to which hop merchants should be invited and the individual directors would visit merchants to explain the aims and objectives of the society in advance of the invitations to attend the display.

When the first AGM of WQHL was held at the Falcon Hotel, Bromyard on 11 July 1985, as Chairman I reported that Mrs Jill Andrews had been appointed Marketing Secretary and that six members were marketing their hops through the society. 20% of all the 1988 crop offered, amounting to 1,000 zentners, (1 zentner = 50 kilograms) had been sold.

Allied at Dormington and Brierley Court

During that winter, 1984/85, Allied asked me to prepare a five-year plan to take out the susceptible varieties of hops at Dormington and to produce a programme to replant with Wye Target and Wye Yeoman. We had already planted 10 acres with Target. This was agreed with the main Allied board and then, after all the time-consuming work had been completed, to my amazement in May 1985 I was told that they had decided to sell Dormington Court. The newly-planted hops were growing well and we had actually strung two hop-yards when Allied said that I was to make all of the men redundant, just shut the gates and leave the farm empty until somebody purchased it. I told them that that was impossible because the hops would get diseased; this would spread to other farms, and especially to our neighbouring farm, so eventually they agreed that we could retain one man to keep the place tidy and both weed- and disease-free. Dr Howard came down and told all the men that they were being made redundant, which was a great shock to them. When this had taken place, the office was moved to Brierley Court, which meant a lot more travelling for me.

Wilt was found at Brierley Court in 1985, but I was very angry because it had been there for at least one, if not two years, before anybody told me about it, and it was even more annoying that the manager at Brierley, Derek Wareham who had been manager at Foley Farms, kept telling the staff that it wasn't wilt. He should have known better and later one of our men, who had previously worked at Foley Farms, said that was what Derek had done at Perton, where they had had wilt at least two years before we had it at Claston. This answered the question we had never been able to solve before about where our progressive wilt had come from. I had all the blame and the unpleasantness for supposedly bringing it to Herefordshire, when it wasn't actually my fault as it had been at Perton at least two years previously. In December 1987, Brierley Court was granted a licence to plant Target.

At Claston by 1985 we had replanted five hop-yards with Target or Yeoman, the latest new variety from Wye, 58 acres in total.

Dormington Churchyard

I had been elected as a Churchwarden in 1956 and for a long period everything ran very smoothly. However, in 1985 we decided to set aside an area in the old churchyard for the burial of cremated remains. It was blessed and dedicated by the new parish priest in April 1986. However, the powers that be decided that after 1 January 1986 anybody wishing to put a stone over the ashes of their relatives had to get a faculty. We had already experienced a long delay in getting our faculty for the area of cremated remains because we had no Vicar at that time. We were very angry about this because not only was it causing extra cost to the relatives of the deceased, but also there was no guarantee that they would get permission to have a tombstone. The reason we had set up an area for cremated remains was to save space in the churchyard, with only a small flat stone, but after the new orders it was perfectly legal to bury cremated remains and have a tombstone in the churchyard, taking up a normal grave-space. However, a small flat stone was not allowed in the area that we had set aside. As the Archdeacon was unable to assist us, I wrote to Mr J.M. Henty in London, who was the Worshipful Chancellor of the Diocese of Hereford, but he was not able to help either. He said that the Archdeacon had explained it to him and although he was more sympathetic he said there was no reason why they should change the rules. In my letter I had told him that I understood that it was the duty of the Vicar and Churchwardens to make the best use of the consecrated land at our disposal, and that it was for this reason that the decision had been taken to set aside the Garden of Remembrance. I went on to say that the PCC and indeed the whole parish were up in arms about the matter, and that unless it was resolved satisfactorily the Churchwardens and PCC would resign and all interest in the Church would be destroyed. Having received Mr Henty's unhelpful reply to my letter, I wrote again on 8th August, saying that the contents of his letter had not allayed our fears, clarified the situation or helped us with our present problem. I also told him that we had taken our problems to the Archdeacon and it was his advice that we should refer the matter to him. I commented that his point about graveyard space was inapplicable because if a small stone were placed flat in the Garden of Remembrance it could not encroach on graveyard space. Furthermore, I told him that it would appear from the regulations that if the ashes were buried in the graveyard, a memorial stone could be erected without a faculty. Mr Henty had agreed that it was not possible because it took eight months for a new vicar to be appointed. I went on to say that Mrs Heavens husband had died and she had wished to bury his ashes in our set-aside area, but permission for a faculty to put a stone there had been refused. "The widow and the congregation all feel that once ashes have been buried in an unmarked grave and the faculty for a memorial tablet refused, as is the case here, there is no visible memorial at all. A precious place will be forgotten quickly, is disturbed frequently and what is to stop further ashes being buried on top? There seems to be no point in burying them in the churchyard at all. She has, of course, made an application to the Diocesan Office and you rapidly turned it down because of the new disputed regulations. We are very saddened at the prevailing situation and would remind you that the churchyard at Dormington has been used and cared for by the parishioners for hundreds of years and that we feel that these new regulations are totally unacceptable for a small village churchyard." I went on to ask him again to make a ruling to enable us to place a memorial tablet over cremated remains in our Garden of Remembrance without the need for a faculty and invited him to Dormington to see for himself that it was entirely the right and proper thing to do. After a long wait, they finally gave in and we had permission to put stones in our area for cremated remains without a faculty. It was a long and unnecessary waste of time, effort and paperwork caused by officials and the hierarchy being completely out of touch with what we were trying to achieve to save valuable burial space in our churchyard.

APPLES AND DAFFODILS

We had a contract with Bulmers to plant apples at Prior's Court in 1986. We were lucky, because they weren't giving contracts at that time, but I think we received one because the daughter of one of the directors was getting married and we allowed them to have the hop kilns at Dormington for her wedding reception. We wondered what to grow on the land between the trees in the early stages of the apple growing and Philip had discovered in a Scottish book about agriculture that daffodils would be a good crop for this purpose. We contacted a producer group in East Anglia, Lynngarden, and decided to

A crate of picked daffodils

Picking daffodils at Claston

plant daffodils in every other row so that we could still spray the apples. This proved to be a very successful crop for us to grow, the contract being to produce the bulbs for Lynngarden. We planted two varieties which they required: Hollywood, which was a very early daffodil, and Carlton. We planted them in August and the following spring we picked our first flowers, which were a bonus if the price made it viable to pick them, and they went mainly to the Birmingham horticultural produce market. It was a two-year crop, so it was 1988 before we dug the first harvest of bulbs. What amazed me was that although we planted them with a special automated bulb planter which dropped the bulbs in rows and covered them 6 to 9 inches deep, the bulbs falling upside down and on their side, they were always upright when they were lifted two years later.

Two varieties of the apples we planted at Prior's Court were fairly early ones, one was called Somerset Red Streak and the other Tremletts Bitter, whilst a third wasn't a bitter-sweet apple but a bitter apple called Browns which Bulmers liked. Bulmers did all the planting but unfortunately the trees had been grafted onto a dwarfing rootstock instead of 106 and they did not plant them deep enough, causing us to lose quite a lot of trees. They did replace them free in later years, but it meant we were losing crop on some of them for several years.

PURCHASE OF DORMINGTON COURT; CHANGES IN FARMING POLICY

I purchased Dormington Court in 1986. It was unfortunate that I hadn't known earlier that the brewery was going to sell the farm, because if I had we probably wouldn't have bought Prior's Court. There were150 acres of good land, a lot of it planted with hops at Dormington Court, between Claston Farm and Prior's Court, so we decided to buy it. It proved to be a good deal in the long-term, because in a few years' time we were able to sell off the kilns at Dormington Court and there were also a number of cottages on the farm which I sold at reasonable prices. Previously, most of them housed either staff who worked at Dormington, or those who had retired and I decided that they should have first option to buy these houses, which they did.

With Dormington Court and some extra rented arable land, our farm had increased to about 600 acres by 1986, including over 350 acres of cereals. Once we had a licence to plant wilt-tolerant hops, Philip suggested we should look into changing our farming policy, as the beef unit had become unprofitable because of the Holstein influence mentioned previously. I asked him for his opinion and he suggested that we concentrated on hops and cider apples and pulled out of everything else on the farm that was reliant on either Government or EEC money. He could see a time coming when that funding would suddenly cease and we would be left high and dry, as without the funding there was no way there would be enough money in other types of farming unless you were doing so on a very, very big scale, consisting of thousands of acres. We therefore sold the beef cattle and sheep, thus releasing in 1987 a lot of the land which we had been renting to provide food and bedding for these animals. That was the start of a complete change in our farming policy.

By this time the abattoir in Hereford, owned by the City Council and operated by Bowketts of Tenbury, had closed, forcing us to transport our animals far afield. This was because unfortunately for Bowketts, who were supplying Tesco with £250,000 worth of meat a week, the agent who purchased the meat for Tesco went bankrupt. As a result, Bowketts lost £250,000. The Council at this time also insisted that extensive improvements were carried out to bring the abattoir up to EEC standards and as a result Bowketts ceased trading in Hereford. I was very upset when a triple-decker lorry came to collect our last load of cattle. Some of these animals had great difficulty climbing on to the top deck of the lorry, after which they had to travel all the way to Anglesey. In my opinion, this very long and traumatic journey should not have to be endured by the animals and I was very relieved that we had ceased to produce any more fat cattle.

PARISH COUNCIL

Up to this present time, the Parish Council had been meeting at the Iron Room at Frome and in October 1986, Major Hereford reported that it was to be taken over by the Parish Council. This obviously was going to cause quite a lot of problems. We had a letter from Sue Harper, from the Association of Local Councils, outlining the responsibilities of the Council taking over the village hall. We had numerous meetings discussing how this should be done and the responsibilities that we would have, and eventually it was suggested that we should set up a charitable trust, drawn up from users of the hall and the Parish Council as custodian trustees and holders of the deeds.

SHARE FARMING AT POMONA

In February 1987, the brewery decided to sell Pomona and a lot of people came to view it because the farm was in good order, with very little wilt there. Eventually, it was sold to John Griffiths and we formed a share-farming partnership with him, so I was able to retain some of the staff who were at Pomona and to keep the farm manager, Dick Walker. Dick was a tower of strength, having been on the staff at Dormington Court most of his working life before going to Pomona. Later, unbeknown to us, John took on the tenancy of the Foley estate hops, which we realised later would work well in our share-farming agreement.

Our share-farming operation was a simple agreement in which both parties had fixed costs, with growing costs shared 50/50, and a joint bank account for all receipts, which were paid 50/50 into separate bank accounts. We had regular meetings to discuss farming policy and the day to day running of the farm. It was agreed at the outset that I had full control of the hop-farming operation while John managed the new cider fruit orchard.

Part of the share-farming agreement with John Griffiths was that I would provide the drying facilities for the Pomona hops at Dormington Court. It had also been agreed that I would commission the old kilns at Pomona for the 1988 crop. However, for various reasons we had to hire the Thinghill kilns at Withington to dry the 1988 crop and shortly after this harvest John decided to sell the old kilns and buildings at Pomona to a developer for houses. For the remainder of the share-farming agreement, he had arranged to dry the hops at Andrew Foley's kilns at Perton. We then sold 140 acres of land at Longworth and Bartestree, keeping only the orchard that we had planted. We did not plant hops at Prior's Court because we had already taken on all the hops at Dormington Court, although we took out a huge acreage because they were the susceptible rather than the resistant varieties.

DAFFODIL WALKS

In 1987, we planted another 15 acres of daffodils and in 1988 had a daffodil walk to raise money for the church. We were overwhelmed with visitors. We had over 200 visitors on the Saturday, which we thought was very good, but on the Sunday 750 people came and we had queues half a mile down the road each way to get in, although there were four of us taking money. Part of the entrance fee included tea and a bunch of daffodils. We ran out of both due to the unexpected number of people and had to hastily go to Hereford for more milk. Some of the visitors who were friends of ours helped to pick more daffodils for the crowds. At the end of the weekend, we had made £1000 for the church, and when I walked round in the evening to collect up the small signs we had placed directing visitors, there was no litter although we had had nearly 1,000 people over the two days. In fact, I didn't pick up even a sweet paper, which showed that some people do take care if you allow them on to the farm-land.

Jenny Jones among the daffodils

We had our first daffodil bulb harvest in July 1988. This was quite a difficult job because the bulbs had been in the ground for two years and the staff walking on the wet rows picking flowers had made the ground quite compacted. Therefore, as it was dry at the time of harvest we did have a considerable amount of trouble lifting the bulbs. For this, we began with a twin-row lifter machine, but we discovered later that it was much more efficient with a single-row lifter. The bulbs were then picked up by hand and put through a bulb cleaner to remove any soil attached to them, before being stored 5 ft deep, in a bulb drying shed, which was a converted cattle shed with vents in the floor to enable us to blow cold air through to dry them, as advised by Lynngarden. When the bulbs were dry, which took about four weeks, they were put through a

John Williams collecting picked daffodils from the field

cleaner to take off the dried skins before being graded according to size. This was a really dusty job but the end result was very satisfying. They were then put into 25 kg nets to be sent to Lynngarden or retained for replanting. Our bulbs were some of the healthiest Lynngarden handled and most of them, during our later bulb growing years, went to America after being passed by an official who used to come over to inspect them.

*Oleg and Pam picking daffodils
for the church*

PHILIP DAVIES

Philip had been suffering from depression for several years and eventually our doctor sent him to a psychiatrist, who used to come to visit him at Claston. When we asked him about Philip's problem and what could be done, he said it was nothing to do with us, but was a private matter between himself and Philip. During the summer of 1988, he arranged for Philip to go into hospital for treatment, but at the end of August when Philip went to see him to arrange this, he came back and said that the psychiatrist had told him he was cured and that no more treatment was needed. The next day, after very heavy overnight rain, Philip and I inspected the hop-yards in case there had been any damage to the wire-work during the night. The staff were all busy preparing for hop-picking which was due to start in only two or three days' time. After breakfast, Philip had to go to Hereford to collect some bits and pieces for the hop-picking machine because we were changing the system to have bine-loaders in the hop-yard for the first time, and sadly he never returned. It wasn't until early evening that I found him at Longworth where he had committed suicide. I called at Drs John & Bridget Wood in Dormington on the way home and they came with me to tell Pam what had happened. As it had been put on the radio late in the afternoon that Philip was missing, I went up to Bartestree to tell our local police officer, who knew everyone in the village very well. Although he was off-duty he very kindly went back to work and attended to the formalities for me. Dr Wood persuaded me to stay with Pam while he went to Longworth with the police officer to make the arrangements for the removal of Philip's body. The debt Pam and I owe to Drs Wood can never be repaid, and without their help I do not know how we could have coped that evening. My secretary, Jenny Jones, was the first person to be informed and she was another tower of strength. She let our families know and to our amazement it was not long before they began to arrive. Pam and I were completely devastated. We went to bed very late, having been given some sleeping pills by Dr Wood. Next day, Jenny took over and told various people in the hop trade and informed our business associates. I had that morning to go and meet the staff to tell them what to do for the day's work. They were brilliant and told me to go back to Pam, they knew what to do and when I went out later in the day they were all hard at work, each one working separately at their jobs. I was then, with great difficulty, able to talk to each one individually. They were all very upset, they thought the world of Philip and would do anything for him. Talking to them was very difficult but made me realise that even if I broke down, it was vital that I talked to people and it would help, especially as everyone was so kind and helpful.

A private service was held at the Crematorium for Philip. At a later date a memorial service was held at Dormington Church, conducted by Rev Churchus and Rev McDonald with great delicacy and understanding, and attended by hundreds of people, many of them going back to Claston for tea following the service. We were overwhelmed not only by the vast number of people at the service, but also by the large number of letters of sympathy which we received and the help and understanding shown by our families and by so many other people.

Planning for the Future

Hop-picking started the day after Philip died, so I was kept very busy, especially as it was the first time we had used the third hop-picking machine, which we had moved to Claston from Dormington Court. Philip had designed a new track which the Bruff engineers had said would not work, but it did work extremely well and was used without any problems from 1988 to 2004 when the farm was sold and tall hops ceased to be grown. Fortunately Henry Rogers from the Hillend was able to come to help during that hop-picking, which proved to be a difficult harvest because so many of the Target bines had failed to go over the top wire during the summer, and were consequently falling to the ground before they could be loaded onto the trailers with the bine-loader.

After hop-picking, we had a great dilemma as to what to do. My sisters said that I should sell the farm and retire, but I was very anxious to continue with the plans that Philip had made and which we had already started – to have 200 acres of cider fruit and 200 acres of hops. Philip had also found in a magazine an article about Border Oak, the firm in Kingsland that made half-timbered traditional Herefordshire houses, and he had already got a fabulous plan to build a village centre in the field behind what is now The Maltings, but was then part of the farm. In this there were seven low-cost houses, plus some better houses of different types, as well as a village hall and a village green. The plan for the low-cost houses was that we would provide the site and the infrastructure, this being half the cost of a house. These houses would be sold for £26,000, whilst they were actually worth £52,000 each. They would go to local people, but if they decided to move on they would only be able to make a profit on the £26,000 and then the house would be sold at that price to whichever local person wanted it next. Five of the houses were actually already taken when Philip died. The problem after Philip's death was that if we

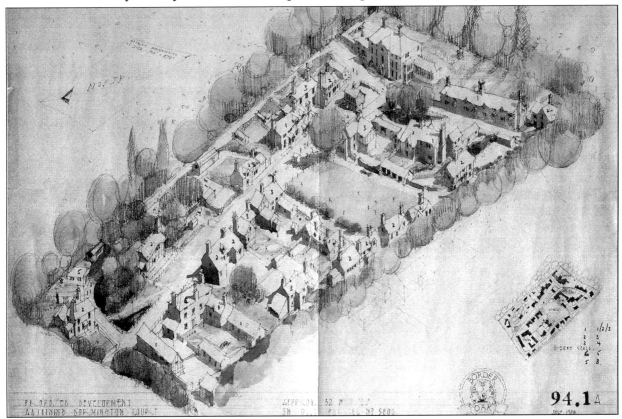

Philip's 'Border Oak' village

115

The proposed village hall

had put in for planning and continued with the scheme, that field would have been valued at £1,000,000, which would have cost us £400,000 in death duty. This was in 1988 when house prices were high, but with no guarantee of getting planning permission we had to abandon it until later. It was very sad because it was a fabulous scheme and Border Oak had actually bought an old barn for the entrance to the village which would have been through the threshing bay of that old barn.

Another reason for not wanting to retire was the fact that I was still heavily involved with the brewery work at Brierley Court and I was enjoying the farm work plus all the various things I was doing. We eventually decided that we would carry on, but we would have to get somebody else to come in to help because it was more than one person could do to manage the various projects. So, we decided to ask Pam's brother's eldest son, Graham Skittery, if he would like to come, which he did and he was with us until we sold the farm.

Having mentioned earlier that the farm diary of 1864/65 showed hops being sold to Flowers, subsequently Whitbread, brewery, just before Philip died the head brewer came to see us and said that he wanted us to take part in a big write-up that they were going to have, saying that they had bought hops from Claston for 125 years. Of course, when Philip died, that all ceased.

It was very different having Graham Skittery with me because his family had been farming a rather different operation, so I had several years training him to get him into my ways rather than theirs, but we partly succeeded, I think. Graham was very good with the fruit and during his stay we planted up a lot of orchards, getting the fruit up to 170 acres. We were lucky because it was at this time that Bulmers were wanting a lot more apples and you could get 30-year contracts to plant trees to produce this extra fruit. It was unfortunate that the one orchard we planted, with two early varieties – Ellis Bitter and Ashton Bitter – wasn't a success as although Ellis Bitter was good, Ashton Bitter was a very difficult tree to grow because

116

it fruited bi-annually, which was a big disadvantage, and also the tree structure was difficult to maintain. They were very fragile trees so in the end we cut them off and grafted them with another variety. The other orchards were planted with Dabinet and Michelin which crop every year and these orchards have proved to be very successful. Other benefits were that Bulmers were prepared to pay for all the fencing, planting and rabbit-proof gates, also for the fruit trees, and you had an interest-free loan that you could pay back over five years. It is a fairly expensive operation to plant an orchard, quite apart from the cost of the trees themselves, which are about £2.50/£3 each and we were planting 300 to the acre. Then you had three years before you had any crop at all, and we always said that it took ten to twelve years before you were back to a clean piece of paper. Some of the orchards did much better and others not quite so well, much depended on the weather conditions when they were planted.

In May 1989 we had a very severe frost. We had 12 hours of frost, with the temperature down as low as -8°C. This was the first and only time that I can remember severe damage to the cider fruit blossom and it also had a catastrophic effect on the hops because we had practically finished hop-training and the shoots were so badly damaged that we had to re-train the whole crop when the shoots grew again. In fact, the ones that hadn't been trained were the worst affected, because not only did the frost destroy the shoots, but when they regrew the new shoots became entangled in these long damaged ones, making it very difficult to retrain them.

WESTERN QUALITY HOPS LTD.

Western Quality Hops Ltd progressed and by 1988 it was finally established as a produce marketing group under EEC rules and was then able to claim EEC hop income support. After invaluable guidance from George Johnson, Miss R. Allen took over as Secretary on 1 January 1988.

In my fifth Chairman's Report in June 1989, I was reporting on the 1988 crop which was the smallest for many years, hop damson aphid and powdery mildew showing in numerous samples. Jill Andrews could not have had a more difficult year as our Marketing Secretary, but she successfully sold all of the group's hops. The quantity of hops marketed through the group continued to rise from 4,900 zentners in 1988 to 6,380 zentners in 1990. Jill and I had been to Edinburgh to sell hops to Scottish & Newcastle Brewery, making a three-year contract. Their hop buyer, Bob Denham, said that we were the first English sellers for ten years to offer them hops and we agreed a 5 year contract worth £750,000 in half-an-hour.

The 38th International Hop Growers Congress was held in Hereford in August 1990, when Western Quality Hops Ltd were one of the sponsors and over two hundred delegates had a tour round the Claston hop-yards.

SOUTH HEREFORDSHIRE ASSOCIATION OF LOCAL COUNCILS

I was made Chairman of SHALC in 1990 and one of the first meetings that I chaired was the occasion when we had a senior person from the Ramblers Association to speak. At the end of the meeting, everybody was against what the speaker was saying. He gave way on nothing. Questions were asked, such as why the Ramblers Association did not help with the maintenance of footpaths and things like that, but he was very abusive, being adamant that everything had to be done by the District Council to keep the footpaths open, and the footpaths and bridle paths kept in perfect condition for the use of the ramblers, regardless of cost.

SONGS OF PRAISE

A few years after Philip died, I was approached by the BBC to see if I would take part in the Songs of Praise programme which was being recorded in Hereford Cathedral and in Herefordshire. I agreed, although I wasn't sure really what they were going to talk about, but they did ask if I would be prepared to talk about Philip's death and how I coped. When they came to record the programme, they spent most of the day doing this and the following is the recording of what I said, being interviewed by Pam Rhodes:

Interview for 'Songs of Praise'

Pam Rhodes: This is a real taste of Herefordshire, down on the farm where the county's world famous cider apples and hops are grown. There's a great tradition, of course Peter, isn't there, of farming families handing down land from generation to generation? Has that happened to you?

Peter: Yes, well my family have been here since about 1864, when my great-grandfather came here as a bailiff for two years before he became a tenant. He was followed by my grandfather and then my father after the First World War. I left school in 1939 and joined the family business. My son Philip was involved afterwards.

Pam R: Tell me about Philip, because he's not here to carry on that tradition. What happened?

Peter: Well, Philip died when he was 33. He committed suicide the day before we started hop-picking. He had been suffering from depression but he had been involved in the farm for about seventeen years, I suppose, and we had made plans for the future.

Pam R: Did you find it difficult to talk about the tragedy, and did people allow you to talk and share it?

Peter: I was determined that I would talk about it and, I am quite honest, when talking to people I broke down, but that didn't matter. If you don't talk and have belief then you will be in a terrible hole and get in a big black hole that you will never get out of and I was determined that that wouldn't happen. I felt that God was helping me and it was very difficult. I was determined that we would go on – hop-picking started the next day and so there was no way you could just hide in a corner and say 'Oh dear'. I am a religious man and I have great faith and faiths that my father taught me and he always said that the first thing in life is that your word is your bond and then he said 'Your responsibilities are first to your family and then to your staff and then to your church and the parish' and those three are very closely knit together and I have always believed in that and worked hard to keep that tradition up. I have a great attachment to the farm, it has been my life, it's been my living and my great joy is to walk around the farm in the evening, especially if I am on my own, and just stop and look, listen and observe and somehow a great feeling of peace descends on you. It is difficult to explain what that feeling is, but it's an incredible feeling. What we have done in the last, well since Philip died in 1988 will go on for ever and it will never be changed. It is there for everybody to see. I mean the orchards that he designed and planted and the hop-yards that we planted, they are there forever.

CHAPTER NINE

A New Era : 1992-2007

It was about 1992 that I discovered that Peter Glendenning, who was in charge of the hop unit at Rosemaund (the ministry experimental farm) had become disillusioned with the way he had to operate there. Fortunately I was able to persuade him to join Philip Davies and Son as our hop consultant, with responsibilities for fertiliser, pest and disease control, and he later became responsible for the development of the hedgerow hop experiments. A few years later he also became consultant to the National Hop Association.

HEDGEROW (DWARF) HOPS

1992 was the beginning of a revolution in hop-growing. If hedgerow hops had been a better-known crop, it would have hit the headlines and there would have been a tremendous amount of publicity. I knew that as a result of the visit to the USA in 1977, Wye College were progressing with their breeding programme to produce hedgerow hops, but I was not expecting it to happen for a year or two. I was absolutely astonished when, out of the blue, in late April 1992 I had a telephone message from Wye College to say that they had got 600 hedgerow hop plants for us, 200 of each of the three varieties, Pioneer, First Gold and Herald, if we would like to have them. Obviously I was delighted but the offer was so unexpected that it did cause a problem because all of our land was already planted. In order to make room for this extra crop, we had to plough up a small area of winter wheat. As we had been propagating hops since 1963 we knew that the cuttings had to be taken by the third week in June and so we put these plants, from which we needed to take cuttings, in the greenhouse to get faster growth in order to achieve this. We grew these tiny plants on until they were big enough to provide 600 cuttings of each variety, enabling us to plant six rows of 400 plants by early July. These hops had to be grown to form an 8 foot high hedge, as opposed to the traditional hops which were grown on 16 to 18 feet wire-work. We had no idea how this could be accomplished, but after much discussion with our wire-work contractor, we decided on the materials which we had always used for the tall hops, adapting them to form a lower frame to support the hedgerow hops.

Five other hop growers had these plants; there were three farms in Kent and two others in Herefordshire. One of these was Rosemaund, the Ministry experimental farm, and the other was another grower and they, in their wisdom, decided to get a propagator to produce thousands of plants, which meant they were propagating right through into August. I knew this wouldn't work, because we had discovered that although cuttings propagated after the third week in June would root, there would not be time for them to produce sufficient root structure to start growth the following Spring. The rooted cuttings must be planted in the hop-yard by the middle of July. So they ended up with thousands of plants, 90% of which died. Of the three farmers in Kent, two were great friends of mine, but on one of those farms, the rabbits took most of the plants and on the other, where Herald, which is very shallow-rooted and delicate, was planted, it wasn't very successful because it was planted on some very heavy clay. However, both of them produced good crops of hedgerow hops in following years. At the other farm, in East Kent, the farm manager didn't agree with the hedgerow hops, saying that they were no good and so they didn't bother with them. I cannot understand why he was allowed to make this important decision.

Over the next three years we tried various support systems for the hedgerow system, using different types of string and plastic netting. The squares proved to be too small in the fish netting which we had thought would be the most successful, but the manufacturers were not interested in developing a more suitable net, although we explained that there would be a market potential of at least 1,500 kilometres. However, eventually in 1997, we found a Spanish company who made us a black net with 9 inch squares, which we had discovered to be the ideal size.

POMONA FARM

In early 1992, John Griffiths said that he was terminating our share-farming agreement, giving a reason which was strictly against the agreement, and soon after announced that he was going to sell Pomona farm. It was obvious that this would have serious financial implications for us, and my solicitor advised us to engage Mr Carter, a Chartered Surveyor, to work out our financial loss. Mr Carter had been involved in setting up many share-farming agreements. As a member of the Lord Chancellor's panel, he had on occasions received appointments from the President of the Royal Institution of Chartered Surveyors to act as a sole arbitrator and as an independent expert.

As a result of his deliberations, Mr Carter assessed that John Griffiths owed us nearly £135,000, in addition to our half share of the remainder of the money in our joint receipts account. John objected to this, eventually forcing us to take him to court and the case nearly ended up in the High Court. We had to engage a barrister who was an expert in share-farming. Eventually John agreed to settle out of court, but we only received £40,000 plus our half share of the joint receipts account. It had cost us a great deal of money in lawyers' fees but if we had not gone to court we would not have received anything.

DORMINGTON COURT FARM BUILDINGS

When the share-farming agreement ceased, we took over the Perton hops, picking and drying them at Claston. We sold the Dormington Court farmyard and most of the buildings to Hereford Hardware Supplies, and Mr Hurd, a local builder, bought the farm builders' yard, known locally as 'Stan Clifton's Work Shop'.

Hereford Hardware Supplies were foolish because part of their planning permission required the demolition of the old corrugated-iron hop-picking machine shed, plus other redundant sheds and the landscaping of the area surrounding the kilns. They failed to do this and the site soon became an eyesore, probably putting off potential customers to the furniture store. This was a pity, because they had done a lot of work inside, converting the kilns into the furniture store.

After a few years, I realised that Mr Eggerton, the owner of Hereford Hardware Supplies, was going to have to sell up. I suggested that he joined forces with me to build the Border Oak village which had been planned on the south side of the site before Philip's death. He was very keen on this idea and we got Border Oak to incorporate a scheme which would join the two systems together, reduce the number of houses on my site and use some on his site to make a really attractive area, with the entrance to the site from the main road. I do not know why, but eventually Mr Eggerton backed off this idea.

WESTERN QUALITY HOPS LTD.

The 1992 Western Quality Hops Limited crop was 21% lower than the 8,000 zentners grown in 1991 due to a very severe downy mildew problem, Target being the most seriously affected, causing very low yields of very poor quality hops. However, our customers were very understanding and took all of the poor quality hops. I believe that we were the only group to have pesticide residue analysis available for our customers and I feel this was very beneficial. Our levels of residues were very low, showing that members were following good agricultural practice.

THE FIRST HEDGEROW HOPS

The first full crop of hedgerow hops

In 1993 we were the only farm to produce a full crop of hedgerow hops, and this was also the first commercial crop grown in the world. Afterwards, I discovered that if we had failed, the whole hedgerow hop operation would have ceased. John Cyster, the man who had suffered the rabbit damage, also managed to produce a few hops. He was already working on building a mobile hop-picking machine for harvesting the hedgerow hops, with parts from a blackcurrant harvester, parts of a hedge trimmer and other bits and pieces. That year, this machine picked our six rows of hops and whilst there were all sorts of problems, the actual picking unit was brilliant, never having been bettered, although it was a very Heath Robinson affair at that time. However, it worked and we picked our hops successfully, having a lot of fun during the process. The following year he improved it considerably, although there were still some problems.

In 1994 we planted some more First Gold hedgerow hops, because this variety appeared to be the best. By 1995 there was a need for a much better hop-picking machine, so John Cyster imported a mobile harvester from Eastern Europe. This was designed to pick seedless hops,

The Cyster mobile hop-picking machine

which are much tougher and more robust. When we started the harvester up in the yard part of it wouldn't work – a motor had failed – but when we rang the manufacturers they told us it would take a fortnight to get a replacement, by which time the hops would have been over-ripe. However, with much research we found a suitable motor in this country, but the main problem was that as hedgerow hops are seeded, they are very delicate and this harvester absolutely thrashed both the net and the hops, which was disastrous. I knew it was much better mechanically, but it didn't pick the hops anywhere near as well as John Cyster's machine.

121

South Herefordshire Association of Local Councils
and The Herefordshire Joint Charter Group

I had been elected Chairman of the South Herefordshire Association of Local Councils (SHALC) in 1990 and the next five years were a very hectic period, because the South Herefordshire Association was the leader in proposing a split from the joint Herefordshire & Worcestershire Association to set up the separate Herefordshire Association. This was because the Herefordshire & Worcestershire County Council was being split into two discrete authorities; therefore it would have been unworkable to keep the joint association of parish councils. SHALC was very unpopular in many quarters, particularly Kington and Colwall, because we were taking the initiative in this matter. In the January of 1994, I invited Mr Szaroleta to a South Herefordshire Association meeting, at which we discussed the progress we were making on the formation of a Herefordshire Town & Parish Council. Mr Szaroleta was the Regional Director for the Local Government Commission for England, responsible for organising all the new ideas for the West Midlands.

We organised a meeting at the Blind College on 31 January 1994 for representatives from most of the parishes in Herefordshire, including Parish Clerks, and also the City Council, as well as Leominster, Malvern Hills and South Herefrodshire District Council, together with Ledbury, Tenbury and Ross Town Councils. I was astonished when one of the first things said at the meeting was that this was the first time they had ever met together. This was a very successful meeting and everybody was agreed that Herefordshire should have its own Association of Parish and Town Councils.

The South Herefordshire Area Committee had prepared a survey, a questionnaire which was sent out to all the Parish and Town Councils in the South Herefordshire area, and this was following the circulation of the Department of Environment's consultation paper on the role of Parish and Town Councils in England, published in the Autumn of 1992. It was sent to the sixty-two member councils and 101 individual Town and Parish Councils in Herefordshire. We had two months in which to respond and in that time 84% of the member councils completed and returned the questionnaire. That represented the views of 449 Parish and Town Councils, which was a very good result. There was overwhelming dissatisfaction with the present Herefordshire & Worcestershire Council, and a similar overwhelming wish to have a Herefordshire unitary authority and a Herefordshire Association of Parish Councils, with the Parish Councils having a much more important role, because they would then know what was happening in the government of the county.

As a result of the questionnaire, South Herefordshire Association made a submission to the local government review, and I believe we were one of very few associations of Parish and Town Councils that actually made a submission. This submission was stating the overwhelming desire to have a Herefordshire unitary authority and a Herefordshire Association of Parish Councils. It covered 102 member Parish and Town Councils, which is 100% membership of all the local councils in the area, and it represents some 520 local councillors in a rural area with a population of approximately 53,000. This was in March 1994.

As a result of all this work, the inaugural meeting of the Herefordshire Joint Charter Group, which was finally set up by Herefordshire & Worcestershire Association of Parish Councils, was held on 26th June 1995. Because I was Chairman of SHALC at that time, I was elected Chairman and served for the period that the Charter Group took to get the Herefordshire Association of Parish and Town Councils up and running.

Before we held the inaugural meeting, South Herefordshire set up a small committee to meet all the Town Councils to get their views on what we were planning to do and everybody was very supportive. As a result of these meetings, a Herefordshire Town Forum was set up, consisting of the market towns of Kington, Ledbury, Ross and Tenbury and this worked very well. The Charter Group had many meetings and most of them were very productive, but we did have a major problem with Colwall, largely because the representatives of the Malvern Hills area were unable to attend the Colwall Parish Council meeting because they had other meetings on the same night. They therefore tried to stop the Charter Group. This problem was most surprising, because the Malvern Hills Council had representatives on the Charter Group.

Hereford City Council, under the Chairmanship of George Hyde, and I as Chairman of the Charter Group, invited every Town and Parish councillor to a meeting at the Shire Hall. The objective of the meeting was to give everyone who attended an update of the progress, informing the Herefordshire Association of Parish & Town Councils. Well over two hundred people attended, mainly being very supportive, but the Colwall councillors had obviously come to be disruptive by complaining about the short notice of the meeting, and saying that the Herefordshire Charter Group was not representative of the rural parishes, both of which were completely untrue. I had already been to a meeting of the Colwall Parish Council to explain that their worries were caused by their two representatives failing to keep them informed. In a letter sent by Mr Brent, the Clerk, he said that his Council was most grateful to me for my 'Daniel in the lions' den' act and as a result of that they had asked to be members of the Charter Group, but as their representatives had already been coming to those meetings, it was a little puzzling. To pacify them we let them have a third member, unlike the rest of the groups who only had two, but we did this as Colwall was such a large parish.

POTENTIAL DEVELOPMENTS AT CLASTON

I had been thinking about building new kilns for several years before it occurred to me that it might be possible to build a completely new farmyard, new farmhouse, house for a farm manager, kilns, cattle sheds and picking sheds. We contacted ADAS, the Government Agricultural Development & Advisory Service, who specialise in research and planning. Mr Finney, the Senior Consultant for Land and Leisure, produced

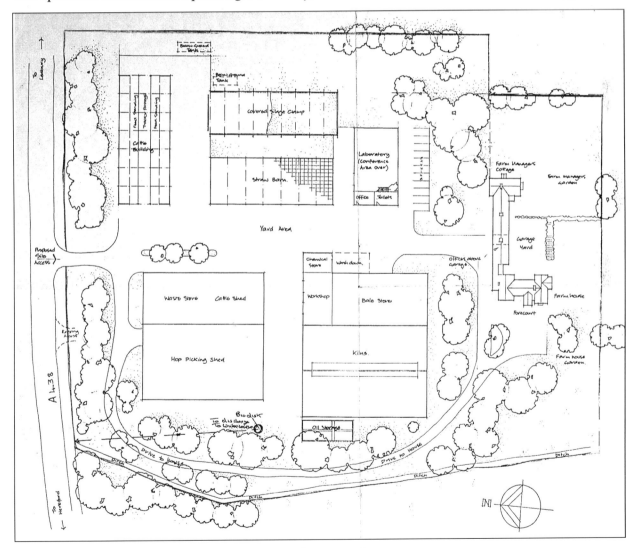

Plans for a new farm

a planning application to build this completely new farmyard in a field to the south-east of Claston, the other side of the road and about 400 yards from the present farmyard. To our amazement we had no difficulty in getting planning permission. Two houses would have been built by Border Oak, and ADAS had actually worked out a timescale and a schedule for the operation to be completed by the end of May 1998.

Before applying for planning permission, we had met a firm called the Marlborough Land Company based in Essex, who were very enthusiastic about buying Claston farmhouse, the kilns and the whole farmyard. We came to an agreement that they would pay £1,000,000 for this, subject to planning permission. They put the planning application in for a mix of houses on the farmyard, and to develop some of the old buildings. Having agreed to our building the new farmyard on a greenfield site, the planners in their wisdom then refused planning permission to develop the old farm site, saying that it was a greenfield site, which was only partly true, as there had been buildings on two-thirds of this area for several hundred years and no buildings on the other site.

We had previously asked an estate agent to explore the potential of converting the buildings for light industrial use, but the cost made it prohibitive. The planners mentioned that they had noted the commercial and economic circumstances which had prompted us to apply for this and the development was fully considered. Whilst they had every sympathy with us, it was not considered that these were sufficient to outweigh either national guidelines or the local land policies, and the application was recommended for refusal. They also said that if we built the farm complex we would have to clear the site of the old buildings and grass it down, which we knew from the Marlborough Land estimate would cost vast sums of money, so we had to abandon the whole operation.

THE MALTINGS DEVELOPMENT AT DORMINGTON : TAY HOMES

Following the failure of the joint plan with Marlborough Land, my solicitor David Matthews had agreed that we could go ahead to apply for planning permission for our village on the south side of the site. This we did but by that time the council had drawn a line round all villages in the county, called a village envelope, outside which planning permission would not be given for any housing developments. Mr Eggerton's land, which was now classed as an industrial site, had been included in the village envelope, but our site had not. By now, sadly, Mr Eggerton had gone into liquidation and unfortunately his bank's application for the 23 houses, which were all reasonably expensive, came before the planning committee at the same planning meeting as ours. Philip's plan, on the other side of the fence, outside the envelope, included a village green, a village hall and the low-cost houses which five local young families were very anxious to purchase. The rejection of my plan regrettably meant that these young people were forced to leave the parish and probably go to live in the city, much against their will. I was very upset that a few local people opposed my scheme, which in fact showed that they had no interest in local young families remaining here, although I felt this was vital to the future of village life. It was a pity that in Mr Eggerton's scheme, which became The Maltings, there were no low-cost houses.

The bank then sold the site to a building company called Tay Homes and following this a director from the company came to see me to get information about existing land-drains, water pipes and sewerage. I tried very hard to work with them, but found them very difficult. The main problem was over the pipe for sewerage, which they wanted to put across our land into the existing sewage treatment plant, which had to be enlarged. Also, there was to be a pipe to carry the purified effluent down to the river, all of which they thought they could do for nothing. They were very angry when I told them there was no way that they could cross my land for nothing, causing disruption and possibly a risk of future trouble and damage to crops from broken pipes and drains, etc. Eventually, when they realised that there was no other option but to cross our land, they agreed to pay us £30,000 to do so. I was horrified when they were actually constructing the pipeline, because in places they dug a trench 9 feet deep, but there was no shuttering in place to protect the men who were working in the trench from landslides. I felt it was very dangerous and, strangely enough, the pipe-work for that sewage system has never been adopted by Welsh Water because it has never been properly passed or examined and adopted.

We had a right of way straight through the centre of the site on a metalled road which they obviously wanted to change. Eventually they agreed to make a road up the other side of the hedge from the actual Maltings site. They did not seem bothered about the land drains that were going through the site, or the mains water supply from the 20,000 gallon reservoir at Backbury Farm that had formerly been used to supply water to Dormington Court and also to take water down to Moor Mills. I explained where all the pipes were, but they completely ignored this. On one occasion when Graham and I had been away at a meeting all day, we came back home and saw a Tay Homes van leaving the farmyard. We were puzzled by this so we came down to the developmentsite and found that apparently when they dug the foundations for the first house they had cut through the pipe from the reservoir and had 20,000 gallons of water flooding the area. It was entirely their own fault, as I had already told them where the pipes were, but we were amazed that after repairing the pipe they still put the foundations for that first house in the next day, although it was like a paddy field. Their final problem was where they could put a pipe to deal with the surface water and the land drain water which they would otherwise have had to connect to their sewage water system. I offered them the chance to go along the bottom of the orchard next to the site, for £5,000, but they would not do that and eventually, at great expense, they put it under the ditch below the orchard on the side of the road. It took them about a month to do it, and because they had to have traffic lights it must have cost them a fortune. At the time I had foolishly forgotten that we owned the verges on the side of the road, so I could actually have made them pay. However, they did make a good job of that and there hasn't been a problem with surface water since.

When Tay Homes had their first sales open day one weekend, Pam and I went down to have a look because I was interested to see how the houses were built. I used to go regularly to the site, getting to know the site foreman and various workmen. We went into the first house, the one now occupied by Ian Morley and Kerry Diamond, and after looking around downstairs went to go upstairs, when to my amazement as I put my hand on the knob on the banister it fell off, which I thought was not a very good example of their workmanship.

EXPANSION OF HEDGEROW HOPS

After the 1995 crop, it was obvious that hedgerow hops were much more environmentally-friendly and labour-saving, therefore being the way forward for the future, and so in 1996 we planted 15 acres at Perton and 40 acres at Dormington Court. Some of them were planted with roots we bought in East Anglia because we couldn't produce the quantity we needed in time, and the rest we filled with either plants that we grew in our own greenhouses, or some that we got Wyevale to grow for us. We had decided the year before that we would have to have our own mobile harvester, and so a local firm, Pattenden Engineering, agreed that they would make one for us. They actually made three that year. Ours was the first and I told them that I wanted it to pick half an acre an hour, up to 15 zentners per acre and this information helped them considerably with the design of the machine. They had a very good design engineer, Robin Peers, who had worked on aeroplane manufacture, then on the static Bruff hop-picking machines and also did much of the work on the Brierley hop-picking machines and kilns. He then produced a fabulous self-propelled machine called the Pattenden Robin and we picked our first hops with it in 1996. They delivered the machine the night before we had planned to start, ready to commence harvesting at 8 a.m. the next day. Our two drivers and the Pattenden engineers went to the hop-yard, having told me that I wasn't to go there until they were ready. At about 11 a.m., John Armstrong, who was in charge of the operation, came back and told me I could go and have a look at the machine, which was working very well. I could not believe it, because our men, Conroy Jones and Clive Huffer, had not driven anything like this before. They were fully in control, the hop-picking

The Pattenden self-propelled harvester
driven by Clive Huffer with my sister Kate

machine was going very well, picking the hops beautifully, without breaking them up or damaging the net. That machine, with a few minor alterations, has worked brilliantly ever since.

When we came to put the net on the larger area that we had planted, we decided to use a white plastic net with 6 inch squares. We eventually found out, after extensive training trials, that the squares were still too small and in later years we went to a black net with 9 inch squares, which was much better and was also less visible. When training, we just put one bine up each of the uprights on the 9 inch square. At first, we were using traditional anchor rods and anchor blocks, digging holes 4 feet 6 inches deep, but then we realised that it wasn't necessary to do that, so we had some new anchor rods made with a big corkscrew on the end. They were 3 feet long and we wound them into the soil, but this wasn't quite strong enough. A lot of them are still OK, but some pulled up so now we use a straight rod with just a small anchor block going in about 2 feet deep.

9 inch netting

It really has been a case of trial and error because nobody had erected any quantity of the fencing necessary for the hedgerow hops before. It was a new concept in hop growing, instead of having wire-work 15 to 18 feet high, with two strings to each plant, for hedgerow hops you have netting 8 feet high and place the plants every half-metre to form a hedge of hops. This has enabled us to use the mobile harvester so that when harvesting hedgerow hops the labour force is dramatically reduced. To pick 5 acres a day in the traditional system with two static picking machines, you needed 32 people, whilst with a mobile harvester to pick the same acreage a day you need only seven people. Also, fewer tractors are needed, instead of eight we now only use two. When using the mobile harvester, the picked hops, comprising mostly hops and leaves, are conveyed to a trailer in the next row and then taken to the static picking machines at the farm, where they are put through the spray picker and cleaners to take out any leaves and other debris. The bine track and bine chopper are not used, but we do use the spray picker, running it very slowly to pick the very few sprays knocked off by the harvester. This reduces the maintenance on the hop-picking machine dramatically.

We were delighted with the yields we were getting – even with our first crop twelve months after mis-propagation we grew nearly 13 zentners to the acre which, compared with the national average for tall hops of just over 11 zentners, was quite remarkable, although our own yields with the tall hops were much higher.

Following several years of fluctuating hop yields, it was astonishing that WQHL members produced 47% more hops in 1996 on a similar acreage than in 1995, but unfortunately there was a virtual collapse of the world hop market so the group only increased its income by 12%, to £1,300,000. This year we grew, for the first time, over 2,000 pockets.

Pam and me with the last hop pocket of 1996

Hop Marketing Problems

When we had sufficient hedgerow hops to market, we made a five-year contract with Morris Hanbury-Jackson at £250 per zentner. Sadly two years' later, in 1998, they became bankrupt and, although the 1998 crop was covered by our credit insurance, we lost the contract for the remaining three years. Western Quality Hops then made an agreement with Thomas Hawkins to market the First Gold hops and, to get into the European market, we had to sell them at very low prices. Forward contracts had become a non-event because of the low price of hops; brewers could buy them much cheaper on the spot market than with forward contracts. We ended up selling hops, for a couple of years, at about £50 per zentner instead of £250, with catastrophic consequences to the profitability of the hops. The alpha price had dropped from £35 per kilo in 1993 to about £12 by this time, in fact it was becoming very difficult to sell hops at all. One Sunday evening, I think it was in 1999, Michael Wiggin, a hop merchant, rang me to say that he would take all the unsold Western Quality alpha hops, Target and Yeoman, at £12 per kilo. He realised that this was a very poor price but said that if we didn't accept it quickly the price would fall much lower. I reluctantly agreed and it was a good thing that I did, because within a few days the price had dropped to £8.

By now, the plant breeding programme was progressing at Wye College and I went down to have a look at their harvesting. They had got a tractor-drawn harvester, which had been made up from an old blackcurrant harvester. It worked very well for their needs, as they only collected sufficient hops for analysis samples and brewing trials. They then asked me, as we had been successful, if we would like to do farm trials of any new varieties which came along. I felt that this was an exciting project and so we made an agreement with them.

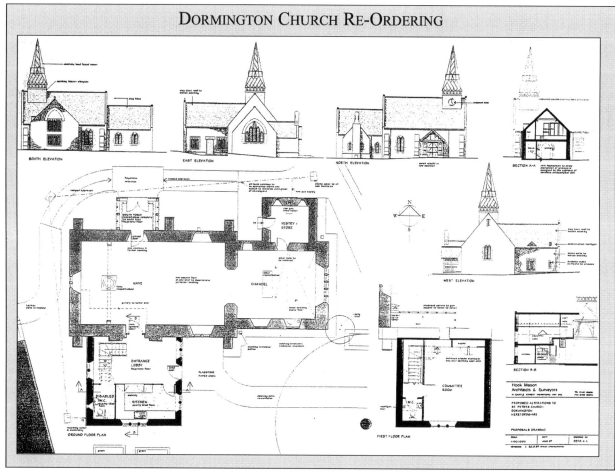

128

Following the architect's Quinquennial Report, a meeting was held on 6 May 1997 to discuss hisestimate of £40,000 to carry out necessary repairs to Dormington Church. The meeting decided that it would be worthwhile looking at the potential of retaining the church as a place of worship, while combining this with facilities for a community centre. The architect produced a plan to move the existing entrance to the north side of the church, where it had originally been, to give space for a two-storey extension. This would provide a kitchen, toilets and a small meeting-room. The total cost of the alterations and the repairs would have been about £145,000.

It was agreed to set up a charitable trust to provide the necessary funding. The architect, who had the necessary expertise and experience to do this, was instructed to make an application for National Lottery funding. Unfortunately he did not emphasise the need for a community centre. Consequently the application failed and this resulted in the abandonment of the alterations. However, through local fund-raising and donations from various organisations, the Trust has already raised £53,000 for church repairs, covering the cost of repairs to the vestry roof, the leaded windows, monuments in the church, the bells and the churchyard paths.

PLANTING HOPS : NEW VARIETIES

Having mechanised the hop-picking, we also mechanised the planting of the hops, continuing to grow the plants in our greenhouse in $2^{1}/_{4}$ inch square Jiffy pots, hardening them off in a tunnel and then using a mechanical planter. We marked out and then subsoiled the row which we were going to plant and while doing this we put in liquid fertiliser mixed in water up to about one inch below where the pot was going to be. We planted one row at a time, placing the plants 20 inches apart. This proved very successful, and in fact, as long as the ground was prepared properly, the plants seemed to do better than when we were planting them by hand.

Hard at work: Hilary Bromage, Carol Webley, Ros Edwards, Joan Williams
with Reg Bufton on the tractor

Two-row sprayer

Providing we got them planted by the middle of July we regularly harvested a full crop the following year.

In 1997 we had another variety of hedgerow hop from Wye, called 9350. This was a very different hop with a very strong aniseed-like aroma, but unfortunately it was very susceptible to downy mildew. One or two brewers used it, one of these was in South Wales and it was interesting that when we had a farm visit the Chairman of Wolverhampton & Dudley Brewery, David Thompson, was very keen that they should try this in one of their beers, but as the head brewer didn't agree, it didn't happen.

In 1998, we had six more new varieties to try and we decided that it would be easier if we called these by ladies names, because the hop plant that produces the cone is female. So we named these after members of the female staff. Of this wide range of varieties, one was an aroma hop which we called Jeanette, which was closely related to First Gold. Another one was Jenny, which was a sister to Herald, which produced a much heavier crop but the alpha was disappointing. Then we had Ruth, a very early hop, which I thought might have been successful because it yielded really well and it had a nice aroma, but the brewers did not like it. Another was Ros, which

Peter and David Thompson

was a very high-yielding variety, susceptible to downy mildew but not as badly as 9350. Ros eventually became a registered variety and is now called Pilot. The fifth variety was Hilary, which was a good yielder but the alphas weren't high enough. The other variety, called Joan, was a very late hop which was naturally seedless with very poor yields, so, after four years of trials, they were all discarded except the one called Pilot.

The next new varieties of hops came in 2001 and one of these was the first hop that had been bred which was naturally resistant to the hop damson aphid. We called that one Jayne and that has become a registered hop, with considerable interest being shown by some brewers and it is now called Boadicea. The other one, Pina, was very disappointing, it produced a very low yield, most of the hops having leaves in them so it was no good and has been scrapped.

The following year we had three more, which showed great potential in early trials as high alpha hops and were called Jill, Kate and Irene. Sadly in our field trials the alphas were too low and so they were not continued.

DAMAGE BY HAIL

We had a monumental hailstorm in June 1999 when the hops were varying from 6' to 10' high. We had never seen a storm like it – the hailstones were more like jagged lumps of ice. Fortunately we insure against hail, having had this insurance since my father started hop growing in 1919. When the assessor came to look the next day, there were 100 acres of tall hops which had been severely damaged, and he thought that there would be a claim of at least £250,000. However, the weather was very kind to us and the hops grew back remarkably well; we were able to train fresh shoots to replace the damaged ones, but although we didn't have a huge crop it was reasonable and the claim was only £80,000 on that yield. It was interesting that the hail hardly affected the hedgerow hops, probably because the upright net forms a fairly solid wall which protects the hops.

MECHANISING THE KILNS

Above: Kiln being loaded by levelling conveyor
Left: Automatic baler

We now decided that it was time to look at mechanising the kilns, where we were employing fourteen people. As it was getting very difficult to find suitable staff, at great expense we built a new set of kilns. These were to be completely automated, computer-controlled, and heated with gas instead of oil. An engineer from Kent

Hops being dried in the new kilns

called Albert Philpin built the kilns, comprising ten units, each 23 feet square. For years, in other countries, they had been using a mechanical device to level the hops, which come straight from the picking machine on conveyors into the kiln, and then onto a levelling conveyor which is an angled belt off which the hops roll and which travels along, loading each kiln automatically. To start it all up you just had to press one button, and when the kiln was full the gas fires were started from the platform which ran up the centre of the kilns. The fires were controlled automatically at the correct temperature, taking four hours to reach 140° which is the temperature we dried at. The temperature was maintained until it was time to turn the fires off. This was very successful and was the largest set of kilns that this engineer had put up.

HOP SUNDAY AT CLASTON

Bishop John Saxby and Revd. D. Bowen taking hop-yard service on hop Sunday

HARVEST FESTIVAL AT DORMINGTON

On 3 October 1999, our annual Harvest Festival service took place in Dormington Church
and I delivered the following sermon:

I have not got a text for my words this evening. Instead, I am going to pose a few questions. Simply, why did or does this happen? I expect most of you are wondering why I am up here talking to you this evening ... I asked our Rector some months ago if he had asked someone to give tonight's sermon and when he said 'No', I asked jokingly whether he wanted me to do it! His eyes sparkled and he said 'Yes, but you mustn't go on about all today's farming trials and tribulations!' As someone who has lived and worked all his life on the land, in this wonderful part of the world called Dormington, I did not see this as a problem!

Harvest Festivals have been held in churches for about 150 years, and I wonder how many people in this country realise their importance, when you can go into a supermarket and buy any fruit or vegetable at any time of the year? And now with the advent of 'ready-cooked' meals, more and more people are edging further and further away from the reality of where their food comes from. I am now going to quote from the past Dean of Windsor, Reverend Mann's speech at a Farmers' Club dinner in London:

> It seems to me that in the countryside things have got a bit out of balance. Too much emphasis is being placed on the urban environment and townspeople, and not enough on the country. Even in the Church of England my local vicar has eight parishes to look after on his own, and that does not happen in towns. Of course, lip-service is paid to the beauty of the countryside, but even that sometimes seems to be regarded as a holiday attraction for the town dweller.

God made the world, but apart from a few areas of natural wilderness, the countryside has been made for the large part in the country by man – and it is the sweat of the British farmers and countrymen and their hard work over the centuries that has created the loveliness of our fields, lanes and villages. That is the background to the country. To work on a farm is not just a job; it is a way of life. There is no such thing as a 'nine-till-five' job on a farm. If you are dealing with stock and the demands of the harvest, you work all the hours of the day. It is also a family concern, with all the best family values and with everyone involved and affected in one way or another. I cannot remember who it was who said that behind every successful farmer there stands an astonished mother-in-law!

One of the greatest blessings that God has bestowed upon us is that we cannot see into the future; I think if we could, we would grow like the modern media, and be tempted to dwell on the sensational and horrible things, while discounting all the good ones. Thank God that we do look to the future, in ignorance but in hope, and that is very necessary for farmers, who all too often have to learn with the bad times, but still in hope. It is rather like the fortune teller's tent at the country fair which had a notice up outside saying, 'Closed due to unforeseen circumstances!'

This ends the quote and sums up what I believe to be the countryside's problems today. But let us now go back to earliest times when man lived off food growing in the wild at that time. I ask the question, why did they start to grow crops? And surely they must have learned where these crops grew best, because they worked the land by hand and knew just where the soil was best. I quote from the *Parable of the Sower*:

And when he sowed, some of the seeds fell by the way side, and the fowls came and devoured them up: Some fell upon stony places, where they had much earth: and forthwith they sprung up, because they had no deepness of earth:

And when the sun was up, they were scorched; and because they had no root, they withered away.

And some fell among thorns; and the thorns sprung up, and choked them:

But others fell into good ground, and brought forth fruit, some an hundred-fold, some sixty-fold, some thirty-fold.

Was this an early instruction to farmers, later to be adopted so neatly by our Lord? How natural it was for Jesus to have used farming ways in so many parables! If we distance ourselves from farming and nature, *can we really appreciate the depth of wisdom* in these timeless parables? I now quote from the *Parable of the Tares* (or weeds):

Another parable put he forth unto them, saying, The kingdom of heaven is likened unto a man which sowed tares among the wheat, and went his way.

But when the blade was sprung up, and brought forth fruit, then appeared the tares also.

So the servants of the householder came and said unto him, Sir, didst not thou sow good seed in thy field? From whence then hath it tares?

He said unto them, An enemy hath done this ...

Why did they believe this? If it was true, who is the enemy who sows all the weeds that grow in our gardens and fields? Now, I have always looked at weeds as wild flowers growing in the wrong place, and most of us know that weed seeds can survive in the soil for many, many years. With those few thoughts of ancient times, let me give you *my* reasons for the importance of Harvest Festival. I believe we should be saying thank you for more than just our harvest of corn, fruit and hops. Shouldn't we say thank you for all that happens in the countryside during the year?

There is the wonder of corn coming up under a blanket of snow in a severe winter. Why do the snowdrops appear when it is often so cold? Have you ever really looked at them closely and wondered at their beauty?

When the weather warms up, the buds begin to burst, giving many vivid shades of green. Then, early spring flowers start to bloom ... the beauty of all the wild flowers ... A friend of mine from the industrial Midlands once asked me who had planted them all ... Have you ever asked yourself this question?

As the grass begins to grow, it is time for baby lambs. When I was in my early twenties, I was looking after the sheep and helped a ewe with a difficult birth. The lamb was perfect, but was distressed, so I was helping its mother to revive it. Sadly, it died in my arms. I remember the ewe looking at me and starting to nudge me with her nose, obviously asking me to do something about it. This was her harvest time and I had failed her in her hour of need, in spite of the trust she had in me; *why* did this have to happen?

And now onto blossom time, when the countryside is a blaze of colour. A time when all of us will be thinking of wonderful crops. Have you ever looked closely at the blossom? Whatever it may be, the intense activity of wildlife working away pollinating the flowers. *Why* does all this happen? How do the bees and the insects know where to go and find their food? Insect populations increase just in time to coincide with the hatching of baby birds! Have you ever watched a nest and seen just how quickly they grow and learn to fly? *Why* does the cuckoo not build her own nest, but lays her eggs in another bird's nest? *Why* does the surrogate mother not react? By now our wild animals are bringing up their young. How many of you have picked up a leveret, a baby hare, and felt the softness of its silken coat, and looked into its wonderful large eyes? ... Perfection!

Swallows, swifts and martins now start arriving. How are they able to travel thousands of miles, some to arrive at the very same nest as last year and begin laying eggs within three days? No assistance from radar or satellite. Why do they travel so far to breed?

Do we really concern ourselves with why there are so many different kinds of birds, of animals, insects and plants, all living together in the countryside? Have we come to wonder and learn, or pay lip service to what is now glibly called 'the environment'?

As the summer passes, ears of corn start appearing across the fields, with their special beauty, as Mary Webb so wonderfully describes:

> It was a great delight to me to look at the standing corn and see it like a great mere under the wind. Times it was still, without a ripple; times it went in waves. Like a storm in Galilee Mere that the King of Love did still. So I watched the grain week by week, from the time when it was all green till it began to take colour, turning raddled or abron or pale, each in his kind. And it shone, nights, as if there was a light behind it, with a kind of soft shining light like glow-worms or a marish light. I never knew nor do I know now why corn shines thus in the nights of July and August, keeping a moon-light of its own even when there is no moon. But it is a marvellous thing to see, when the great hush of full summer and deep night is upon the land, till even the aspen tree, that will ever be gossiping, durstna' speak, but holds breath, as if she waited for the coming of the Lord.

And now onto harvest, so greatly changed with the advent of the combine harvester. This has led to the decline of a beautiful creature, the harvest mouse, which used to produce and rear its young in the stooked sheaves of corn. And now it is time for the migratory birds to leave, how do they know when to go, and which way?

And into autumn with the beautiful colours of flowers, leaves and berries. How many realise the importance of fallen leaves to life in the soil? Have you ever noticed how they are pulled down into the ground by the earthworms; eventually to become part of the food for life in the soil.

All these inexplicable happenings during the year, and the beauty of it all through the changing seasons, are my reason for being at our Harvest Festival.

There is, however, one other reason. In the late 1920s, my sister and I were taught by an old Scottish governess. Every day, she took us for a walk and taught us about the countryside. To do this she made us stop, look, listen and observe. I have always remembered this, and when I am walking around the farm in the evening, I do just that. It has taught me to be able to relax and, for a few moments, leave aside the immediate problems in my life. It is a constant wonder to me, the sense of peace that comes from stopping and listening. I believe that the discipline of taking time to be close to His creation can help us all to get closer to God. How many of us can say thank you for this?

If only *all* children were taught at school about food production in this country and to respect its importance, not only to the economy but also to conservation of the countryside! As the Reverend Mann said, 'Of course lip service is paid to the countryside', but *I* believe very little is understood of its true importance....

I will end with a brief passage from one of Adam Nicholson's weekly views from Perch Hill:

Nature is no more than the word for everything that is not us. It is a myth of Adam's nudity in Eden: a dream of unclothed and uninterfered-with perfection that does not and never has existed, at least not as far as anyone has experienced it. Do I believe that? Not entirely.

Kipling, feeling old and sad, wrote to his friend Rider Hadder: 'I know life has got to end somewhere; I just wish it wasn't such a cold and desolate place'. It doesn't have to be. I step outside. The swallows are swooping-circling over the pond. You can feel their vivid urgency; their live beauty, like the gestures of a Jackson Pollock made flesh, repeated over and over again, for no other reason than the swallow's desire to be itself. For a moment or two anyway, Eden can be here and now.

And so, when *our* time comes to leave this earth, is that our Lord's Harvest? Let us ask our Lord to help us all to be truly thankful for the harvest He provides for us; and help us all to stop, look, listen and observe, so that we can learn from Him.

CLASTON HOP SEMINAR, 2000

When the National Hop Association was formed in the 1980s, it became obvious that in due course it would have to join with the Association of Growers of New Varieties of Hops and eventually this happened in about 1995. This meant a cessation of the annual farm walk, so in the year 2000, Thomas Hawkins of Hawk Hops, together with Hops from England, Western Quality Hops, two producer groups operating in the West Midlands and a local hop merchant, Charles Fareham of Malvern, decided to join with us to have a joint farm walk at Claston. Because of the problems of attracting people to attend just a farm walk, which was really more or less a jolly, we decided to have it on a more professional basis, with papers by various people in the hop industry. We put a tremendous amount of work into this promotion and to our amazement we were overwhelmed by the response. We had papers by Dr Peter Derby on the current programme of hop breeding at Wye College, Peter Glendinning, who was then working for me, spoke about growing new varieties of hops, and I talked about a grower's point of view and the history of Claston in the hop industry. We also had a publican who talked about the promotion of beer in his pub, how he operated and also about drinking beer from different types of glasses. Finally Thomas Hawkins talked about the current marketing situation in the hop industry and about how the quality of hops should be described on the bottle labels more accurately, naming the variety of hop and country of origin, not just 'finest hops'.

We invited people from all the large breweries, our major customers and senior people from the NFU, the Brewers' Society and others but we also said that if anybody wanted an extra ticket it would cost £95. To our amazement, on the actual day 87 people came, including several extras who paid their £95. We even had a couple of brewers or maybe more who came from Belgium. When people arrived they were given coffee and then during the papers, each table of ten was given a different beer to taste so that at the end of the day they had about five or six different beers. Also, we had a range of cask beers for people to drink during lunch-time and we provided a good cold buffet. In the afternoon, we arranged visits to look at the new varieties of hops, and harvesting the hops, our new kilns and also the static picking machines.

I was amazed at the comments we had afterwards and the letters we received saying how worthwhile the day had been. It showed that the hop industry was not dead as had been described in various newspaper articles, especially one, I think it was *The Times*, saying that lavender and herbs were going to take the place of hops and that hop growing in the U.K. was finished.

On the second day, we invited all the small brewers and micro brewers and we were overwhelmed, we had 166 people which really tested our system of taking people round the farm, the catering and other arrangements. We gave them a simpler lunch and only charged people £25 for that day, but the papers were the same. Again, we had a fantastic response, people saying how much they had enjoyed the day and how worthwhile it had been, so all in all it was a very worthwhile effort. It had cost us quite a lot of money, but at least I am sure that it helped our sales in our producer group in future years.

FIRE!

We did have a major problem in 2000, the first year of the new kilns, because all the conveyors in the kilns consisted of rubber belts, running over a metal sheet. Hops are very sticky when harvested and these rubber belts were getting gummed up, causing over-loading of the motors, so we knew that this was something we would have to alter for the following year. Unfortunately, after we had been picking for about two weeks, the whole set of kilns burnt down. There had been a misunderstanding between Flogas, who supplied and installed the gas tanks plus all the pipe-work, and a firm from Essex, Niche, who put the burners in. Flogas thought that the burner people would put in a liquid gas trap and Niche thought that Flogas had put it in, but neither firm had actually done this. Unfortunately, one morning when Flogas were filling one of the gas tanks, liquid gas got down the pipe and put the fire out, but of course the liquid gas went straight into the kiln. As soon as the liquid gas stopped, the automatic equipment was activated to ignite the burner. We had a massive explosion and the kilns were burnt down in about twenty minutes. We were very lucky that nobody was hurt, because three of our women were on the platform above cleaning up, and the force of the explosion blew one of them over. One of the others with her picked up and returned her broom, but didn't help her up! This caused some amusement when related later on. They all suffered from severe

After the fire

shock for quite a long time after and so did the hop-drier, Reg Bufton, who was on duty at the time. It was a horrific experience, but it did enable us to carry out improvements when rebuilding the kilns for the following year, raising the kiln floor and replacing the rubber belts with chain-driven ones.

It was amazing how quickly we had support from neighbouring hop growers to assist in completing the harvest. The first was a fax from Andrew Foley offering the use of his unused kilns, which I gratefully accepted. Julian Cotton, who had spare drying capacity, also agreed to dry hops at Pomona Farm, but altogether it was quite an expensive operation because it meant we were having not only to haul the hops from the yards to the picking machines, but also having to haul the loads of green picked hops to two sets of kilns in opposite directions. We used two or three old kilns of our own as well, so we had three different drying units. Another neighbour, John Probert, lent us a trailer which was a great help. The loss of the kilns was all covered by insurance, but it was a very difficult operation to organise the picking and drying of the hops and keep everything under control. Everybody was marvellous – they all buckled down and we successfully picked all of the hops.

TARRINGTON SCHOOL

Tarrington School was built by Lady Emily Foley in 1874 for the benefit of the children of Dormington, Stoke Edith and Tarrington. The Foley family had been building schools in the Midlands to enable them to have the advantage of better-educated staff for their various business enterprises. The Tarrington school would have improved the quality of the numerous future employees required for the running of the extensive Stoke Edith estate, many of whom would other wise not have been able to read or write. Sadly, the school was closed in 1998 by Herefordshire County Council, who were managing the school, due to insufficient numbers of pupils.

Later, the Council put up signs to sell the school building and the school house, claiming that they had ownership of these properties. A small committee, representing the three parishes who actually owned it was set up, comprising Andrew Foley (Stoke Edith), Stella Bradstock, Pat Jenkins and Angela Stock (Tarrington) and me (Dormington), to prevent this sale. It took a decade to prove that the school was not the property of the Council, but that it belonged to the Trustees of the parishes, of which there were none still living.

We had invaluable legal advice, without charge, from Christopher Hann, a solicitor whose mother was a member of the Richardson family, who have lived in the village of Tarrington for many years, and also from Lord Denning who, when we visited him, we discovered was fighting a similar local case. Our case nearly ended in court, but the Council gave in at the last moment. Under the guidance of our architect, Angus Jamieson, the school has been converted into one of the best village halls in the county. The inaugural meeting of the Lady Emily Community Hall standing committee was held on 13 June 2000 and the hall was officially opened on 12 August 2000 by Emily Foley aged 5 (the eldest daughter of Andrew Foley) and Elsie Hill, who was 90 years old and had been the local post lady for many years.

WESTERN QUALITY HOPS LTD. REACHES ITS 21ST BIRTHDAY

Crops and hop prices fluctuated violently from 1996 to 2000. When we held our first meeting in 1984, other growers said that Western Quality Hops Limited would not last long, but how wrong they were. WQHL provided 18.8% of the UK's national crop in 2000 and 75% of all hedgerow hops. Our first year of marketing with Hawkbrand hops was very successful. In 2001, the group produced a record crop and, in spite of declining hop prices, our income was £1,700,000. In my 21st Annual Report I was able to announce better sales prices, but sadly the decline in WQHL production continued. In spite of this we are now producing 20% of the national crop.

ANOTHER FIRE

Following the kiln fire, we reconstructed the kilns and they worked extremely well, but unfortunately two days before the end of hop-picking another disaster struck. One Saturday, when we were busy harvesting apples rather than hop-picking, Winston Price came running up to me in the house to say that there was a small amount of smoke at the end of the bale store. We had been putting the bales in the cattle shed and there must have been about two thousand of them. I went quickly out with him, and by then it was obvious that the bale store was alight, but what astonished me was that the whole building was ablaze within a matter of a very few minutes. I know hops, when you get sufficient heat, will burn; otherwise they only gently smoulder, so it was quite amazing why the building was set alight so quickly. Of course, by the time the fire was extinguished the heat had been so intense that all signs of evidence as to why the fire had started were destroyed, so we will never be able to find out the real cause of the fire.

A FOOD AND DRINK CENTRE?

When we were starting to think about our new kilns, we wondered what we should do with all our old barns and the lovely old stone buildings which had been the original hop kilns. I had an idea that perhaps we could do something on the lines of a Food & Drinks Centre, because I knew there were lots of small producers who were producing super goods in Herefordshire but were having problems marketing them. I went to see George Hyde, who was then Leader of the Council and he was very excited about the idea, saying that it was something that he had been thinking about and wondering where it could be done. So he contacted Geoff Hughes, Head of Community & Economic Development for the Council, who came to see me. He was also full of enthusiasm about my project. He said that he thought the best thing to do would be to put me in touch with the Chamber of Commerce and they would advise me on how to set about planning and designing it. So they came up with a list of several architects and I selected John Hewitt, who was working from Colwall at that time. They said that he was excellent and they had done a lot of work with him. After several meetings and discussions he came up with the idea of the Herefordshire Food & Drinks Centre. He said it would cost a lot of money to do this, so we needed to look at some way of funding it. He suggested having some Border Oak houses, all with workshops, some of which were to be expensive houses, others less so and people could only occupy them if they were involved in either agriculture, the Food & Drinks Centre, tourism or something connected with Herefordshire. There were also to be five low-cost houses.

We agreed that first of all he would carry out a feasibility study, which would take 3½ days, to include measuring the buildings and doing a survey. Then draw up a site master plan, an outline of proposed uses and presentation materials, which would take 4 days and then he was going to take 3 days establishing a

Restoration of the old cooling room by Roger Lloyd as part of the proposed Food and Drink Centre

management mechanism for sustainable project delivery. The funding strategy would take 1 day, economic justification 2 days and the planning strategy $2^1/_2$ days and then a $^1/_2$-day presentation to Herefordshire Council, a total of $16^1/_2$ days. Stage Two was to develop an architectural and proposed usage business plan content, in the light of the feedback from the presentation to the Council and then it was going to take $24^1/_2$ days to work out a future funding strategy. The whole thing was going to cost £14,760, of which the Chamber of Commerce paid a substantial amount. So it can be seen that it was a very comprehensive study and resulted in our final plan, which sadly had to be amended. The whole project was approved by the Chamber of Commerce, who worked closely with John in the preparation of the final plan. There was in fact a contract between the Chamber of Commerce and John Hewitt.

John came up with a brilliant plan to convert one of the cattle sheds into a farmers' market, to convert the bottom of what was the new cooling room into a shop, open five or six days a week, with a history of each product so that if a farmer wanted a stall there, he would not have had to be there all the time, as we would have had staff to manage it, but details about his farm and how he produced the goods would be shown. Upstairs in the old kilns we were going to have a restaurant, where originally the idea was to have a hop museum, but we felt that there probably wouldn't be enough visitors to warrant having somebody to look after it all the time, so we decided to make that into a restaurant and convert the round kiln into a little bar. Upstairs in the new cooling room, built in 1976, we planned a conference centre and the upstairs of what were the new kilns, which had been built about 100 years ago, was to be a meeting room, with a kitchen at one end, under which toilets would have been situated. The straw barn was to have been converted into workshops for people to start up businesses.

Part of John's strategy was to have a meeting at an early stage and to invite various people who might be interested, food and drink producers and tourist people. We arranged to hold this at Claston on 28 June 2001, six weeks after John had started on the project. This meeting was very well supported, although things were at a very early stage. A number of the people who had agreed to come offered to bring some of their products, we provided a buffet supper but with their help it was a much more successful event. Whilst there were various queries about the project, on the whole everybody was very supportive and very excited about the whole idea.

We had a lot of interest and a number of people came forward wanting workshops, one person wanted to rent one acre of land to have a living furniture workshop, and one, who actually went ahead, was Paul Harris who converted one of the old kilns into a brewery. This was written into our planning application and Paul gave evidence at the subsequent enquiry. Two other people who were really interested were Simon Gourlay, a former President of the NFU, and Nick Saphir, past Chairman of Food From Britain, who wanted to run the shop. They hoped to have five of these shops all over the country and had had planning applications refused in one or two places, but they were very optimistic about this one, where they planned to have a bakery as well. If it had happened, this would have been a great relief to me because I always had worries about how to manage the shop. Sadly, because of the long delays, Simon and Nick eventually backed out and started up a similar scheme in France where they had no difficulty in getting planning permission.

I then talked to the Highways Authority about the project, who suggested that we should put the entrance on a roundabout at the junction of the A438 and the road to Mordiford, where there were various problems and there had been a number of accidents.

We put in our first planning application in 2001. We had done a lot of work getting ready for this and had also spoken to various bodies about funding. We had great problems with the planners. When that application had been put to the Council, they obviously had to notify everybody nearby and I thought it would be a good idea to have a meeting in the church to explain what our thoughts were. There was uproar. I have never been to such a difficult meeting in all my life. Somebody started to complain even before Nick Brewin, who was chairing the meeting, could explain the plans. Residents of The Maltings were up in arms about the planned roundabout, which I would have thought would have been of great benefit to them. Everybody was so abusive and angry at that meeting that I tendered my resignation from the Parish Council the next day, because I could see no reason to spend my time representing people who could not even speak civilly at a meeting.

We talked to the Council about this and I withdrew that planning application. We then suggested a new entrance to the Food & Drinks Centre at the existing farm entrance. This planning application was submitted and we had a site meeting with the Council Planning Committee, when everybody was very much in favour of the project. The main objection from most people was the fact that we were building houses to help with the funding. It was quite interesting – we even had one letter which said that if the project could not be funded on its own then it could not be viable, which was nonsense. At the site meeting, the then Chairman of the Planning Committee, together with our local Councillor, went into one of the buildings but unfortunately a few days before the planning meeting there had been a local election and I had put up some signs promoting Bill Wiggin, the prospective Conservative candidate. I had asked the men to take them down and they had left them in the bottom of one of the kilns. As soon as this person saw the posters, she said to our Parish Councillor that that was it, the application would not go through.

After a lot of deliberation, the Council came back and said that the plan included too many houses. The first thing we had to do was to take out the low-cost houses because they weren't necessary, which was absolutely crazy because it was part of the project so that if somebody wanted to start up a small business they would have a low-cost house on site. We also had to cut down the number of other houses by two. A few days later, I spoke to the Housing Officer of the Council when she came out to have a look at the site. I explained what we were doing and she replied that those low-cost houses were desperately needed and it was an ideal idea, but she said that the planners had told her that she was to tell me there was no need.

Another idea that we had for the Food & Drinks Centre project was to have a pub. A lot of people thought this would be good. Border Oak had actually built some pubs for the Wolverhampton & Dudley brewery so they had got a plan of a half-timbered pub with accommodation above and that was put in as a secondary part of the planning application. The application actually went before the planners in April 2002, but because of various objections we had had to keep withdrawing it and when it finally went before the planners it was approved, but they said that because it was outside the structure plan it would have to go to the Government for approval. There was only one person who didn't vote in favour of the plan. The application had cost me over £9,000.

The Government then decided that there must be a local enquiry. This was a very expensive operation because we had to get all sorts of evidence together and it cost me about £50,000, and it must have cost both the Council and the Government just as much. Before the enquiry, we had to get somebody to do a visual appraisal and although the Council officer dealing with that had already done this, we had to have a separate opinion. Also, we had to have an assessment of lighting impact and traffic appraisal as it was very close to the main A438 Hereford – Ledbury road, which the Highways people said was an ideal site. There were a number of other things which we had to do, as well as having a full surface water and sewerage system planned and an electrical scheme, which was a pretty big operation. We also studied various ways of organic heating. After consultation with Bulmers, we had come up with the idea that we could burn all the apple prunings within ten miles of the site, Bulmers saying from a transport point of view there would be about 10,000 tons of prunings. The problem was that there is only a very short time for collection when the orchards are dry enough, generally in March and up to the middle of April before spraying commences, therefore it would have been impossible to handle 10,000 tons of prunings in the six weeks available. We then looked at using one of our gas burners, installed for the hop drying, and this would probably have been the system we would have adopted.

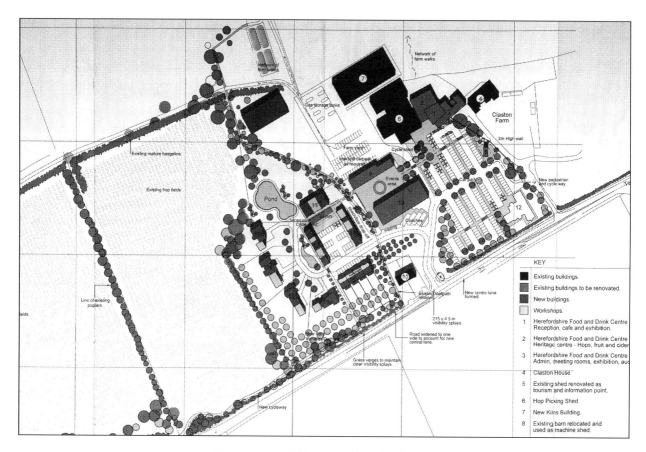

The proposed Food and Drink Centre

Following planning permission, it took until 3 December 2002 for the local enquiry to be held. Amazingly, there were no objections whatsoever to any of the proposals at the enquiry, in spite of a number of people who had previously objected. One of the main contentions was whether the houses planned were a necessary part of the project, but the Inspector agreed that they were. Peter Evans, the Chief Planning Officer, considered the houses to be primarily workshops with ancillary residential accommodation and the Inspector said that was a reasonable approach to a novel form of development. We had expected to create fifty jobs, but the Inspector, when he went through all the potential for jobs, was convinced that after a few years when the whole development was under way and the Food & Drinks Centre increased, we would actually create two hundred jobs, either directly or indirectly. The Inspector's comment on the work units stated that they were 'not comparable to a normal dwelling but were a new concept which was particularly applicable to a county such as Herefordshire, where there is a long tradition of individuals working in small workshops associated with a dwelling, often in remote rural locations'.

At the time of the farm walk, our brewery was not quite up and running, but it was nearly ready and the Institute of Brewing were very interested in this and in the project. They wanted it to be their centre for young brewers to come to learn about hop growing and the hop industry, and they would have held training sessions in our conference centre. They were very disappointed when we were unable to continue with the project (see pages 148-9).

DEVELOPMENTS WITH THE PARISH COUNCIL

As regards Parish Council work during this period, several very interesting problems cropped up. One referred to Richard White wishing to develop the old cottages on Tower Hill, which had originally been the farm cottages for Claston Farm. He had done a lot of work up there without planning permission and had enlarged the double dwelling, making it into one house. Also, foolishly, instead of sticking to the bridle-path which had been used for access when people were living there until about forty years ago, he had bulldozed a way through the little bit of wasteland which was a mini common owned by Mr Foley, so you can imagine that this caused considerable problems. The other problem that occurred was that Mr Foley had illegally planted up with trees all of the gardens belonging to the three cottages, before Richard White had bought the cottages from the Green family. In spite of planning refusal, Mr White continued with this renovation work and there were various appeals but I do not think that the end of it has yet been heard. Mr Foley took Mr White to court about doing the road, but I never heard the outcome of that although I imagine that Mr Foley must have won. It was a pity that Mr White did not obtain planning permission before doing the cottages up because they were in a beautiful spot and it seemed a tragedy to let them fall down. Philip, years before, had tried to buy them from the Green family, of the Prospect, because he wanted to make the bottom one into a nice house to live in himself. He offered them £2,000, but they refused and the buildings became derelict, people just went to help themselves to timbers and stone, etc.

Mr & Mrs Len Byard, the last occupiers of one of the houses on Tower Hill

At a meeting on 10 February 1997, a planning application for the change of use of existing yard and buildings at Claston for residential use came up as well as for the new farmstead. I left the meeting, having declared an interest. There was much discussion about this, but in the end the Council supported my application.

Another application that caused a lot of discussion was from Checkley, where Mr Hankinson wanted to set up a youth hostel in an old barn. There were typical objections from local people saying that it would increase the traffic dramatically, but it was a good idea because it was for a very limited number of people to go there just at week-ends and in holiday time, although I believe that application was eventually refused.

Rules for Annual Parish Council accounts were being tightened up and the Council was reminded that although the Parish Clerk did the accounts, the Councils were responsible for raising and dispensing Parish and Town funds in accordance with the law. They were advised that it was important to remember constantly that most of these sums were public monies. The accounts should not be just a book-keeping exercise; they should represent a profile of the Parish or Town Council and be a management tool for the Councillors, as well as the means by which the public are able to monitor progress on an annual basis.

A major development by this time was that the Beat Officer for the area, PC Sally Fisher, used to attend the meetings which was very helpful when we had highways problems. We did have a major problem because of the traffic going through Rotherwas to get to and from Hereford on the Rotherwas road. This heavy traffic was starting to come to Mordiford and then through to Dormington. The heavy lorries were damaging roads and buildings in Mordiford village so the Council banned any lorry over the weight of 7.5 tonnes from taking this route. The large amount of traffic on the road from Mordiford to Dormington has become a major problem for the Parish Council, and this increased when they started to build the new roundabout at Belmont for the Asda store. Although that has now been completed, traffic has got so used to coming this way that the problem remains.

It seemed quite strange that most of the things the Parish Council supported the District Council refused and vice versa. By this time, of course, The Maltings development had started, the first houses being completed in 1996 and we were having problems with accidents on Dormington corner. It is a miracle that no-one was killed because one person, coming from Mordiford was going too fast and went through two trees, hitting one then going across the road, into someone's garden and then turned left, through another hedge, across the main road and ended up in the hop-yard on the other side of the road. After much discussion and various meetings, with much pressure being put on the Highways Department of Herefordshire Council, a lot of signs were put up plus a 40 mph speed limit through Dormington. It was a pity that the Council hadn't supported Tay Homes, as they wanted to make the junction about another 5 metres to the east of where it is now which would have enabled people to see the traffic coming from Ledbury more clearly.

THE CHARTER GROUP AND THE HEREFORDSHIRE ASSOCIATION OF LOCAL COUNCILS

I am sure that we had not realised what a difficult operation it would be for the Charter Group to set up a Herefordshire Association of Local Councils. We were greatly helped during all these meetings by our Secretary, Linda Wilcox, who was a tower of strength; not only was she involved with SHALC, but she was also secretary to the Charter Group and various Parish Councils. She was a great authority on the workings of Parish Councils.

As a result of the meetings between the South Herefordshire Association of Local Councils and South Herefordshire District Council, a format was drawn up, which the Charter Group was able to use for the new Herefordshire Unitary Authority. The newly-appointed Chief Executive of this, Neil Pringle, with George Hyde and other councillors had meetings with the Charter Group, in which we evolved a sensible plan for the future working together of the Unitary Authority and the Herefordshire Association of Local Councils. One important factor was to persuade the Herefordshire Unitary Authority to appoint a Local Councils' Officer. Jane Jones, who was the first of these officers, was very efficient, forming an excellent liaison between the two bodies.

The final meeting of the Joint Charter Group was held on 1 April 1999, immediately prior to the first meeting of the Herefordshire Committee for the Herefordshire Association of Local Councils. One thing that we regretted was that we failed to get permission for Parish and Town Councillors to go to planning meetings.

It was suggested that I should be the first Chairman of the new Herefordshire Association, and although I realised that it was a great honour I rejected that idea, because I had not sufficient time to carry out what I knew would be a heavy workload, especially in the early days of the new Council. It was unanimously agreed that the purpose of the Herefordshire Committee was to bring together a body properly representing all Parish and Town Councils in Hereford county, to provide a forum for on-going regular and relevant meaningful democratic consultation with the unitary authority and other statutory bodies. One of the initial problems in all these discussions was that Hereford City wasn't parished, but eventually this took place on 1 April 2001. This was following a government regulation that any area in the country that was not parished could be so divided, provided the people there wanted it.

FRUIT COMPETITIONS

In 1997, 1998, 1999 and again in 2002 I entered the Top Fruit class in the Grower of the Year competition, which included hops. To my surprise, we were a finalist in 1997 and 1998 and to my astonishment in 2002 were awarded the Norah Stucken Award for Individual achievement. Finalists were invited with their guests (mine being Pam and Graham and Pina Skittery) to the dinner, at which winners were announced. I received the prize from Sir Ben Gill, President of the NFU, in front of several hundred guests. Winners were expected to make a short speech, which was not too difficult, but what I had not noticed when previous winners were speaking was that close-up pictures of them were being shown all around the room, so I was amazed when I was speaking as I could not help but see a picture of me whichever way I looked. This was very disconcerting! I was also invited to enter The Worshipful Company of Fruiterers Environmental Competition in 2002 and to my amazement we won the overall award. Pam and I went to the Mansion House in London to receive the prize, which was a cheque and a magnificent cut glass rose bowl, from the Lord Mayor.

GOLDEN WEDDING

On 23 April 2002 we celebrated our Golden Wedding with a short service of re-dedication in the church conducted by the Rev. David Bowen. This was followed by a buffet supper prepared by Len Gee of the Yew Tree Restaurant, Frome, for friends and family and staff at Tarrington Community Hall. Part of my response to the toast to Pam and I by my cousin, Digby Blanche, who was best man at our wedding was as follows:

Today I stand here feeling very humble and very honoured to have been lucky enough to have been the husband of this very special lady. I am not sure whether Pam has been so lucky. She has already cooked over 70,000 meals for me. I know that Pam is not only loved by me but by many others. She is a wonderful person of many talents. Firstly for putting up with me for 50 years, also as a mother and home-maker. She loves her gardening, upholstery and is a gifted amateur artist. She also helps to make sense of my writings and 'talks' as well as being involved in the farm. Pam has been 'chief hop propagator' for 38 years now and, with her trusted team of ladies, has overseen the production of more than a million plants. Add to this all the help she gives her brother, her involvement in the parish and finally all the work she does for her church. Pam is a very gentle person. Once during hop picking she scratched her face on a hop bine and one of the hop-yard staff, collectively known as 'the Coventry Boys' said she looked liked a piece of cracked Dresden china!

THE CHALLENGE OF MARRIAGE
I believe marriage is like an oak tree –
In a passage from John Wyatt's *Reflection on the Lakes* he writes about an oak tree:

No writer could ever match the poetry expressed in the form of a single tree, for it speaks from its roots, through fibres of its stem, the shape of its trunk, the turn and spread of its branches, the twisting and reaching of the twigs. A tree speaks. It speaks of a hundred summers and a hundred winters. Of storms and droughts and floods and snows, of plague and gales, of rocks and soils and hidden waters of air and birds and pollinating insects. The whole of the message is contained in the way it has grown, precisely, to make use of what its environment has provided. It states in essence: 'Here I am, and where I am is what I am'. The way of saying can only be purely truthful. The natural laws make it impossible to lie. If a tree appears to be beautiful, it is because beauty is truth and truth is beauty.

Perhaps the marriage ceremony is like planting an acorn, and the success of the marriage depends on how, together, you overcome the challenges of life. I am sure that we shall not survive for hundreds of years, as an oak tree does, but we have made a good start. Great times with the family, the excitement of the birth of our son, Philip, and the wonderful 33 years that we all had together. The sadness of his tragic death.

In spite of Philip's tragic death, life has to go on. His death was like a violent storm that, in the case of the tree, would rip off some of its major branches. They had played a major role in the life of the tree, just as Philip had in ours. At that time, my family suggested I should retire. I was 65, but we decided that we should accept the challenge to complete Philip's vision of the farm.

As Pam and I walk round the farm on a Sunday evening, we see this vision taking shape. It was back in 1982 that he suggested, and I agreed, that we should change our farming policy, to get rid of everything that the Government and the E.U. had anything to do with. At that time we had a 300 herd beef unit, 250 ewes for fat lamb production and 400 acres of cereals, as well as 125 acres of hops and 40 acres of cider apples. His vision was to have 200 acres of hops and 200 acres of cider apples, with the hope that the hops would eventually be hedgerow hops. With the help of our nephew Graham Skittery, and Peter Glendinning, ably assisted by our wonderful staff and much hard work, that vision has largely been fulfilled.

In Philip's short life he achieved much, for not only was he an excellent farmer, he was an astute businessman. He was given £2,000 worth of computer programmes by Farmplan for his assistance in designing a new business plan; he was a good engineer and designed a hop-picking machine bine track, which manufacturers said would not work, but it did; he built a grain drying system with a blower to take the grain through the roof of a cattle shed which worked, to the surprise of many. He also worked part-time with MI5 for some years that resulted in catching a spy. He gave that up when he discovered that most of the MI5 people were using drugs.

To go back to the tree – when that acorn was planted, there was no certainty that it would survive, just as when we were married there certainly was no great expectancy of us lasting together for 50 years, but we have, with the help of the love and friendship of our families and friends.

Although Pam and I are now maturing gracefully from wrinklies into crinklies (antiques) we still have great plans and challenges for the future. As I said earlier, marriage is a challenge, and I believe that if you do not always have a challenge ahead of you, you will soon fade away, and anyway a challenge is always exciting.

The oak tree states in essence: 'Here I am and where I am is what I am'. I think after fifty years together we can safely say 'Here we are, and where we are is what we are'.

WOODLAND AND WILDFLOWERS

During the long period of obtaining planning permission for the Food & Drinks Centre, we had decided to join a stewardship scheme which involved grassing down all the river meadows and planting them with wildflowers, also to have two large ponds and eight acres of woodland. This was quickly accepted by the Forestry Commission and DEFRA and a 10-year project was set up. There was very substantial funding for this. When the Inspector heard about this, he commented that this would be an additional attraction to visitors to the Food & Drinks Centre, because we would actually create picnic areas and wheelchair access to the wildflower meadows, woods and ponds and we were going to provide proper footpaths right through the area. The Inspector's recommendation was 'that planning permission be granted for both applications, subject to conditions'. The conditions were all reasonable and ideas that we built into the scheme. It was amazing how much paperwork the public enquiry generated, with every person taking part producing large quantities of paper describing their particular aspect, and there had to be detailed maps showing the site position, the effect on the countryside and photographs from various aspects showing what the impact would be. This was largely caused because the Inspector insisted that both the Council and the applicants prepared the necessary documentation for each part of the different aspects of the planning application.

THE FINAL BLOW TO THE FOOD AND DRINK CENTRE

Following the local enquiry in December, it was not until 21 August 2003 that we had a letter from the office of the Deputy Prime Minister saying that he had approved the planning application for both projects, and that he was very impressed by the applications and was fully supportive. During all this planning period, we had had meetings with Advantage West Midlands, DEFRA and various other bodies to explore the potential of funding. Advantage West Midlands said that it would be better if they provided all the funding and eventually it was agreed, when we had worked out the total cost, that they would only provide 26% of this funding.

MEMBER OF THE ORDER OF THE BRITISH EMPIRE

It was most astonishing, in fact quite unbelievable, that in the Queen's Golden Jubilee Birthday Honours List on 15 June 2002 I was awarded the MBE for services to the hop industry. I was very surprised but delighted to receive such a large number of congratulatory letters.

The investiture was held on 11 November 2002 and I was accompanied to Buckingham Palace by Pam and my sister Joan, who had a marvellous view of the proceedings in the Palace. I shall never forget the moment when I heard my name announced, then walking forward, bowing to the Queen, receiving the MBE medal, shaking hands and then being asked a question about farming. It took just a few minutes, but the memory is for a lifetime. This honour was more than I could ever have imagined possible to have bestowed on me.

After our photographs had been taken in the Palace courtyard, we went to the Farmers Club for lunch before going to Westminster Abbey, where we saw the moving number of poppies in the Garden of Remembrance, after which we had a fascinating tour of the Abbey. In the evening, we were taken out to a celebration dinner by Joan's eldest son, Andrew – a marvellous way to end such a wonderful day.

Elizabeth the Second, *by the Grace of God of the United Kingdom of Great Britain and Northern Ireland and of Her other Realms and Territories Queen, Head of the Commonwealth, Defender of the Faith and Sovereign of the Most Excellent Order of the British Empire to Our trusty and well beloved Philip Alfred Donne Davies Esquire*

Greeting

Whereas *We have thought fit to nominate and appoint you to be an Ordinary Member of the Civil Division of Our said Most Excellent Order of the British Empire*

We do *by these presents grant unto you the Dignity of an Ordinary Member of Our said Order and hereby authorise you to have hold and enjoy the said Dignity and Rank of an Ordinary Member of Our aforesaid Order together with all and singular the privileges thereunto belonging or appertaining.*

Given *at Our Court at Saint James's under Our Sign Manual and the Seal of Our said Order this Fifteenth day of June 2002 in the Fifty-first year of Our Reign.*

By the Sovereign's Command.

Grand Master

Grant of the Dignity of an Ordinary Member of the Civil Division of the Order of the British Empire to Philip Alfred Donne Davies, Esq.

After receipt of planning permission from the Government, we called a meeting with Advantage West Midlands in October to go through the phasing in of the project, together with a schedule for their funding, because it was going to take about three years to complete the whole project. To our amazement and horror, Advantage West Midlands then announced that there was no money and there would not be any for three years, although the scheme, once we had got planning permission, had gone through their funding committees and had been given full approval and top priority. After so many years of exhausting effort with so many setbacks, to get planning permission and agreement by Advantage West Midlands, this really was a death-blow to me, because we had been working hard on the farm to develop it and to bring it into the next century. To be told this really made me decide enough was enough and so I abandoned the scheme.

I am sure that there had been a lot of dirty work going on behind the scenes, politically, and I feel sure that Heart of England Fine Food played a big part in preventing our getting funding. For some reason they were very jealous of the scheme and I know that at various meetings they had expressed concern about the project and felt it should not go ahead. I have no idea why, because they are basically a promotion body, but they have never actually set up anything themselves although they have stands at various meetings and lots of publicity. It could have been one of their showcases but I have a strong belief that they played a big part in stopping the scheme.

Advertisement for Sovereign Hops

149

NEW HOP VARIETIES

In 2003, we had another hop variety, TA200, which we called Pam. This was the first hedgerow aroma hop and it is proving to be very successful. It produces superb yields, very low bittering levels which the brewers want from an aroma hop, and has a very delicate aroma. This hop, in 2006, has been registered as a variety named Sovereign.

In 2004 we had another variety which we called Sylvia. This had remarkable results at Wye where the hops were picked by hand but for some reason on one side of the hedge the alpha yields were very high whilst on the other side the yield was low. Our first crop in 2005 was very disappointing, the alpha was low, so we are doing one more trial but I think that hop will disappear.

In 2005, we planted the first hop which is not being bred for brewers. There are many constituents of the hop but the three main ones are alpha acid, which is the bittering which the brewers require to give the beer its bitter flavour, the oils which give the taste, and beta acid, which is a preservative and which has been discovered to have great pharmaceutical properties. It is used in the sugar industry and in animal feedstuffs. On many experiments, beta acid has proved more effective than penicillin. We have planted two acres and two other growers are also planting these beta acid hops on a 6-year sales contract. Instead of selling it as an aroma hop or paying for its bittering, this is going to be paid for on its beta acid content. If the trial is successful, there is tremendous potential for this variety, because the requirement could be enormous. The difference in this hop and the normal hops is that in normal hops you have $2\frac{1}{2}$ times as much alpha acid as beta acid, but in this one it is reversed.

CLASTON FOR SALE

Claston – The dining room

Because of the disappointment caused by Advantage West Midlands saying that there would be no money for the Food & Drink Centre for three years, in spite of their repeated promises to the contrary, and the catastrophic drop in hop prices, I reluctantly decided in 2004 that it was time to sell the farm and retire. I had been looking at land prices for a while and, after talking to various land agents, came to the conclusion that it was unlikely that land prices would increase; in fact there was a possibility that prices may even drop back because of the unprofitability of farming in general. I decided in the spring of 2004 to put the farm on the market. As it turned out, it was the correct decision, but it was difficult to know which estate agent I should market the farm through. We had always used Sunderlands for all our business in the past, but I thought that as this was a bigger sale it might be wiser to engage a national estate agent to give a wider advertising base, so we chose Knight, Frank. Looking back, I am not sure that it was the correct decision, as they generated very little interest outside Herefordshire and some of the administration left much to be desired. Mr Smith, who dealt with the sale of the farm, was very helpful but I was annoyed that, having arranged an open day for potential buyers to come to view, they sent only one junior person to speak to people, which I thought was pretty poor, especially as about twelve prospective buyers attended. There were too many visitors for one person to deal with. Nevertheless, we eventually sold the farm for a very good price – more than I had expected.

I hadn't realised that selling a farm would be such a major operation. It was not the actual selling of the land but also organising the details for all the contracts for the cider apples, hops and the woodland which were very involved. The Stewardship scheme had to be dealt with, as well as the planning permission for the Food & Drinks Centre. I had hoped to be able to sell it to a buyer who would agree to complete this Centre, and I had several people who were interested, but that interest waned due to the many delays and did not materialise.

Claston – The drawing room

Before the sale of the farm, we sold the orchard at Longworth to Henry May, who has formed the 'Tidnor Orchard Trust' and is growing the apples organically. He is planting very old varieties of cider apples and at the moment has 250 varieties. He has now been awarded a National Collection status for '*Malus* (cider making)'. When the farm was sold, the farm and buildings on the north side of the A438, were sold to Derek Thomas from Perry Hill Farm, Clehonger, and the rest of the land on the south side of the road to Glyn & Richard Williams of Ross-on-Wye.

The sale was completed in October 2004 and the next major job was organising the farm machinery sale, which was held in December. This sale was handled very efficiently by Sunderlands. There was a huge attendance, people came from all over the country, with over 300 potential buyers registered. Prices exceeded all expectations. The sale got off to a great start with a huge heap of scrap iron, comprising anything which was metal but was of no use, and it made over £700.

Somewhere to Live

I had retained a plot of land in the walk orchard on which we had applied for planning permission to build a house. After several meetings with the planning officer, he finally refused planning permission for the house, but unbelievably gave us planning permission for a mobile home for three years, saying there was no proven need for a house on that site.

It was agreed that we could live in the farmhouse at Claston until October 2005, but it was not until August that we were fortunate in finding a house in Dormington, adjacent to the nursery hop-yard. We found out that number 12 The Maltings was on the market the day before the house was to be sold, but when I rang Derek Craddock to ask him if the house had been sold he said it had, but invited us to go and have a look anyway. We went that evening at 7.30 p.m., had a look and Derek told us that as he was a little concerned that the potential buyers might not have the money, if we agreed to pay the asking price, which was £5000 more than the agreed sale price, and confirmed by 9.30 a.m. the next day, he would sell the house to us. We were very pleased about this and quickly made up our minds to buy and the sale was then agreed the next morning. Thus we had somewhere to move to when we left Claston just before the agreed date in mid-October 2005.

One astonishing thing happened during the purchase of the house, as on the day that we were agreeing to exchange contracts my solicitor and I hoped to meet Derek and his wife with their solicitor to sit round the table at one of the solicitors' offices to finalise the deal. His solicitor would not agree to that, so it was arranged that we would be in our solicitor, Gordon Lutton's, office and they would be in their solicitor's office. When we rang to check that everybody was there ready to sign, nothing happened for over an hour because my solicitor, David Hartwell, who phoned several times, was unable to make contact with Derek's solicitor. Eventually, they got through to us very irate and asked what was going on. Apparently, because they had told their secretary that they were not to be disturbed by any telephone calls, she wasn't putting the calls through, and the deal nearly fell through due to that misunderstanding.

I had originally decided to retire when we had replaced all our tall hops with hedgerow hops and had the Food & Drinks Centre in full swing. However, with the collapse of the hop market, we did not continue to replace the hops because it was obvious that it was very unprofitable to plant hops at that time. As none of these things came about, I expected when we had sold the farm that I would retire, but Richard Williams asked me if I would like to continue growing the hedgerow hops for him, which meant that I could also continue with the hops which I had been growing on rented land at Stoke Edith. I readily agreed. We moved the greenhouse so that I could continue propagating hop plants. I did not think we would need planning permission to move it from one part of the farm to another. However, somebody objected and the Council insisted that we had retrospective planning permission. That was no problem, and it only cost me £50. I learnt afterwards that it would have cost the Council another £450 which the ratepayers would have to pay simply because somebody had complained about us moving the greenhouse.

We were both very sorry and sad to leave the beautiful old Claston farmhouse, which had been my family home for 141 years, but now that we have been living at The Maltings for some time we realise what a good thing it was. It is a much easier house for Pam to care for, and we are very happy, with no regrets now about moving to our new home.

In the twenty-one years since its conception, I believe that Western Quality Hops Limited has exceeded the original members' expectations. The dedication and competence of our Marketing Director, Jill Andrews, and the enthusiasm and willingness of all the directors to take on any extra task has enabled us to achieve this success. A special mention, however, must be made of John Andrews in not only helping with the handling of the crop, but also the original bulk buying operation and the immense and invaluable work he has carried out in hop research.

At the end of 2005, the Government announced that all research funding for hops would cease on 31 March 2007. This meant that the Department of Hop Research at Wye College in Kent would have to close. The National Hop Association finally agreed to take over this research work, the major part of the work to be carried out at Tony Redsall's farm in Canterbury. I agreed to take on all of the testing of the selected plants from the initial trials. Peter Darby, who was head of the Hop Research at Wye College, was made redundant but has agreed to continue with this work for the National Hop Association.

Dormington Court farm buildings – now the Maltings

The low price for hops remained until 2006, but now, after the very short crop in 2006, all brewers are making new forward contracts for hops at much better prices. The regional brewers, however, have always made forward contracts and their sales have increased because they are producing better beer.

In 2006 we had 79 days with very little rainfall and temperatures were, on many days, 30°C. What a change as I finish my writing! In 2007 we have had 12.2" of rain in the equivalent period of time. This has resulted in the greatest summer flood that I can remember, but luckily this has caused very little damage here compared with other parts of the country, where some farmers have had their crops destroyed entirely.

In my long farming career, I have known both good and bad times, and have enjoyed dealing with the many companies who have supplied our farming requirements, some of them doing so over a very long period of time, during which I have got to know them very well.

In conclusion, I would like to pay tribute to my loyal, skilled and hard-working staff, and also to the casual workers who have all given faithful service over many years: John Albrecht, Clive Bennett, Beryl Bowen, Hillary Bromage, Reg Bufton, Ros Edwards, Miss Gladwin, Bert Green, Mrs Harding, Terry Holden, Jack Hoskins, Clive Huffer, John Jones and his son Conroy, Mrs Peters, Ruth Philips, Winston Price, Michael Pudge, Michael Pullen, Aldy Smith, Caroline Smith, Shane Smith, Jeanette Stephens, Ivy Tomkins, Fred Webb, Carol Weobley, Joan Williams, John Williams, never forgetting Jenny Jones, who over many years was my secretary and, later, more my personal assistant.

A Farming Calendar

Extracts from *Herefordshire County Life*

A magazine called *Herefordshire County Life* had a new editor, Peggy Grayson, who lived in Tarrington. She asked me if I would write a farming diary for this monthly magazine. Although I had never done anything like this before, I agreed and the following extracts were published over the course of two years:

SEPTEMBER 1979

The great day has arrived, hop-picking has begun. Have we enough pickers? Will the hops weigh? What will the picking price be? Shall we have a strike? Soon we shall know the answers.

These thoughts were in all hop growers' minds before the advent of the hop picking machine. On a hop farm in those days every job had to be done either before or after hop-picking and choosing the day to start was probably the most important decision the hop grower had to make in the course of the year. You never quite knew if there would be enough pickers and once started you were dependent on the weather, and could not speed up the picking.

I can just remember the hop-pickers coming to our farm by special hop-pickers' trains, with the waggoner collecting their luggage from Stoke Edith station with horses and the largest farm wagon. After this, the pickers with the children would follow back to the farm, but the majority would go to the local pub for a booze up, and it was not until the following day that you would know how many pickers had arrived. The Station Master always had great problems making sure everyone had a ticket, and force of numbers generally caused him to give up the unequal struggle!

By the time I left school and started to work on my father's farm, buses had taken over from the railway and bus loads came from Hereford, and as far away as Tredegar. The 'first morning' was always a very lively one in the hop-yard, and I shall never forget the first time I had to help to organise the pickers, with their cribs, into their correct 'Houses'. The cribs we used were exactly the same as the ones shown in the 1899 hop-picking scene, and did not change until we ceased using them with the advent of the hop-picking machine after the Second World War. A 'House' was a number of hop plants in the time of pole work, and each House had to be marked, but with the arrival of wirework it was generally the distance between two main wires, about 50 plants. Everyone would arrive from about 5 a.m. onwards. Prams, umbrellas, boxes, food bags and lots of squawking children, 'I want to be next to Mrs So & So', 'These hops are much smaller than the next row', 'Where are the faggots? I want to boil the kettle', were some of the calls, and if you did not tactfully and fairly reply you were in trouble from the start.

Bushelling – that is taking the picked hops out of the crib with a special basket and tipping them into a large sack called a green sack – always started late on the first day. Bushelling was a great art, a job I loved doing, because the basket used did not have to be filled, so you can imagine the arguments that took place, because the pickers were paid on a piecework basis on the number of bushels picked. Eight bushels were put into the green sack and the number of bushels called out in a loud voice by the sack holder. 'Nine, ten,

155

eleven', the numbers echoing across the yard, 'Mrs Jones has done well today, wonder if she has nicked a sack?'

'Bloaters, kippers, roll up, roll up'. The fish vendor had arrived. I shall never forget the marvellous smell of bloaters cooking over a wood fire. The first busheller I can remember had a bloater for his dinner, but he always cooked it outside the kiln on his wood fire.

Before I was old enough to do the measuring, I had to haul the sacks from the hop-yard to the kiln on a wagon with a team of horses. The sacks, which were nearly as big as I was, had to be loaded in a special manner and not trodden on any more than could be helped. One day, when the going was heavy because of a lot of rain, driving along the headland with a full load, the horses in complete control as usual, me hanging on for grim death, seeing, to my horror, a camp fire, cups, saucers, plates, the lot, right in my tracks; you can imagine the result! I could not stop before, I did not try afterwards! The shouts of abuse made the horses go faster, but all was quiet on my return.

On arrival at the kilns, the sacks were unloaded on to a hay elevator which had been adapted for hop sacks. The sacks would be quickly taken and emptied into the kilns where the hops would be evenly spread over the drying floor about 24 inches deep. As soon as the kiln was loaded, rolled sulphur would be burned on the floor of the kiln and the fumes passing through the green hops give them the pale yellowish green colour required to obtain the best price. Hops which have not been sulphured remain a dull green colour and look most unattractive.

Two of our kilns had anthracite open fires to dry the hops until the early 1940's; in the evenings the Welshmen used to come into the kilns and sit by the fire and we used to have wonderful discussions sitting in the firelight with the hum of the fans and the smell of the hops creating an unforgettable atmosphere.

The hops took about 10-12 hours to dry in those days and the dryers would always be able to count on extra help to unload the kilns. A horn of cider for a reward and everyone was happy.

How hop-picking has changed today! Instead of hundreds of people, we have two large hop-picking machines which only need about 50 people to operate them. Tractors whizzing everywhere, the roar of the machines and a constant flow of hops coming off the final belt is a different scene, but to me the attraction of hop harvest is still there.

I shall never forget the look of horror on my father's face when he saw the first hops, picked by machine, cascading down from the banks of pluckers. It looked a most brutal operation and it seemed impossible that any hops could remain whole. That first year, we had intended to pick half the hops by hand, but it was so wet that we had to pick most by machine, working until late at night. Everyone in the hop-yard got soaked most days, but large cans of hot coffee, well laced with rum, kept everyone going.

In those early days of picking machines, Fuggles and Goldings, grown on low wirework, were the main varieties to be picked and were much more easily damaged than the new varieties bred at Wye College in Kent by Dr Neve. Wye Northdown and Wye Challenger, grown on 15 ft wirework, are ideal for the machine and can be picked with little damage and waste.

Today's machines are much bigger than the original ones, with a much, much more sophisticated cleaning mechanism; in fact, today's machine-picked hops are more whole and contain less leaf than hand-picked hops. The bines (a bine is a string of hops, and normally there are two per plant, giving about 3,000 bines per acre) travel through the picking mechanism at about 15 per minute, about $2\frac{1}{2}$ acres per day on each machine. On our average yield of $13\frac{1}{2}$ zentners (=50 kilos) per acre, our two machines pick enough hops each day to make over four million pints of beer!

Kilns too have changed over the years. Nearly all the old round ones, with their characteristic cowls, have disappeared and been replaced with much larger square ones. Nylon carrying sheets have taken over from goat-hair ones and half-inch wire mesh has taken the place of the old horse-hair kiln hair (the mat which used to cover the floor of the kiln). The open fires had been replaced with massive furnaces and automatic stokers some years ago, but these have now gone and oil-fired fan furnaces have taken over. These are much more efficient and are able to heat more air, so you can dry a deeper load of hops more quickly.

The technique of hop-drying, however, has not changed much for many years, and it still depends on the skill of the dryer to produce hops of the correct appearance and dryness. After drying, the hops are cooled and then pressed into the traditional hop pockets. These are large sacks, clearly marked with the growers name, farm, parish and county. Today, however, special E.E.C. marks also have to be stencilled on the pockets. In spite of al the changes, hop-picking is still the great event of our farming year: everywhere there is the indescribably wonderful aroma of dried hops, the time of year when the whole place becomes alive, a happy occasion with a real sense of comradeship amongst the staff. Against the noise you can still hear the women singing, and in spite of all the problems, it would be a sad day if hops were to disappear from the Valley.

OCTOBER 1979

Readers will no doubt be aware that my farming diary has to be written several weeks before it is read. Sitting in the office, with the rain beating against the window, writing this month's diary, I am beginning to wonder just when the corn harvest will be completed. Our own combining was completed before hop-picking. This was achieved by combining very wet grain and drying it in the hop kilns, an expensive hobby, but it had to be done because Hop-picking and Corn-harvesting together are an impossible combination. We finished baling the straw this week but are still struggling with the bale hauling.

Hop-picking started on 3rd September and, much to our surprise after the heavy rains and lack of sunshine in August, the hops seem to be of a good quality and are reasonably ripe for the beginning of the harvest. The hops pick easily and they seem to be up to last year's high yield. The varieties Northern Brewer and Wye Northdown have very large hops this year and so take longer to dry than usual. This is because we normally spray these varieties at the end of May, when the plants are at a certain stage of development, with a chemical called Gibberellic acid. This delays flowering and makes the plant produce more and smaller hops. Due to the cold Spring we were unable to use the spray this year.

Last week, I purchased 30 Welsh Half Bred (Border Leicester x Welsh) Yearling ewes from the sale at Builth Wells. The prices were about the same as last year and are, I think, too high for the economic production of fat lambs. I wanted 50 ewes, so to make the numbers up I went to a ewe sale in Hereford and bought 20 Suffold x Clun yearlings at half the cost. I like to lamb some ewes early and it seems a problem to get the Welsh Half Bred to do so, so maybe I shall have saved money and achieved my objective.

The recent heavy rain will make autumn ploughing much easier than for a number of years. On our own farm last year we were unable to plough some fields until late November. Winter cereal planting will start soon under ideal conditions, with a much better chance of even germination, resulting in a stronger and better plant population.

The cider apple crop this year is very small but the few apples there are, are growing to a good size, which should help to increase the yield. I would not expect harvesting to start until the end of October.

Another benefit from the rain has been the flush of grass and, as a result, the beef cattle and lambs are thriving. If the weather continues to keep warm and wet there will be enough grass for the livestock without additional food until later in the year, which will help winter stocks.

In addition to running our own family farm with my son, I am also Managing Director of Dormington Court Hop Farms. This is a company within the Allied Brewery network and, until recently, the company consisted of two neighbouring farms, Dormington Court and Pomona Farm. These two farms are entirely devoted to hops, about 240 acres in all. On 8th August they purchased Brierley Court, a 400 acre farm near Leominster. A large part of this farm will eventually be planted with hops. The farm will not be under my control until the end of September, the sale of implements and livestock belonging to the previous owners is being held on 18th September, so at the moment planning is the only job in hand. There are no hops at Brierley at the moment and the kilns are very small, so a completely new picking and drying unit will have to be built. No new British Hop-picking machines have been built for a number of years but C.W.F., the company which has taken over all hop-picking and drying work for the Bruff at Suckley, are going to build their first machine for us. Last week Mr M. Jolly of C.W.F. and I flew out to Germany to look at Wolf hop-drying equipment and plans are in hand for a new drier to be imported from Germany for the 1980 crop. This winter, about 55 acres of hops will be planted, with another 150 acres to be planted with winter wheat and barley. There are no staff on the farm at present, so I have made arrangements with contractors to plant both the cereals and hops. Normally, I like to drain any field that is to be planted with hops, but time will not allow this to be done this year and as the Welsh Water Authority are embarking on a large flood allevi-ation scheme this winter, it would seem prudent to plan the drainage scheme later.

The TV weatherman has just forecasted a warm and sunny week, so maybe summer has come at last. A pity the hop bines are so rough, or the girls in the hop-yard could at last have got a suntan.

Ledbury Ploughing Match takes place near Ledbury on 9th October and Trumpet Ploughing Match at Withington will be held on 18th October. Finally, on 19th October our Harvest Festival will be held at Dormington Church. This little church, one of the gems in Herefordshire when decorated with the flowers and fruits of autumn, is a marvellous place in which to give thanks for the wonderful blessing of the Harvest.

November 1979

Apples are one of the major talking points in the farming world at the moment. The whole of Europe is prac-tically sinking under the weight of dessert apples, so our own fruit growers are having difficulty in even selling their crop, let alone getting a reasonable price.

It seems very wrong that the British market is being swamped with French apples, whilst we are not allowed to send English lamb to France. I hope the one or two grower critics of the Hops Marketing Board will soon realise how fortunate hop growers are, because without the disciplines of the Board, this year's excellent crop of hops could have put us in the same boat as the apple growers. What is more, the expected production of English hops for 1980 and 1981 has already been sold.

November is the best time of year to harvest cider apples, and what rapid changes in harvesting methods are taking place. Last year, eight cider fruit growers formed a syndicate to harvest cider fruit mechanically, and after many difficult problems we were able to pick up about 900 tonnes with a Tuthill harvester. Gone also is the day of shaking the apple tree, now it is vibrated mechanically with an apple tree shaker, now being made in Hereford by Graham Rivers at his Central Components factory. In an effort to get all of last year's record crop picked up in time, we had to work up to nine at night, well after dark. In foggy condi-tions in one very large and thick orchard, the harvester, tree shaker and three tractors hauling the fruit from the harvester got completely lost. This was one problem we had not foreseen! This year's crop is very poor due to the biennial cropping of most cider varieties, and to the very cold weather at pollination time. In fact, it was so cold that no self-respecting bee dared venture from its hive. It is because of the tendency to bien-nial cropping that I favour our half-standard type of semi-intensive orchard, as opposed to the intensive bush system. In our orchards, we are able to graze sheep for eight months of the year. The shelter of trees is also of great benefit to young lambs in the Spring, and is an added bonus to the grazing, so that in years such as this we are getting some return from the orchards.

The ewes which have been running with the rams for some time now look in very good condition. We still have about 200 lambs to sell, but, since Fat Lamb prices have collapsed to a lower level than last year, we shall not be selling any until prices improve. There are two main reasons for the collapse, the late mat-urity of fat lambs earlier in the summer has brought an excess number on to the market, and the closure of the French market. A fresh outbreak of a sheep disease called Scab a few years ago has resulted in the compulsory dipping of all sheep between September 3rd and November 11th. We shall be dipping ours shortly, and at the same time treating any foot rot which the odd sheep may have. While talking about sheep, readers may not know much about the wool crop, which is quite an important part of sheep revenue. Different breeds cut very different weights of wool, and also there is a great difference in price per kilo. Of the sheep we keep, the Suffolk Clun Cross ewes produce the best quality wool, with the Scotch Half Bred cutting the biggest fleeces, and the Welsh Half Bred cutting smaller fleeces of poorer quality.

Corn planting has gone well and will soon be completed, although it was surprising how dry the land became in early October, especially on grassland that was being ploughed up for cereals.

Winter feed crops of turnips, kale, etc look especially well, and as I write the grass is still growing. All our beef cattle are in the yards now, and have been treated for worms and warbles. I could never understand farmers not treating their cattle in the autumn for warbles until it was compulsory to do so. I was always convinced that cattle thrive better when free of this pest. The autumn Weaned Calf sales are just about to begin. We shall be buying about 85, but prices at the moment are uncertain. Last year's prices were considerably higher than the previous year, but should not rise as much this year.

DECEMBER 1979

As the days shorten and the evenings lengthen, life on the farm is beginning to slow down for the winter. All the winter corn is showing through the ground and looking well. Given a few more weeks' reasonable weather, it should survive any severe frost coming after Christmas. Last year we were late planting our winter oats because of the dry conditions, and there was insufficient time for the plants to make enough root growth to survive the severe frosts.

This year, much to my surprise, weaned calves were cheaper than last autumn and, as a result, Geoffrey Thomas, an expert cattle buyer who purchases cattle for us, has been able to send us stronger and better cattle than last year at less cost to us. The first 18 that arrived at about 7 in the evening managed to open the fold yard gate a few hours later. We knew nothing about this until an anxious motorist came to inform us that an animal was on the main road. Luckily, this was the only one to go on the main road, and it had raced to Tarrington, where it had been hit by a car whose driver had failed to stop. Another kind person, however, had chased it back to Dormington where it had disappeared into a field. It took seven of us two hours to round up the remainder, which were in small groups scattered all over the farm. We were lucky, I suppose, to find them all, because looking for black cattle on a moonless, foggy night was a bit like looking for a needle in a haystack.

Our next problem was an outbreak of Transit Fever, to which weaned calves are very susceptible. The stress and excitement of being hauled around the country in lorries, standing around in the market and being frightened in the sale ring causes the fever to break out, and the midnight venture made it worse. It is very contagious and took about three weeks to clear up. One of the best of our two-year old cattle, due to be sold fat after Christmas, had a throat infection which spread rapidly to its lungs, and although the vet tried every known drug, it died six days later. Apparently, occasionally animals will not react to modern drugs.

Cider apple harvesting has been completed with disappointing yields. Our half standard orchard was the only one to produce a worthwhile crop – a little over five tonnes per acre. This has given us an average of over ten tonnes per acre, over the last four years, in the ninth to twelfth years of the orchard's life. We still have a lot to learn about mechanical harvesting, this year's problems being quite different from last year's. Leaves and dead grass in the apples were the headache last year, mud and molehills caused trouble this year.

The length of dead bines left on each hop plant at hop-picking have now been cut off and burnt, and most of either the shoddy (wool waste) or farmyard manure has been spread. The final resin or alpha analyses of the dried hops have now arrived. They were about 10% down on last year except for the variety Wye Challenger, which held its own. Our biggest crop was in Bullion, which fell by over 15%. A lot of work

159

is being carried out at Wye College in Kent to try to find out why in some years alpha is much higher than in other years. Growers have standards to reach fixed by variety and get paid about £8.00 more per 1% alpha above, or £8.00 less per 1% below the standard per 50 kilos, so considerable amounts of money are involved.

This is the time of year when most country folk look back on the happenings of the past twelve months. In some ways it has been a fascinating year, with most crops yielding well in spite of the cold, wet start to the growing season. This weather stopped livestock thriving, but they caught up well by the end of the year.

It has also been a year of considerable change. We have new chemicals, two of special interest to us. One is a systemic fungicide for the control of a different range of fungal diseases and the other is a new insecticide based on pyrethrum. I have seen new hop-drying and picking systems, as well as a mechanical hop bine loader.

The change in government has brought a big change in policy which will allow great rewards for those companies and businesses prepared to compete with overseas competitors. Many prophesy a difficult year ahead – they may well be right – but I also believe it will be one of great opportunity for those prepared to work.

JANUARY 1980

This month is the beginning of a new farming year and I suppose as good a time as any to look forward to the coming twelve months.

As a result of the marvellous autumn weather, we are way ahead with the winter work. All of the hops due to be taken out, as well as some wilt-infected areas, have been grubbed and a lot of farmyard manure has been spread on the yards. This will be a great help in reducing the workload in the coming weeks, during which time I hope we shall have at least a short spell of severe frost, which is beneficial to the dormant hop roots. There is no new wirework to erect at Claston this year and, in fact, we shall have a reduced acreage for two reasons. Firstly, we could not grub hops last autumn in time to have a sufficient rest period before replanting. It is vital to fallow the soil for about two years after grubbing hops before replanting, to enable a particular form of eel worm to become free of one of the viruses which causes a disease in hops called Nettlehead. The eel worm is a carrier of the virus and passes the virus to the hop plant. This disease can not only wipe out large areas of hops, but can also reduce the yield of hops which appear relatively healthy. The second reason is that certain areas of hops have had to be grubbed in an effort to control Verticillium Wilt. This disease is our biggest worry at the moment, and is a problem which has to be overcome fairly quickly, if we are to continue growing hops successfully.

Farmwell Ltd. have delivered all our fertiliser requirements and, thanks to their advice, before the recent price rises. What a pleasure to deal with a company who are not only very competitive with their prices, but also give fantastic service – not what one usually gets at the present time. If our Post Office telephone service was a quarter as efficient, we would not have had to wait four months for our new telephone installation!

This has been the first winter that apple tree pruning has started before Christmas and, providing the weather is not too severe, it will continue during this month. The fruit bud on the trees looks strong and prolific, and has the potential for a good crop this year.

Our first fat cattle sales are usually starting at the beginning of this month, but as I write I am not too hopeful of a very good return. It costs about seven pounds to feed a beef animal per week, so too low a price will, in the long term, have a serious effect on future beef supplies. The same can be said of a lamb, with prices at the end of November lower than they have been for a long time.

This causes me to have serious worries about the 21% rise in agricultural wages. I have always believed that our staff should be well paid, but I am sure that with the present prices and the rapid increase in fertiliser, chemicals and machinery costs, there will be a fairly large number of men losing their jobs. In our own case, we shall not be engaging another student, and we shall be laying off our men above pension age. This to me is a tragedy, because there is always a place on a farm for a senior citizen, not only for the work they do but also for their ability to pass on their skills to the younger members of staff, and I think most farms could do with one extra man.

Our hops are being valued on the 8th of this month – always an important event, not only because of the financial implications but also because it enables you to get a complete picture of the crop compared with other growers.

After reading the diary, readers will understand some of the challenges and problems which face us in the coming year. A year of great hope and, in many ways, excitement, which I hope you will enjoy reading about in the coming months.

FEBRUARY 1980

All work on the land came to a halt after Christmas due to the wettest December, in fact the wettest month for many years. Nearly seven inches of rain fell during December and the first few days of January.

Land drains were running more freely than for a long time but, even so, it is quite surprising how quickly flood water disappears if the land is properly drained. Even one of our hop-yards at Longworth, which was under several feet of water, was free of water after a few days, although obviously too wet to work on, and this was after the water level had been so high that it overflowed over the flood bank into the flood catchment area. In spite of the flood, I believe the River Authorities are doing a wonderful job with their flood alleviation schemes. It must take time to overcome the various problems that are bound to occur, and it is most unfortunate that houses get flooded sometimes as a result of the Board's work.

Our ewes have been housed since early January and the first lambs are due now, with the main crop towards the end of the month. Having the ewes indoors makes life easier for the shepherd as well as reducing lamb losses. This is because the ewes are under no stress from adverse weather conditions and, as a result, the lambs are stronger at birth. Also, a newborn lamb can survive much more easily on a dry bed of straw than out in a cold wet field, or one that is frozen. You do, however, have to be careful to ensure that the ewes are healthy when they come in, and that the sheep pen is clean and well disinfected, because any contagious diseases spread much more quickly indoors. It is also important to ensure the ewes do not get too hot; you just need a dry airy shed for them.

During the Christmas holidays, I found an interesting book on cider fruit, written in 1886 by Robert Hogg and produced by the Woolhope Field Cub. It starts with a line by Dryden, 'Not every plant in every soil will grow'. How true today, as every one of us knows to our cost.

The Authorities of the 17th Century recommended light sandy soil for cider fruit, 'look where the full-eared sheaves of Rye grow wavy on the Tilth, that soil select for Apples'. Not quite today's recommendation.

Mr John Watkins of Pomona Farm, now one of our hop farms, describes how he made his cider, and it is a surprising fact that he won second prize at the Royal Agricultural Society Exhibition in 1879 with a cask of cider that had been frozen for several weeks.

It was interesting to note the large increase in areas of fruit trees of any kind between 1877 and 1883, some 25,000 acres, with Herefordshire growing a total of 27,081 acres, whilst Kent had only 17,417 out of a total area of 185,782 acres. In fact, Devon and Somerset also had more than Kent, with 50 counties in all having recorded areas of fruit, the main counties mentioned having mostly apples and pears. In 1977 there were about 163,000 acres, about the same as in 1877, but a rapid decline will surely happen in the next few years.

The Woolhope Field Club introduced several new varieties of cider apples to Herefordshire from France during the 1880s, one of which, Michelin, is still considered one of the best varieties grown today. Nearly 200 varieties of cider apples are described, including one called Ten Commandments. We still have a few trees of this variety, which was so named because, when cut across, it shows ten red spots around the core.

I would be the last person to criticise our Prime Minister in her difficult task, but I was quite amused to see another variety called Maggie described as 'a Gloucester cider apple of fair repute. The tree bears well and the fruit has a very acid, austere taste'.

In conclusion, Tennyson's charming description of a flask of cider as the crowning enjoyment in 'The Picnic' would seem a good way to end this month's Diary, when Summer seems so far away.

> There on a slope of orchard, Francis laid
> A damask napkin, wrought with horse and hound;
> Brought out a dusky loaf that smelt of home,
> And, half cut down, a pasty costly made,
> Where quail and pigeon, lark and leveret lay,
> Like fossils of the rock, with golden yolks
> Imbedded and injellied; last with these
> A flask of Cider from his father's vats
> Prime, which I knew; and so we sat and ate.

MARCH 1980

And so we come to March, I believe one of the most crucial months in the farming year. A cold, dry period with plenty of wind to dry the soil is essential. During the month, spring barley should be planted, and, if planting is not completed, the delay can greatly reduce the yield. The sugar beet growers like to get the seed in by the end of this month. Both of these jobs need to be done when soil conditions are good. A large proportion of the lamb crop is due during March, and wet conditions can be disastrous to the newborn lambs.

Warm, humid periods can also bring their problems. Blackcurrants, apples and pears would start to grow or even show signs of blossom, which may be irretrievably damaged by a sharp frost. It could also start cereals and grass growing, which would also be damaged or checked by cold spells later.

I hope readers will now be able to understand how vital the weather conditions during this one month can be to the yield of crops the following summer, and that I am not just another farmer grumbling about the weather.

Apple tree pruning was completed by the third week in February, and potash and nitrogen were applied. It is essential to get the fertiliser early onto the orchards under-sown with grass, so that it can get washed into the soil, so benefiting the trees and not just the shallower-rooted grass. We shall be applying potash and phosphate to the hops early this month, with the first application of nitrogen going on at the end of the month or in early April. Simazine, a chemical to stop weeds germinating, with Gramoxone added to kill any growing weeds, if necessary, will be sprayed onto the hops as soon as possible. Non-cultivation in hops only started on a commercial scale about twelve years ago. Before that, hops were ploughed during March and the soil which had been ridged around the plants the previous summer, rather like earthing up celery, had to be removed by hand, and the uncovered thickened pieces of bine were cut off at ground level. This was a hard and laborious job, which if not done correctly could damage the hop plants. The pieces of bine which had been cut off would quite readily root if planted and by the following Autumn be large enough to plant out in the hop-yard. Hop-stringing will commence at the end of this month.

At the time of writing, our first lambs have just arrived. The ewes are looking very well, and I hope for drier weather before the new arrivals appear in quantity. Our old stockman, John Jones, is retired now, but happily is still able to come over to the sheep pen whenever he wants to. Housewives should be finding lamb a good buy, because farmers are receiving about 3p to 4p per pound less than this time last year, and I cannot see much hope of any improvement for a while.

In recent weeks, you may have read of some dissent amongst hop growers about the forward prices for the 1982 and 1983 crops, which they have had to offer for sale by the end of January. These very few growers, not more than four or five, are, in my opinion, quite unjustified in their complaints. In fact, a lot of growers are worried about the increased planting of hops in Germany and the USA, and by 1984 we could be in the same position as the apple growers if we do not give the Hops Marketing Board 100% support.

I was interested to read Mrs Biggs' account of Butter Making Classes held at The Hyde, Woolhope. This was Mother's old home and she well remembers them. She also attended the classes, which lasted a fortnight, and were given by lecturers supplied by the County Council. As a result of the instruction, she went on to win a prize in a Butter Making Class at the Three Counties Show.

April 1980

April is the time for daffodils, primroses and violets and during the last few days of the month we shall witness the arrival of our summer visitors, the cuckoos, swallows and martins. It is a time when the countryside comes to life, with hedgerows and trees stirring from their winter's rest. And so it is on the farm. Winter cereals, which will have been rolled to firm the soil loosened by the winter frost and top-dressed with nitrogen, will be growing quickly and, depending on growth stage but normally during the middle of the month, sprayed with weed killers and fungicides. Winter barley is especially prone to mildew which, if not controlled, quickly can ruin the yield.

The fruit buds on most of the cider apple trees will just begin to open towards the end of April, and the first spray for the control of scab and powdery mildew should then be applied.

The hops, too, will be growing now. In an early year we have even started training during the last week of the month, and as soon as the young shoots are six inches, or should I say 150 millimetres, high will also be sprayed for downy and powdery mildew. These early sprays of both crops are vital and can give as much disease control as two or three applications of chemicals in July, at very little cost, because of the very small amount of plant growth to cover. In years gone by, young hop shoots were considered a great delicacy, tasting rather like asparagus, but I would be reluctant to try them nowadays when they would be covered with chemicals. I believe they are still on the menu in Belgium.

We have had a super crop of lambs this year, a number of our ewes having had triplets, and both ewes and lambs are now grazing in the orchards. It gives me great pleasure to watch young lambs lying in the grass enjoying the sunshine, or running races in the evening. When the lambs are about six weeks' old they will be injected with a chemical to prevent a disease called pulpy kidney, which otherwise always seems to kill the best of the flock.

The young cattle which we purchased last autumn will be turned out to grass towards the end of the second week of the month, providing the weather is reasonably warm.

In my March diary, I wrote that I could not see much hope of any improvement in lamb prices. How wrong I was! Prices rocketed at the end of February, lambs making up to £5 a head more than two weeks earlier. In one week, lambs from our own farm increased by £4. This highlights one of the problems of marketing farm produce – the 15% rise was quite unpredictable and one over which producers had no control.

May 1980

What is this life if, full of care,
We have no time to stand and stare?

I believe these lines by W.H. Davies sum up life today. Everyone seems to be in such a hurry, with no time for anything or anyone. On the farm, especially during May it is very important for the farmer to stand and stare.

Practically all planting will have been completed and most crops will be growing vigorously at this time. Winter cereals, particularly barley, in a normal season are showing signs of coming into ear at the end of the month. Time must be taken to look for any signs of disease which, if found, must be eliminated quickly.

Cider fruit trees will be in full blossom and it is vital to spray at late green cluster for aphid, caterpillar, scab and apple sucker. You have to look carefully to see if the spray is being applied properly, because it costs just as much for the chemicals for a poor spray cover as for a good one. I refuse to spray during blossom time, even with chemicals which are harmless to the bees which are put in for pollination. At petal fall, it will be necessary to spray again for scab, mildew and red spider. Weed control in the orchards must be carried out early in the month, but only a narrow weed-free strip on each side of the trees will be made this year. The apple harvestry was made difficult, you will remember from the December diary, by the problem of mud clogging the machines, so we shall hope most of the ground will be covered with grass by next November.

During this month, the hop fields will be alive with the sound of women's voices while hop training, which is still one of the major tasks of the year. It takes a lot of time to train two or three shoots up the strings, three thousand strings to the acre, and then pull out the remainder. What a task it must have been before the days of wirework, because you not only had to train the shoots up poles, but also had to tie them up with raffia! When the young shoots have grown to about five feet we shall be applying a chemical called Cytrolane and water, at a diluted rate of 4 fl ozs, to the crown of each hop plant. This will be absorbed into the plant through the base of the young shoots and gives excellent aphid control for the whole of the summer. By applying the chemical in this way we do not damage predators, which hopefully will build up their numbers in sufficient quantity to be able to kill any aphids still alive in the late summer. Other problems are the control of downy and powdery mildew. Look carefully, and if there are fungi present, you will easily see the tell-tale signs of stunted growth, and the black spores of downy mildews or the familiar white blotches of powdery mildew.

Our young lambs are thriving and, in spite of the very wet March, soil temperature was high enough to keep the grass growing and we should have quite a number fit for sale by the end of the month. Regular treatment for lung and stomach worms is necessary during the summer and watch must be kept for early signs of infection which, if missed, can easily prove fatal. If the grass, especially in the orchards, gets too long, particularly during a wet spell, the young lambs may get little ulcers between the cloven hoof, which makes them very lame and causes rapid loss of condition.

Dairy farmers will be making silage by the end of the month, but it is unusual for us to start haymaking until the first week in June, although if the grass is at the right stage and the weather looks settled we sometimes do.

This month's diary, describing the speed of development of crops and livestock, will, I hope, illustrate the message of the importance of stopping, looking and becoming aware. This applies I believe not only to the farm and the garden but to life in general.

Finally, congratulations to two members of our staff – Bert Gwilliam, who has just retired at the age of 80 and Bert Green, who has worked on the farm for 47 years – on receiving Three Counties Long Service Awards. These two men have always given of their best and are craftsmen of the highest standard in their field.

JUNE 1980

What a strange year we are having weather-wise! After four mild, wet months, April was one of the driest of the century, with only two days of significant rainfall. May has, so far, been just as dry, but fortunately it has been very cold, consequently most crops are not too far forward, so the very dry weather will not have had too serious an effect on future crops. A substantial fall of rain is, however, urgently needed on most crops.

Hops should be growing quickly during June, reaching the top of the strings by the end of the month. Our biggest enemy from late May until the end of June can be wind which, as well as causing considerable leaf damage, can, if strong and prolonged, blow the young bines away from the strings and they then have to be hand trained back onto the strings. Once the bines are more than 10 feet high, this becomes a major problem, with special tractor-drawn platforms needed, so that the women can reach high enough for the training. This can be a long and tedious job, which everyone hates.

Training was completed by the end of May and any further growth from the base of the plant will be burned off chemically during the summer. I remember my father telling me that as a small boy he used to 'mind the sheep', which were put in the hop-yards in those days to eat off the unwanted leaves and shoots. This is done for two reasons, firstly to make sure all the plant energy is put into the trained bines and secondly, to help with disease control. The dense foliage of hops during July and August is very conducive to fungal diseases; keeping the bottoms of the bines clear of any foliage enables more air to circulate through the crop, and so reduce the risk of infection. The last application of nitrogen will be applied to all mature hops during June.

In the cider orchards, we shall be keeping a sharp look-out for red spider and, if necessary, adding an acaricide to one of the mildew and scab sprays. Last year scab was more prevalent than for a number of years so, if warm, wet conditions occur, extra spraying will be necessary.

Sheep shearing will be done in early June. Very few farmers wash their sheep today. What a job this used to be, submerging the ewes in either the river or a pond with clean, deep water and scrubbing them during the process with a piece of wood on a long handle. It was usual for one of the staff to get ducked as well!

The most nutritious hay is made in June, but since the grass is still young and lush it takes longer to dry than later in the summer, and it is often difficult to get dry enough to bale without damage by rain.

I hope any of you who may be walking or picnicking in the country during the summer will please take care not to damage crops, or leave broken bottles about, which can cause serious damage to livestock. Farmers are only too pleased to help you to enjoy the countryside, but animals straying through gates carelessly left open, onto the roads, can easily cause serious accidents. Finally, take great care if you light a fire – one spark or smouldering embers can easily set alight hedgerows, ripe corn fields or woods.

JULY 1980

I suppose July is, to most people, the first of the two holiday months. Schools close down for the summer recess and our coastal resorts, weather permitting, will be packed with people. On the farm, however, pressure increases as we come to the end of the farming year and harvesting of the various crops begins. Haymaking, hopefully, will have been completed and winter barley will be ready for harvesting by the middle of the month. How quickly farmers have reacted to the benefits of the new systemic fungicides and the improved varieties of the plants raised by the plant breeders! Until a few years ago, winter barley was hardly a worthwhile crop because of fungal diseases and low yields, but it is now grown in ever-increasing quantities and, this year, is probably the cereal 'crop of the year'. Another point in the crop's favour is its early maturity, especially on a hop farm where it is always a struggle to get the harvest completed before hop-picking. To be able to clear a crop in July is a great help. Winter wheat and oats look well, although yields, especially wheat, may be a little disappointing, because the plants did not tiller as well as hoped for in the spring. Spring barley has had to struggle in many cases, because of the very dry conditions since planting time. The June rains have helped the crop and some farmers irrigated in May, with good results. The recent heavy rain has caused some lodging of our winter oats, but the winter barley, which I felt was at greater risk, has so far not been seriously affected.

The lambs continue to flourish but, as I write, prices are beginning to fall. Sheep farmers, at the moment, are uncertain as to when to market their product. Lambs should be sold when they weigh between 33 – 40 kilos, and are in good condition. However, when the new E.E.C. sheep agreement comes into force, probably not until September, producers will receive a higher price. Whatever the market prices, an E.E.C. subsidy will increase the producers' return to an agreed level. This new arrangement is a great step forward in the Common Market farming policy and will be beneficial to both farmers and housewives.

It is many years since the hops were as forward in growth for the time of year. At the present time they are at least fourteen days ahead of normal. Possibly the foliage will become too dense, with a resulting reduction in yield. I hope not, because the demand at the moment for English hops is excellent, with good export sales.

Powdery mildew is proving quite a problem this year. The mass of young growth on the plants and the hot humid weather conditions are ideal for the fungus.

A new chemical for defoliating the base of the bines is being used on our farms this year after two years' trials by Fred Dickens at the Rosemaund Experimental Farm. It is proving more effective than tar oil, which we used to use, and is more useful in weed control.

In the cider orchards, the apples are swelling rapidly and crop prospects are good, but I gather from the dessert apple growers that Cox are not too abundant.

One of the largest hop growing areas in America is in Washington State. These hops are grown on volcanic soil and at the moment are covered in between 1.5 – 6 inches of ash from the Mount St. Helens volcano. This, I understand, will be beneficial to the crop, because it will replace plant food which has been removed over the years by irrigation. The growers are, in fact, worried in case the crop is so heavy that the wirework may collapse. However, if they have rain, the hops would be destroyed by gases which would form, and it could take up to three years for full production to be regained, and this would completely upset the world hop market.

What a great achievement by Vivian Samuel to win the World Ploughing Championship recently held in New Zealand! I am sure all our readers would join me in congratulating him on his wonderful effort. He is the third Herefordshire ploughman to be World Champion, joining John Gwilliam and Ivor Goodwin. Well done!

AUGUST 1980

As I write this month's diary, with the north wind howling against the office window and thick, black clouds sweeping in over the hills bringing more rain, it would not be too difficult to imagine it was at least late autumn. However, in spite of the wettest June for many years and the cold, wet early July, I believe most crops look well. The spring barley, which has made a remarkable recovery, now looks a useful crop. Winter barley, which is ripening very slowly, urgently needs hot sunshine to speed up the process.

Haymaking has, so far, been a non-event. The grass which we cut several weeks ago has only just been baled and we think it will just be palatable to the cattle. The hay crop has declined rapidly during the past few years, to be replaced by silage and Claston is certain to be a convert next year. This will mean a big change in storage facilities and feeding methods, which will have to be carefully planned during the coming winter.

The cold weather has slowed down growth in the hops and some wind damage is becoming apparent. Hail has caused damage to hops on a number of farms and for the first time about 20 acres have been affected at Pomona. Seeing the ground between the rows covered with small pieces of leaf and the ends of laterals was a very unpleasant experience, but hopefully there was sufficient undamaged foliage for the plants to recover, without seriously affecting the yield.

Powdery mildew is still proving troublesome in some hop-yards because, I think, insufficient systemic fungicide was applied in the early sprays. I was very surprised to hear recently that some hop-yards have very heavy infestations of red spider mites. These normally cause problems in very hot, dry weather. On our farms, we always apply a control spray at the end of May, when the mites first appear, as it is much easier to get good spray cover then than when the foliage becomes dense later in the summer.

166

Scab has been a major problem in some orchards, but our early spray programme has enabled us to obtain excellent control. Considering the mass of apples on the trees, the June drop was not as heavy as I would have expected because, no doubt, the trees were not under stress from a moisture deficiency.

During my recent visit to Germany to inspect the drier, I spent a day looking at the Hallertau hop growing area. This is the largest concentrated area of hops in the world, but most of the farms have only 12 acres of hops or less. Not many hop-yards are more than 2 acres; the rows, which are sometime curved, run in all directions whereas in the U.K. most of them run north to south. They make a very interesting pattern, rather like a patchwork quilt. The wirework is over 20 feet high, compared with 15 feet here, and the rows look very narrow, being only 5 feet, 2 – 3 feet narrower than ours. Full cultivation is still carried out with specially designed equipment for the narrow rows.

There did not appear to be many cattle or sheep, although most farms had pigs. These were kept in large barns which were attached to the mostly large farmhouses, to form a courtyard. Many of the barns also contained the hop-picking machine and a kiln or drier. On one farm, we were shown the kiln, and to get to it we entered the main hall through the front door of the house, then went upstairs on to a large landing and then up another staircase to the cooling room, which was over the bedrooms, with the kiln at the far end of the room.

I was most impressed with the tidiness of the farms and was amazed at the equipment they had. It was quite normal to find a 100 HP four-wheeled drive tractor and a 50 HP one, as well as a narrow hop-yard tractor, on a 30 – 40 acre farm with 10 acres of hops. In one small field I saw a large tractor baling hay with a modern baler, another turning the hay with a swathe turner and several women raking it into swathes for the baler. This amazing mixture of up to date equipment and ancient practices can be seen in the fields everywhere.

I always stay at a little hotel in Wolznach, a small town in the middle of the hop growing area, about 40 miles from Munich. Opposite the hotel is one of the three farms, complete with muck bury, which are near the town centre, and some of the hop-yards on the outskirts of the town are surrounded by houses. Most readers will know that Germans are great beer drinkers, but will be surprised to hear that there was always someone drinking beer when I was having breakfast at about eight in the morning!

SEPTEMBER 1980

It seems only a very short while ago that I wrote my first diary for September 1979. So much has happened on our farms during the past twelve months, with everyone working to maximum capacity, that it is difficult to imagine, at the moment, that industry is in a deep recession. I cannot understand why it is so difficult to get quick delivery of simple standard engineering products, when firms are crying out for orders. No-one seems really interested. On the farms, the approach is quite the reverse, with every member of staff giving their best, knowing full well that if the farm fails to produce good crops, they will be out of a job.

Most farm products are giving poor returns at the moment; lamb, beef and potato prices in particular are lower than last year, but I very much doubt if these lower prices have reached the housewife.

Because of holidays, this month's diary has to be written earlier than usual, so it is too early to say much about cereal yield. We have combined some winter barley, which did not need drying thanks to the wonderful hot, dry week at the end of July, and the yield was excellent. The violent storms have done considerable damage to winter wheat and oats and a spell of hot fine weather is urgently needed to dry the badly flattened corn.

Haymaking was eventually completed by the end of July and, in fact, the last fields to be cut yielded well, with hay of very high quality, because the grass was still young having been grazed very late.

The recent warm weather has helped most varieties of hops. Northdown and Northern Brewer, however, were badly checked by the cold weather and are too far into flowering for much improvement, but other varieties should give a good yield. Powdery mildew continues to be troublesome and weather conditions are now ideal for a rapid spread of the fungus. An extra spray or two will be needed to control it. The soil drench used to control aphid has again worked extremely well, but growers who have just relied on a normal spray programme have again had problems controlling the pest.

And so we come to hop-picking! Already the build-up has started – we are being inundated with telephone and personal calls from people wanting work during the season. In fact, it is more like the old pre-picking machine days, when this was the normal occurrence. The advent of the picking machine obviously had a dramatic effect on hop-picking because of the reduction in the numbers employed.

In those days, one important part of our hop-picking was the coming of the Church Army caravan, stationed at Dormington. The ladies manning the caravan, not only came to the hop fields to organise hymn singing, but were also skilful nurses who attended to the many minor injuries. In return, we had a crib at which all visitors were expected to pick, and the proceeds were given to the Church Army to help cover their costs. Incidents of these times, such as the tale of the missing cockerel, seldom occur today. This much-valued cockerel was missing from a neighbouring farm and the local bobby came on the Sunday morning to investigate the theft. He went to the cook-house to see if anyone could give him help to find the culprit, but of course no-one could, and then he thought he could smell chicken cooking. No-one would admit to it, but one old lady was boiling a large pot which appeared to be full of clothes. He told her to take out the clothes, and there to his delight was the missing cockerel, which was being cooked in the same pot!

In contrast to the sudden change in picking methods, drying processes necessary to reduce moisture content of green hops from about 80% to 10% have changed more slowly. Hops are dried by blowing hot air through the bed of hops spread over the kiln floor. When I left school, in most kilns the air was heated with anthracite coal fires. The first development I witnessed was the introduction of an enclosed coke furnace, which heated the air as it passed round it on its way to the hops. It was very difficult to keep accurate temperature control, but this was soon overcome with the introduction of the automatic stoker, which produced a blacksmith-type fire in the heater. Small pieces of coal were burned and it was a very dirty job, handling the huge quantities required. This system was used for many years, until the oil-fired fan furnaces were introduced in the early sixties, and it is still used today.

OCTOBER 1980

In spite of some of the worst summer weather for many years, a good hot spell in mid-August enabled the bulk of the cereal harvest to be combined under ideal conditions. Yields have been excellent, our own being much better than expected.

Hop-picking started on 2nd September, a day earlier than last year, in perfect weather, but yields are well down this year. The varieties Northern Brewer and Northdown, as mentioned in the September Calendar, have been affected more by the weather than I predicted and it looks as though these varieties could be down by 30% on last year. Powdery mildew has also had an effect on yield, the new systemic fungicides having failed to control the disease for the first time. There are two reasons for this – one, the high incidence of infection in the early growth which was never stopped and two, the perfect weather conditions for the continual spread of the fungus, which proved too much for the fungicides.

Much more care will have to be taken next year to ensure a complete clean up of the fungus by the middle of May.

Apart from Verticillium Wilt, which continues to spread, our hops seem to be free of other pests; however downy mildew, another fungus disease, has affected hop cones on many farms, especially varieties of hops which are fairly resistant to this disease. I know many growers have believed that spraying was unnecessary, but the many warm, wet spells of weather have proved this to be a fallacy.

It was most interesting to see a small area of hops, at the Rosemaund Experimental Farm, completely dessicated by hop damson aphid. Looking at the yield records of hops pre-1912, you find that on occasions only 1.5 cwts per acre were grown and it was simply because the whole of the UK hop crop had been destroyed by aphids. Seeing these hops at Rosemaund made me realise how vital the skill of the scientist is to farmers and gardeners. Growing crops is a constant battle against pests and diseases and, although I know nature comes to our aid very regularly, we still cannot manage without modern chemicals. I wholeheartedly agree that they should be used sparingly and with great care, but I disagree with the do-gooders who want farmers to go back to the very old methods. I wonder if they spray their roses?

Cider apples continue to grow rapidly and the trees are bowed to the ground with the weight of the fruit, in fact, some trees have broken branches. This has made it impossible to cut the grass, which could make harvesting difficult.

Reading a most interesting article *The Woodlander* by E. Heath-Agnew brings back many boyhood memories. However Bert Green, one of the senior members of our staff, remembers Barlow's death fifty years' ago, but agrees with me that the farm was then re-let to Joe Booton, who farmed there until 1960. He planted more hops and installed a modern coke heater and hop press. My father helped him with his hops and he, in turn, brought a team of horses to Claston to help during haymaking and harvesting.

I well remember walking over Tower Hill with my father to look at these hops which were grown on poles, the only such yards I have ever seen. Many years ago there were several hop farms in Checkley and the remains of the kilns are still there. I spoke to our farm manager at Pomona, Dick Walker, about burning ash wood to kill aphids and he told me that when he was a boy at Dormington the owner, Mr Beale, would make him collect all the debris from the hand-stripping of the hop bines and, when fairly dry, burn this on the headlands to help stop aphids.

November 1980

Last November, apples and lambs were the main topics of the month and they are again this year, but for different reasons. Last year, dessert apple growers were having great difficulty in selling their produce. However, this year present prices are reasonable. This is due to a number of factors – growers are grading and marketing to a much higher standard, an immense advertising publicity campaign has made the public realise that there are other and better apples than French Golden Delicious, and I also hope and believe that people are beginning to realise that, by buying foreign goods, jobs are being lost in this country.

Cider apple growers are having a problem to sell the record crop they have produced this year, because two poor summers and the recession in industry have resulted in a reduction of cider sales. Consequently, the two largest buyers of cider apples, Bulmers and Showerings, have not purchased any cull dessert apples and, at the moment, are not able to cope with all of the cider apples. Our own crop will easily be a record one, but this has caused considerable damage to a number of trees. Most varieties of cider apple trees tend to crop biennially and an experiment is on to try to overcome this problem. By spraying one half of the tree with a chemical at petal fall to destroy these apples, better apples are produced on the other half of the tree. Although this reduces the crop, the following year a good crop is produced on the sprayed half of the tree and early trials have shown a marked increase in yield over the two-year period.

At last the lamb war is over. An agreement has now been reached which will enable a free market to exist in the E.E.C., coupled with higher prices to producers of about £4 per lamb. A new and, I think, more sensible grading system will be introduced. At the moment the lean carcass, which is what the housewife wants, is not always up to the required certification standard and so the subsidy of about £7.50 per lamb is lost to the farmer. He has thus been forced to produce over-fat lambs. These over-fat lambs will not be certified in the future and the gradable maximum weights of lambs will also be reduced. It does seem crazy that it has taken over a year to reach this agreement. Fat lamb production should now be more profitable and this will, in time, lead to much higher numbers of fat lambs coming onto the market, ensuring ample supplies of English lamb for the housewife. At 'Sheep 80' (a sheep demonstration held at the Three Counties Showground at the end of July), there was an exhibition of lamb carcasses of different sheep crosses and the carcasses, using a Texel ram, had the leanest meat. As a result of this observation, I have just purchased a Texel ram. I intend to use this ram with the Welsh Halfbred ewes I purchased at the Welsh Halfbred ewe sale, held at the Royal Welsh Showground. This was the first time I had been able to attend this. 20,000 sheep, as alike as peas in a pod, made an impressive sight. The movement of sheep from the pens to the sale ring was carried out so smoothly and quietly. Dogs were used and up to forty sheep at a time were being sold every minute.

Conditions have been ideal for autumn cultivation and we were able to complete our cereal planting before apple harvesting. Yields are always higher on cereals planted by the end of October.

December 1980

Over the last few years, the area of land planted with winter cereals has rapidly increased. This is due to a number of reasons – increase in yields over spring plantings, better varieties of winter wheats and barleys and new fungicides especially for the control of mildew. The fine weather in early October quickly changed to produce a very wet autumn, which has caused a serious delay to the massive planting programme and many acres may not be planted, unless we get a long spell of fine weather and, with snow falling as I write, this seems unlikely.

Our forefathers always kept a balance between the areas of winter and spring planting. They must, however, have been very efficient with their autumn work, because in 1868, 3.6 million acres of wheat were grown, over half-a-million acres more than today, and remember only four-legged horse power was available. In one way, it would not be so easy now as it was then, because so much of England's farmland has been eradicated. During the last thirty years about 50,000 acres a year have been turned into roads, industrial or building usage and consequently an area larger than Herefordshire has disappeared from farming.

Harvesting of our syndicate's massive cider apple crop has nearly been completed. Well over 1,000 tonnes of the fruit have been picked up by our machine harvester. The new tractor-mounted Tuthill machine has worked very well, but unfortunately is unable to work in all types of orchard. This wet autumn has show up the benefits of well-grassed orchards for machine picking, because where clean weed and grass-free herbicide strips occurred, the fruit did not keep as well and the apples were covered in mud after harvesting. Due to the very large crop, many cider orchards may remain unharvested and it would not surprise me to see a fairly extensive grubbing of cider orchards.

Market prices of cattle and sheep have continued to fall and housewives should be stocking their deep freezers, especially with lamb. It cannot be too long before supplies drop and the problems of the export market are resolved, when prices will rise.

Fat stock prices have affected the store cattle sales, with the result that our cattle buyer, Geoffrey Thomas, has been able to buy the best animals that I think we have ever had, at a reasonable price. For the first time, a large proportion of the cattle are Charolais or Simental and only 10% Herefords. This to me is a tragedy, but because the present day Herefords are much smaller than Continental or Friesian Cross cattle, which also provide leaner beef, they are not suitable and reluctantly we have to move with market requirements. I am confident, however, that it will not be too long before the Hereford breeders will be producing the right type of cattle again.

Canon Shaw, in his wonderful Harvest Thanksgiving address at Dormington Church, spoke of the patience needed in agriculture. However large or small your equipment may be, be it a 150 HP tractor with a multi-furrow plough followed by a large drill, or, as it is in some foreign countries, a team of oxen ploughing, with the seed sown by hand, you still have to wait the same period of time for the following harvest. When planting a hop-yard, you have to wait about two years for a full crop, with an orchard, much longer. You have to be patient and wait for the fullness of time for your efforts to be rewarded. The problem today is that we all want instant everything.

In 1880, agriculture was in a very depressed state because of a series of deficient harvests and low prices, very similar to today, but farmers are quick to adapt to changes of circumstance and the problems of fuel crises, pests and diseases and poor returns will be overcome, so that the housewife will be kept supplied with her requirements.

In these difficult times, the passage from John Masefield's *Grace before Ploughing* seems very apt:

And here we are now, like Shakespeare, in some doubt saying, 'What's to come is still unsure! To most of us it seems very unsure, but then it always has been and we who have seen great changes must have great hopes.

JANUARY 1981

The beginning of a new year is always a good time to look back at the lessons learned on the farm over the past year, and see how we can put them into practice in the coming year.

1980 was the year of powdery mildew on hops and we were never able to completely control this fungal disease. The problem started in April, and growers will have to make sure this year that full control is obtained at least by mid-May.

Cider apple orchards produced a record crop which, for the first time, resulted in more apples being produced than could be sold, causing some growers to suffer considerable financial loss. Manufacturers, whose sales have been below expectations for the past two years, did remarkably well to purchase so much unwanted fruit, to the benefit of growers. The Chairman of H.P. Bulmer Ltd. told competitors at the Orchard Competition Dinner that his company had processed 49,000 tonnes by the 4th December and would be paying growers £2,900,000 for their apples this year. Congratulations to Douglas Blandford of Huntleys, Much Marcle, on winning the coveted Golden Apple award for the best orchard.

The Prime Minister's visit to H.P. Bulmer Ltd., at her request because of their wonderful record in man management and ever-increasing productivity, is a just compliment to the company.

Sadly, the Hops Marketing Boards will have to end in the near future because its statutory powers are incompatible with E.E.C. rules. The Board and the N.F.U. have fought long and hard to retain a marketing system which has worked efficiently for over forty years. It will be vital for all hop growers to join the new Producer Groups which will take its place.

Last week, when looking at hop samples at Paddock Wood, I was given a book called *The Hop*, written in 1899. The virtues of hops have been recorded for more than a thousand years and they have been culti- vated and used for brewing for over five hundred years. Wild hops were growing in England before the time of Columbus and came into prominence when their culture was introduced into Kent by Flemish immigrants about 1524, and hop growing was legalised by Parliament in 1554. Some interesting growing costs are given for 1880, which I will compare with 1980 figures. I understand from my bank manager that £1 in 1880 would be worth £20.87 today.

The total average growing costs in 1880 were £30.30 per acre, about £635 at today's value. 1980 costs will have been over £1,000 per acre. Manure costs were £6, or £125 at today's value, per acre. Our costs this year were £90. Chemical costs (yes, chemicals were used in 1880) were £2.50, making £52 per acre. 1980 costs were well over £100 per acre. So you can see some costs were higher and some lower. The yield was 8 cwts per acre, compared with 13 or 14 in 1980. Sale price was 10 pence per lb in 1880 and £1 per lb in 1980.

Having compared hop prices of today and 100 years ago, I thought it would be interesting to look at other farm produce from the Claston Farm diary of 1880, belonging to my great-grandfather. He was selling yearling cattle at £6 per head or, at today's value of the pound, £125. This winter I paid about £285. On May 25th 1880, my great-grandfather sold a fat lamb for £2 4shillings, at today's value £45.91. On June 4th in 1980 we made £30. Wheat was a bit over £11 per ton, equalling £230. Today's price is just over £100. Yields in those days would have been well under half those of today, so that per acre wheat gross returns would be about the same.

FEBRUARY 1981

In spite of many wet spells during the last few months, the land is much drier than at the same time last year. You will remember last year at this time the land was completely sodden from seven inches of rain in December and the land drains were all running freely, but this winter they have hardly run at all. This has enabled us to catch up with the Autumn work which had been delayed while we were harvesting the record cider apple crop. Grubbing of hop-fields infected with Verticillium Wilt is continuing, a further sixteen acres will be taken out this winter. Because many weeds and garden plants are susceptible to this disease, nurserymen are not allowed to sell hop plants for gardens.

The enormous weight of cider apples carried last year caused considerable damage to the trees. Since Christmas, we have been cutting off the broken branches and, in a few cases, even trimming some tree trunks. The large saw cuts, when covered immediately with Santar to reduce the risk of disease, heal quite quickly and around the edges of the wounds emerge young shoots which can be trained to take the place of the original branches. Another chemical, a pre-harvest drop hormone, can be mixed with Santar to stop shoot emergence if required. The only other pruning this year on the older trees will be taking out branches which are rubbing one another, crossing the centre of the trees, or are too low on the driving alleys. Heavy pruning tends to promote too much wood growth, which reduces next year's fruit buds.

Lamb prices have risen quite remarkably since I wrote the December diary and look likely to reach the guaranteed E.E.C. level fairly soon. I hope readers took my advice and made their lamb purchases at the time. Fat cattle prices have also moved up, but joints of the cheaper cuts of beef are still excellent value and, with careful cooking are, I believe, much tastier than steak. A traditional butcher will always give good advice on which joints are the best buy. Our first lambs are not due to arrive until the beginning of the month, with the bulk of the crop expected in March. The first ewes to lamb have been housed in the lambing pens since before Christmas and will be treated with a combined serum to combat tetanus, pulpy kidney and lamb dysentery fourteen days before lambing commences. Lamb dysentery kills baby lambs when they are two or three days old and the first time I was responsible for lambing the ewes, I can remember twenty-five lambs dying in two or three days from this disease. Pulpy kidney can kill lambs when they are over four weeks' old – the serum controls the disease until they are six weeks old, when they have to be treated again. Our in-lamb ewes are not given any supplementary feed except hay until six weeks before lambing, when a mixture based on oats and barley is fed twice a day. This feed is given on an increasing scale to a maximum of fourteen days before lambing. This helps the ewe to produce stronger lambs, which obviously have a better chance of survival in their first few hours of life, and also increases the milk supply which in turn increases the lambs' daily weight gain.

The new E.E.C. sheep pricing could encourage a larger early lamb production and, as the maximum weight for guaranteed price is being reduced, it will be interesting to see if some of the breeds of sheep which are out of favour at the moment, as they are early maturing and produce smaller carcasses, come back into prominence.

I have been reading recently an interesting little book by William Cobbett called *Cottage Economy*, written in 1882. 'Economy means management and nothing more', he writes and then goes on to describe how country folk of that period survived by being, to a large extent, self-sufficient in producing their own food. On a quarter of an acre, a large part of the staple diet was produced and brewing and bread making seemed to be two of the main occupations. Until about 1780, it appears that every village family brewed its own beer, with different strengths of brew for different times of the year. Most families kept a cow and pigs and it appears that a large part of the garden was planted with cabbages and turnips to feed the cow. The pigs fed on bran from the wheat flour used in bread making and the barley malt after it had been used in making the beer. The manure produced by the cow and the pigs was sufficient to fertilise the garden. The author was very critical of the introduction of potatoes and tea, saying that it made people lazy and was also responsible for an increase in fuel consumption. This was because it took more fuel to make tea and boil potatoes than it took to make beer and bread. Although the standard of living at the time must have been very primitive, their way of life did show how, with a lot of hard work, a family could produce a large proportion of their own food. I am not suggesting that we should return to their way of living, but perhaps we should be moving away from the more expensive pre-packed and instant foods.

MARCH 1981

I am writing this month's diary while on holiday in Sierra Leone, which is a small country, about the size of Wales, on the west coast of Africa. My wife and I decided to come here because we thought the weather would be perfect for a restful holiday, and also because we wanted to visit a country which had not yet been spoiled by tourism. Our hotel stands a few yards away from a sandy beach which extends for several miles, with a warm sea and a background of timber-covered mountains. Occasionally, a ship appears on the horizon on its way to Freetown, the capital of Sierra Leone. This is the dry season, which generally lasts from November to April, January and February being the pleasantest months of the year, whereas April and May can be unbearably hot. A sea breeze cools the air and the heat of the sun is kept back by a dust haze caused by the 'Harmattan', which is a cod dry sand-carrying wind from the Sahara desert. During the rainy season from May to October, up to 125 inches of rain falls, making life very difficult for everyone.

One day we drove twenty miles from Freetown to a place called Waterloo. There we left the main road and drove on a sandy track for about five miles to a village near a river, where the 250 native inhabitants live in mud brick houses of one room, with thatched roofs. The way of life is only just beginning to change, the people being farmers and fishermen. They cultivate by hand, their only tool being a short-handled hoe, about five to ten acres of land, and grow cassava, a plant which produces a root vegetable, also sweet potatoes, maize, groundnuts and tapioca. Two crops are grown per year, rice being grown in the rainy season. Growing around the village and cultivated areas were palm trees for oil, bananas, breadfruit, mangoes, pawpaws, coconuts and oranges. Chickens, goats and a few cattle are kept which, with fish from the river, provide a staple diet for the village people. We were taken for a trip down the river in native boats which were crudely made from tree trunks and are normally used for fishing.

The land is communally owned by the tribe, but legal ownership is vested in the Chief, on trust for the whole tribe. Although a member of the tribe is entitled to a parcel of land for farming, he is normally limited to the size he can cultivate. We had to call on the Chief for permission to visit the village and secure a safe passage. After the visit, we called to thank the Chief, who is elected by the people for life. In these tranquil surroundings, the villagers appeared to be happy and the children well-fed, but in the towns there seems to be much poverty and very little work.

One evening we were taken to see a modern farming project which started three years ago. This was supposed to be a new system which would enable the people to produce crops for sale. The thirty acres of land was split into plots, ten plots to the acre, each belonging to one family. They were being taught by the Chinese to grow water-melons, egg plants, cucumbers, peppers, radish, courgettes and 'Up

Country' and Chinese corn and, as in the villages, rice during the rainy season. The soil was a very deep loam, not unlike some of our soil at home, with an abundance of water. The crops standing in the hot sun obviously had to be watered, but they only had to dig a hole three feet deep to find plenty of this, should the piped water supply fail. The results of their labours were pitiful, with only a few plots having good crops, as the farmers, who were keen to learn new skills but had very little money, were unable to purchase enough seed and fertiliser. There was a Government official who was supposed to help train the people and demonstrate on a Government-owned plot, but he was unable to do so owing to a pending Court Order on ownership of the plot. It does seem strange that a former British Colony with a fantastic agricultural potential should be so undeveloped, but we hear that, since the British left, most of the agricultural skills which we had taught the people have been abandoned. Memories of the heavy workload we used to have ten or twelve years ago, when 'throwing down and cutting' the hops at home during March, were brought back to me when watching the people working the crops with their hand-hoes.

Pruning, or 'throwing down and cutting' as it was known, used to be one of the most important tasks in the hop growers year and had to be completed by 26th March or yields could be reduced. Prior to this, in the autumn after the dead bines had been cut off and burnt, the alleys between the rows of hops were ploughed, two furrows to the right and two furrows to the left, leaving a drainage gulley up the centre of the alley. These furrows were ploughed back in the early spring and the remaining soil, which had been earthed up over the base of the growing bines the previous summer, was removed by hand, and the bits of stem uncovered were cut off with a sharp hook.

These bits of bines were called 'cuttings', and would grow into hop plants if planted. Hop cutting was a hard job and, if wet, even more difficult. I can well remember ploughing the rows with water following in the furrow, which must have been damaging to the soil structure. Nowadays, most hop farmers use a 'no cultivation system', spraying the land with Simazine and Gramozome if weeds are prevalent. This has to be done before the young hop shoots appear and the system seems to control most weeds. Because the hops are not being pruned, they tend to shoot earlier, so stringing now starts in March instead of April. The best young shoots are in the centre of the plant, but if stringing is left until the shoots are three to four inches high they can be damaged. Present day wirework was not used on many hop farms until after the First World War. Until then, the young hop shoots were trained up chestnut poles, which were produced in the many chestnut copses seen in our area, two poles being used to each plant. A special bar was used to make a hole 18 inches deep, into which the pole was firmly fixed. This operation was known as 'pole pitching'.

During this month, as most of our ewes are due to lamb, we shall be hoping for a dry spell of weather to enable us to turn the ewes with their new born lambs onto dry pasture. A dry spell is also essential for planting spring barley, sugar beet and early potatoes as, if these crops cannot be planted in March, serious reductions in yields can occur, hence the saying 'a speck of dust in March is worth a peck of gold in May'.

APRIL 1981

April is the month when the countryside normally comes to life, but this year the very mild spell at the end of January and early February stirred plant life into growth both in the wild and on the farm. While buds in the hedgerows, blackcurrants, pears and plums were beginning to burst, cereals and grass fields were a lush green. Nature generally keeps things in their correct season, and the three weeks' cold spell in February will have saved many crops and plants from severe frost damage by checking growth and preventing fruit buds from bursting too soon. The heavy fall of snow will also have helped to protect the lush cereal crops from frost scorch during the severe weather. 'Now that April's here' every bit of plant life will again be stirred into action by the spring sunshine. The cereals, which will now be growing quickly, will need top dressing with nitrogen and spraying with fungicides and weedkillers. The ever-increasing areas of winter cereals and the mild winter have made ideal conditions for mildew, which must be controlled at this time of year. Once the corn gets thicker and taller, it is impossible to get a good spray cover and so control the fungus.

You will remember reading in last year's diaries the problems caused by powdery mildew in the hops. This created a very high population of over-wintering mildew spores which, as the temperature rises and the hops begin to grow, will be bursting into life in vast quantities causing primary infection. It will be necessary to spray as soon as the young hop shoots are a few inches high, hopefully killing the fungus before much secondary infection takes place. Last year we failed to do so, mainly I believe because not enough chemical was applied to the acre in the early stages of hop growth. During April for the last two years we have been applying a new chemical, Ridomil, as a soil drench to control downy mildew in hops. This has worked so effectively that we have seen no signs of the disease since its use. Unfortunately, the effectiveness of the fungicide has broken down in Ireland and Holland on Potato blight (a similar fungus disease to downy mildew) because new races of previously controlled fungi have developed and so it has been taken off the market. Aphids also seem to be able to develop tolerance to new groups of chemicals quite quickly.

Our cider apple trees look to be very free of the over-wintering eggs of red spider mite aphid and other pests. They also look remarkably free of fruit buds, but after last year's record crop this is to be expected on some varieties. A full spray programme will, however, still be necessary to keep the trees free of pests and diseases, and to enable them to produce strong healthy fruit buds for next year's crop.

As I write, lambing is at its peak and our ewes are producing an excellent crop of well-developed lambs. A number of surveys and predictions about the future of lamb production in the U.K. have been made recently by a number of eminent people. As usual, there is a difference of opinion as to what type of lambs farmers should be producing. Some say small and well-fleshed carcasses are required, while others say large lean ones are wanted. They all agree, however, that the young housewives of today are not buying much lamb. In the last ten years, the number of housewives buying lamb has fallen by 19%. This seems strange because lamb during the past two or three years has probably been the cheapest red meat you could buy.

In the January diary, I wrote about William Vevers who lived at Dormington Court in the early 1800s. I have since received a letter from his great-great grandson, Dr G. Vevers, who is now living in Hereford. He told me that Charity, the Grand National winner, was buried in the garden at Yarkhill Court. The present Yarkhill Court, now owned by Roland Stedman, whose family followed the Vevers to Yarkhill, was built by Lady Emily Foley in 1872. The old house stood on an island, surrounded by a moat on the other side of the road. Dr Vevers has been searching for information about his ancestors and he is meeting me shortly at his ancestral home, Dormington Court.

Many of you will have heard of the theft of the famous door knocker from Dormington Church. The knocker, shaped in the form of a feline head, is about 750 years old and is probably the only one of its kind in the country. It had been on the present door since 1875, when the church tower was rebuilt. My great-grandfather was Churchwarden at that time. The Rev W.I.O. McDonald aptly remarked that the person who took the door-knocker was 'someone with enough intelligence to know its value, but not enough moral intelligence to leave it where it belongs'.

The very ugly figures often found on the outside of churches took away the evil spirits from church-goers as they went into church. The present holder of the door-knocker could well be affected by the many evil spirits it has collected over the 750 years of its existence. A £200 reward will be given to anyone who can give the necessary information leading to its return.

May 1981

The rush and scurry to get everything done at once seems to have taken over very early this year on the farm. This applies especially to the hops, which are growing so quickly that they are at least fourteen days ahead of normal. Training the young shoots up the strings is normally a May job, but this year it will be finished 'the first time over' by the end of April. My prediction in last month's diary that powdery mildew would be rampant as soon as the young hops started to grow, has proved correct and the hops will have been sprayed three times by the end of April. This year we are using one of the older chemicals called Afugan for the control of the disease, and so far it appears to be effective.

Towards the end of the month, for the first time, we shall be making silage. This is a new venture, but I am confident that we can produce a high quality feed for the cattle and sheep next winter. Last year's disastrous hay-making, which was not only costly and time-consuming, but resulted in a practically worthless product, has made many farmers change from hay to silage.

The very wet weather in March caused many fields of winter cereals, especially on the heavier soil, to go yellow. This was because the roots had become waterlogged and was also due to lack of nitrogen. In the most severe cases this will reduce yields but, when applied, the above average soil temperature will help the nitrogen to work more quickly and so bring the crop back to full health.

The lamb crop has been variable this year, with some areas having very low lambing percentages, while farmers in other areas have had record crops. We were fortunate to have a record crop, but one flock was attacked by dogs which severely mauled a number of lambs. It took the vet, my son, my secretary and the foreman over two hours to clean up, clip and stitch the wounds. Sheep worrying is a major problem to farmers; if only the owners of the dogs could see the torn, mangled and suffering bodies of the sheep maybe they would take more trouble to keep their dogs under control.

Thanks to the great efforts of the police and the wide publicity in the newspapers, we have recovered the Norman door knocker stolen from Dormington Church. It was recognized by an antique dealer in London and as soon as the thief is caught we hope to have it back in the church.

JUNE 1981

Readers may think I am nearly always mentioning the weather in my monthly farming calendar. I make no apologies for doing this, because farmers can do very little to combat extreme weather conditions, such as those of the last weekend in April. Crops this year were at least ten days early at that time and so were in too delicate a state to withstand the severe battering from the northerly gale, which whipped up the heaviest snowfall of the year, coupled with several night frosts, one of which was quite severe. When walking round the farm after the storm, it was heartbreaking to see the freshly trained young hop shoots blown from the strings, with a lot of the tips of the shoots broken off or shrivelled up. Many of the strings up which the hops are trained were blowing freely in the wind, having been either broken or released from the ground pins, which had pulled up.

In the orchards, the trees now covered with leaves and blossom buds had had branches broken by the weight of the snow. Fortunately, I could see little evidence of damage to the cider fruit flower buds, which open later than dessert apples. I understand that up to 90% of the blossom has been destroyed in some dessert apple, plum and pear orchards, causing more problems for die-hard pressed-fruit farmers.

Winter cereals and silage grass looked as though a steam roller had driven over them, but no permanent damage had been done. However, in other parts of the country where large areas were flooded, serious damage will have been caused even on grassland, where silt will be left behind. This can have serious effects on livestock, either when they are grazing the affected pastures or eating fodder harvested from them.

Nature has tremendous recuperative powers and we shall still be expecting the hops to have reached the top wire by the end of the month. Aphids will be appearing at the beginning of the month, but have been successfully controlled for a number of years with a chemical called Cytro-lane, applied to the base of the growing hop bines at the end of May or early June.

Our lambs have thrived on the abundance of grass this year and we have been able to start selling them four weeks earlier than last year. At present, the price is higher than last year, but as more lambs come on the market it will begin to fall, although I expect it to remain higher than last year, especially if the exporting problem to the E.E.C. countries can be resolved.

Finally, the Three Counties Show, which takes place this month, is an event looked forward to by most farmers. It used to be much more of a business event, with farmers buying a lot of machinery, but nowadays has become more of a social occasion still, however, keeping its tradition of having large quantities of the best quality livestock competing for coveted awards.

JULY 1981

In most years, the size of the hop crop is controlled by weather conditions in July. The hop plant will produce most of its fruiting growth during this period and then come into flower towards the end of the month. This puts a great strain on the rootstock, which therefore needs all the help it can be given by the hop grower, who can do his part by making sure that sufficient fertiliser is available to the plant and also that it is free of pests and diseases. However warm weather, both day and night, with sufficient moisture in the soil, can easily increase the crop by 30%. To get a clean crop at harvesting time, growers have to ensure that no hop damson aphids, powdery mildew or downy mildew are present at flowering time. Aphids cannot be eradicated once they get into the actual hops.

Many people will no doubt have read a lot about Progressive Verticillium Wilt during the past few months. This fungal disease kills the hop plant very quickly – the foliage of an infected plant will die in about fourteen days. Disease symptoms normally begin to show during this month and continue until the hops are harvested. The fungus is present in the dead and dying leaves, particles of which, when carried by animals, birds, tractors or people to clean areas, will infect them, causing a very rapid spread of the disease. This is why it is so important that the very few footpaths through hop-yards are not used until further notice.

Winter barley has come 'into ear' earlier than usual, so we should be harvesting this month. This will enable us to spread last year's hop waste on the winter barley ground before we start the wheat harvest in August. This waste has proved most beneficial to the very light gravel-based soil on part of our farm and has increased the worm population enormously, which in turn has resulted in several more hundredweights of corn per acre.

The very heavy rainfall during May delayed silage-making so that the second cut of grass will not be made into silage until late June or, most likely, the beginning of this month. The yields of grass will have been increased but the quality of the silage will be lower.

AUGUST 1981

The continuous winds in June caused a lot of damage and re-training the growing bines back to the strings when they were 12 feet high was a long and tedious job. However, the hops have recovered well and, given sufficient rainfall and sunshine, could produce a good crop.

For the first time we have sprayed our winter wheat to control mildew and septoria at ear emergence. This was done by an aircraft flying at two feet above the crop. The pilot's skill was quite unbelievable and an examination of the crop next day showed that he had made a marvellous job, covering the leaves with the fungicide perfectly. I hope this results in plumper grains of wheat.

The fire risk on farms is greater during August and early September than at any other time of the year. The ripe corn will be tinder dry and the smallest spark can set it on fire, and at the twinkling of an eye the year's work is lost and hedgerows and trees destroyed. The full hay barn and stacks of bales of straw are also especially vulnerable, so please be careful when out in the country at this time.

I recently paid a visit to the new Courage Brewery in Berkshire, just off the M4 near Reading. Work started on the project in the summer of 1976 and in 1980 the plant went into production. The $9^{1}/_{2}$ acre covered area is one of the largest in Western Europe, and the whole project cost over 90 million pounds. Quality control throughout the whole plant is of the highest standard and is very different to days long ago. Then the beer inspector, or whatever his title was at that time, would walk into the inn wearing leather breeches. He would order his quaff of ale and would then proceed to pour some onto the wooden bench at his table. He would then sit on the spilled ale for half an hour. At the end of that time he would attempt to stand. If his breeches had stuck to the bench, the ale was of good quality, but if not it was of a poor standard.

APPENDIX

Trumpet Hedging (Agricultural) Society

On 21 October 1944, the *Ledbury Reporter & Guardian* reported that the enterprise of the recently formed Trumpet & District Home Guard Hedging Society, in organising their first annual ploughing match during the war, was amply justified when the event took place at Marley Hall, Ledbury.

There were only three classes for hop samples, plus seven special classes for hops on which different products had been used. Mr W.J. Rimell won eight First prizes and had the prize for the best sample in the show. He later judged the hop competitions for many years. The product prizes were for Ford's organic fertilizers, Fisons manure, Shews Heaters, Plant Protection and Brandam Brothers Sublime Flowers of Sulphur. These special prizes continued until Philip Davies & Son won seven prizes with one sample. This situation caused much dissatisfaction and by 1955 the rules were changed so that there were four Open classes for either hand-picked or machine-picked Goldings and Fuggles, and similar classes for members only.

In 1964, I became Chief Steward of hop classes, taking over from Martin Skittery, who had held this post for many years. The first class for any new variety of hand or machine-picked hops was then introduced, also for the first time there was a prize for the Champion sample of hops in the show. These changes were necessary because of the number of new hedgerow varieties of hops, such as Herald, Pioneer, Pilot and the aphid-resistant variety, Boadicea. Growers were also beginning to meet the new demand for the old, tall varieties such as Progress and Early Choice. These changes enabled the small quantities of these varieties to be shown in competition with other hops.

In 1967, when I became Chairman of the Society, W.R. Robinson took over as Chief Steward of Hops in my place. For the first time, in 1969 there were classes for named new varieties of hops – these were Northern Brewer and Bullion. Also, a new innovation in 1970 was for a Bullion class in which the judges awarded 60% of their decisions on analysis of the bittering levels. Classes for the new varieties, Wye Northdown and Wye Challenger, were introduced in 1972 and 1973.

Alastair Young became Chief Steward in 1980, when the distinction between hand and machine-picked hops ceased to be mentioned, as also did the Bullion analysis class, which had failed to create much interest. In the 1981 hop schedule, notice was given that growers who had Progressive Verticillium Wilt on their farm were requested not to bring samples to the show.

The class for another new variety, Zenith, was introduced in 1982 and the class for under 10 tons of quota was changed in 1984 to under 10 hectares, and later changed to under 6 hectares. Growers who had P.V.W. on their farms were allowed to show again in 1985 and a class for a new variety called Omega was also introduced that year.

The judges would have liked to have awarded the winner of the first wilt-resistant class for Wye Target Champion sample in the show in 1987, but felt that it would be so unpopular with other growers that they decided against it.

In 1996, the first class for the hedgerow hop, First Gold, was introduced and the class for under 6 hectares of hops was replaced by one for members, Target. A class for another wilt-resistant variety, Phoenix, as well as one for any variety not in any named class, was started in 1988

At the 2005 show, the classes were completely reorganised and reduced, leaving classes for any aroma variety, named or not, and a similar one for high alpha hops, this being the term used for the bittering level of the hop. There was also another class for the latest new variety, called Pilgrim.

By the time John Probert took over as Chief Steward in 2006, the rapid decline in the acreage of hops grown in the U.K. resulted in the considerable reduction in the number of samples entered in the competition from about 1964 to the present.

The hop competition has always created a great deal of interest both among hop growers and members of the general public.